CHEMISTRY IN THE EARTH SYSTEM

NGSS   INTEGRATING CHEMISTRY AND EARTH SCIENCE

CHEMISTRY IN THE EARTH SYSTEM

Meet the writing team

Kent Pryor
I have a BSc from Massey University majoring in zoology and ecology and taught secondary school biology and chemistry for 9 years before joining BIOZONE as an author in 2009.

Tracey Greenwood
I have been writing resources for students since 1993. I have a Ph.D in biology, specialising in lake ecology and I have taught both graduate and undergraduate biology.

Lissa Bainbridge-Smith
I worked in industry in a research and development capacity for 8 years before joining BIOZONE in 2006. I have a M.Sc from Waikato University.

Richard Allan
I have had 11 years experience teaching senior secondary school biology. I have a Masters degree in biology and founded BIOZONE in the 1980s after developing resources for my own students.

Cover photograph

Volcanic landscape (composite photo)

PHOTO: © Jagoush/stock.adobe.com

Volcanoes are a result of the Earth's internal heat. They form on the over-riding tectonic plate along subduction zones. The internal heat of the Earth produces convection currents in the mantle that move the tectonic plates. Where cracks in the plates form, magma may reach the surface as lava, producing a volcano.

ISBN 978-1-927309-71-1

First edition 2019
Fourth printing with minor corrections

Copyright ©2019 Richard Allan
Published by **BIOZONE International Ltd**

Printed by REPLIKA PRESS PVT LTD using paper produced from renewable and waste materials

Thanks to:

The staff at BIOZONE, including Mike Campbell for design and graphics support, Paolo Curray for IT support, Allan Young for office handling and logistics, and the BIOZONE sales team.

Purchases of this book may be made direct from the publisher:

BIOZONE Corporation
USA and Canada
FREE phone: 1-855-246-4555
FREE fax: 1-855-935-3555
Email: sales@thebiozone.com
Web: www.thebiozone.com

Contents

CODES: **Activity** is marked: to be done   ✓ when completed

Chemistry in the Earth System: A Flow of Ideas

This concept map shows the broad areas of content covered within each Instructional Segment of Chemistry in the Earth System. Anchoring phenomena are indicated in red boxes and dashed red arrows show conceptual connections between topics. Green boxes show some of the crossing cutting concepts linking some of the topics. Can you find other connections?

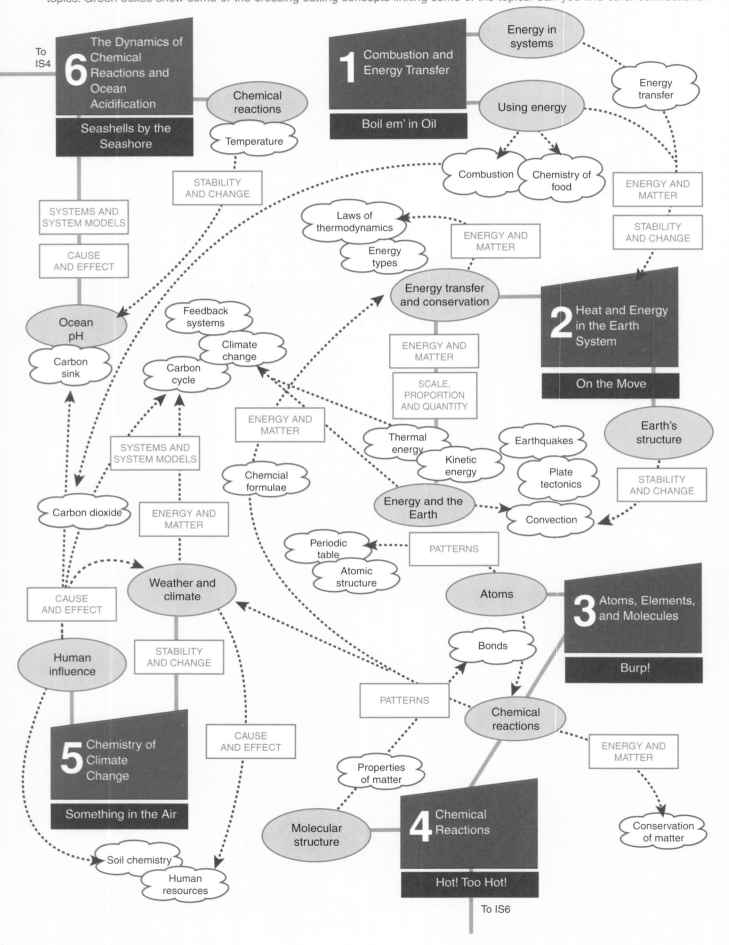

Using This Book

Activities make up most of this book. These are presented as integrated instructional sequences over multiple pages, allowing you to build a deeper understanding of phenomena as you progress through each chapter. Each chapter begins with an **Anchoring Phenomenon**. This is something you would have seen or experienced (e.g. cooking fries) but may not necessarily be able to explain. The anchoring phenomenon is revisited at the close of the chapter. The remaining activities in a chapter are designed to lead you to an understanding of that phenomenon. Each activity begins with a task to **engage** your thinking, asking you to review your current understanding of a phenomenon and setting the scene for the content to follow. The activity then allows you to **explore** related content through modeling, experimentation, or data analysis. You can then **explain** phenomena described through models, simulations, data, descriptions, or photographs.

Many activities will also require you to **elaborate** (expand) on the ideas covered and then to **evaluate** your understanding.

Structure of a chapter

Chapter introduction

Identifies the activities relating to the guiding questions.

Summative assessment

This can be used as a formal assessment of the NGSS performance expectations addressed in the chapter.

Anchoring phenomenon

The first activity is always centered around an anchoring phenomenon. It introduces a phenomenon that is explained by the rest of the activities in the chapter.

Anchoring phenomenon revisited

Once you have completed the activities in the chapter should be able to explain various aspects of the anchoring phenomenon more fully.

Activity pages

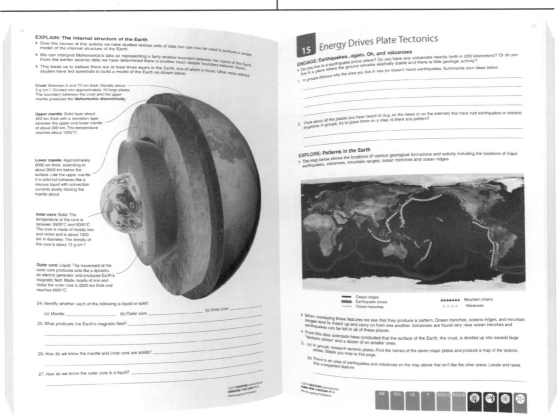

Chapter Introductions

This identifies the Instructional Segment to which this chapter applies.

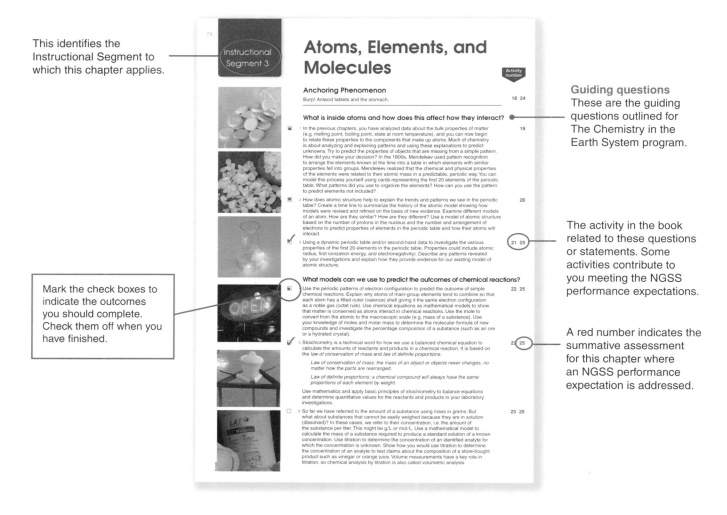

Instructional Segment 3

74

Atoms, Elements, and Molecules

Activity number

Anchoring Phenomenon
Burp! Antacid tablets and the stomach.

18 24

What is inside atoms and how does this affect how they interact?

1 In the previous chapters, you have analyzed data about the bulk properties of matter (e.g. melting point, boiling point, state at room temperature), and you can now begin to relate these properties to the components that make up atoms. Much of chemistry is about analyzing and explaining patterns and using these explanations to predict unknowns. Try to predict the properties of objects that are missing from a simple pattern. How did you make your decision? In the 1800s, Mendeleev used pattern recognition to arrange the elements known at the time into a table in which elements with similar properties fell into groups. Mendeleev realized that the chemical and physical properties of the elements were related to their atomic mass in a predictable, periodic way. You can model this process yourself using cards representing the first 20 elements of the periodic table. What patterns did you use to organize the elements? How can you use the pattern to predict elements not included?

19

2 How does atomic structure help to explain the trends and patterns we see in the periodic table? Create a time line to summarize the history of the atomic model showing how models were revised and refined on the basis of new evidence. Examine different models of an atom. How are they similar? How are they different? Use a model of atomic structure based on the number of protons in the nucleus and the number and arrangement of electrons to predict properties of elements in the periodic table and how their atoms will interact.

20

3 Using a dynamic periodic table and/or second-hand data to investigate the various properties of the first 20 elements in the periodic table. Properties could include atomic radius, first ionization energy, and electronegativity). Describe any patterns revealed by your investigations and explain how they provide evidence for our existing model of atomic structure.

21 25

What models can we use to predict the outcomes of chemical reactions?

4 Use the periodic patterns of electron configuration to predict the outcome of simple chemical reactions. Explain why atoms of main-group elements tend to combine so that each atom has a filled outer (valence) shell giving it the same electron configuration as a noble gas (octet rule). Use chemical equations as mathematical models to show that matter is conserved as atoms interact in chemical reactions. Use the mole to convert from the atomic to the macroscopic scale (e.g. mass of a substance). Use your knowledge of moles and molar mass to determine the molecular formula of new compounds and investigate the percentage composition of a substance (such as an ore or a hydrated crystal).

22 25

5 Stoichiometry is a technical word for how we use a balanced chemical equation to calculate the amounts of reactants and products in a chemical reaction. It is based on the law of conservation of mass and law of definite proportions.

Law of conservation of mass: the mass of an object or objects never changes, no matter how the parts are rearranged.

Law of definite proportions: a chemical compound will always have the same proportions of each element by weight.

Use mathematics and apply basic principles of stoichiometry to balance equations and determine quantitative values for the reactants and products in your laboratory investigations.

22 25

6 So far we have referred to the amount of a substance using mass in grams. But what about substances that cannot be easily weighed because they are in solution (dissolved)? In these cases, we refer to their concentration, i.e. the amount of the substance per liter. This might be g/L or mol/L. Use a mathematical model to calculate the mass of a substance required to produce a standard solution of a known concentration. Use titration to determine the concentration of an identified analyte for which the concentration is unknown. Show how you would use titration to determine the concentration of an analyte to test claims about the composition of a store-bought product such as vinegar or orange juice. Volume measurements have a key role in titration, so chemical analysis by titration is also called volumetric analysis.

23 25

Guiding questions
These are the guiding questions outlined for The Chemistry in the Earth System program.

The activity in the book related to these questions or statements. Some activities contribute to you meeting the NGSS performance expectations.

A red number indicates the summative assessment for this chapter where an NGSS performance expectation is addressed.

Mark the check boxes to indicate the outcomes you should complete. Check them off when you have finished.

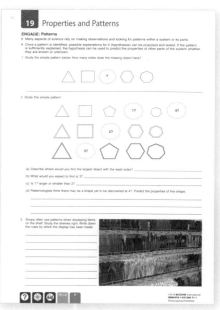

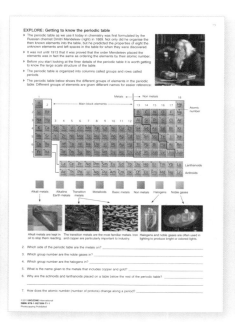

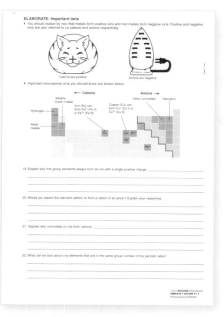

Group discussions, informative articles, simple practical activities, and modeling, are used to **engage** with and **explore** material related to the activity.

You will need to use your knowledge and the evidence presented to **explain** trends in data or how a particular system works.

You can **elaborate** on the skills and understanding gained during the activity and **evaluate** your understanding using further modeling and data analysis.

Practical Investigations

An important part of chemistry involves carrying out experiments and carefully observing and recording what occurs during them. Throughout the book you will notice green investigation panels (like the ones shown below). Each investigation has been designed using simple equipment found in most high school laboratories. The investigations provide opportunities for you to investigate phenomena for yourself. The investigations have different purposes depending on where they occur within the chapter. Some provide stimulus material or ask questions to encourage you to think about a particular phenomenon before you study it in detail. Others build on work you have already carried out and provide a more complex scenario for you to explain. The investigations will help you develop:

▶ Skills in practical chemistry

▶ Skills in observation

▶ Skills in analysis and problem solving

▶ Skills in mathematics and numeracy

▶ Skills in data collection and practice in maintaining accurate records

▶ Skills in working collaboratively and in groups

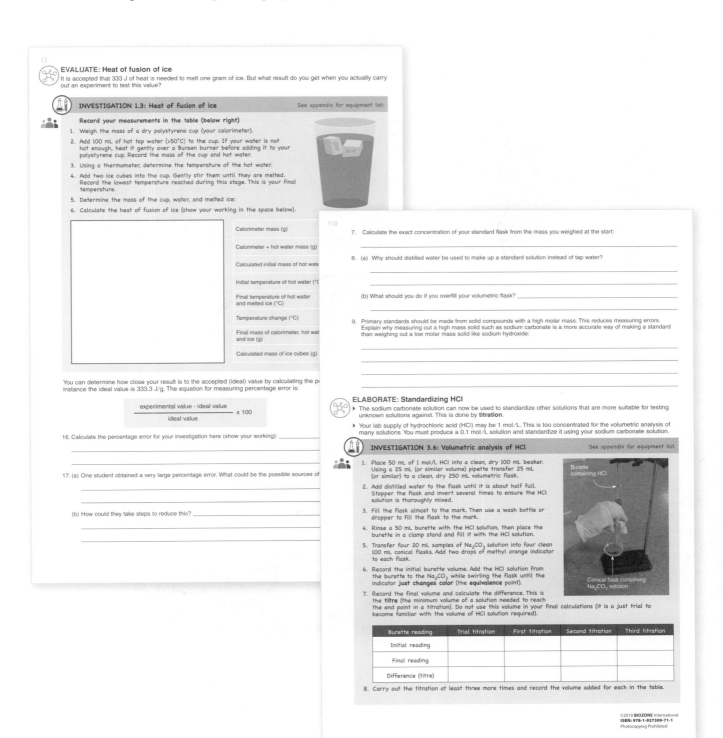

Using BIOZONE's Resource Hub

▶ BIOZONE's Resource Hub provides links to online content that supports the activities in the book. From this page, you can also check for any errata or clarifications to the book or model answers since printing.

▶ The external websites are, for the most part, narrowly focused animations and video clips directly relevant to some aspect of the activity on which they are cited. They provide great support to help your understanding.

www.BIOZONEhub.com

Then enter the code in the text field   **CES1-9711**

Search for an activity here.

Instructional segment (IS) and chapter title.

Click on an activity title to go directly to the resources available for that activity.

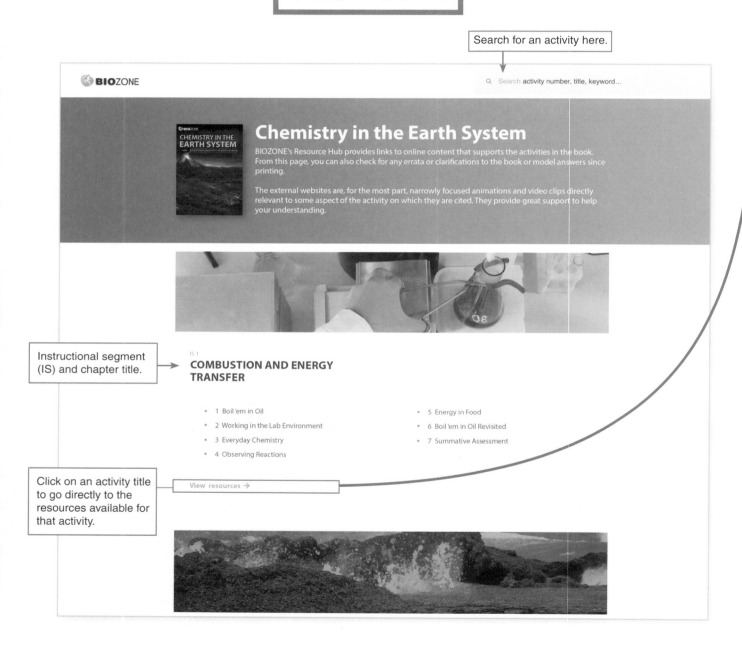

IS 1

COMBUSTION AND ENERGY TRANSFER

- 1 Boil 'em in Oil
- 2 Working in the Lab Environment
- 3 Everyday Chemistry
- 4 Observing Reactions

- 5 Energy in Food
- 6 Boil 'em in Oil Revisited
- 7 Summative Assessment

View resources →

Activity

Search for an activity here.

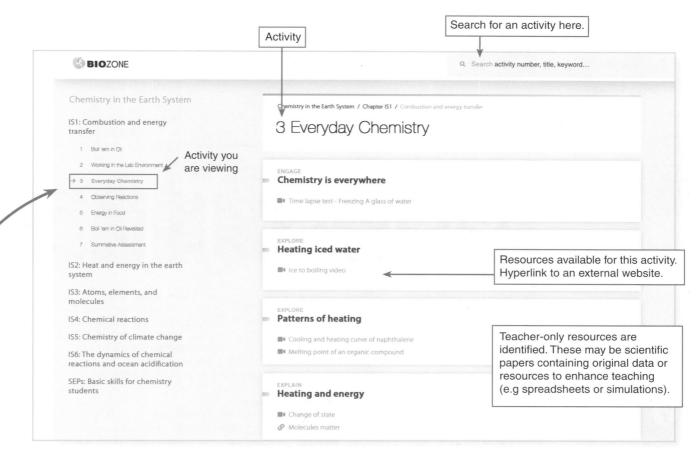

Chemistry in the Earth System / Chapter IS1 / Combustion and energy transfer

3 Everyday Chemistry

Chemistry in the Earth System

IS1: Combustion and energy transfer

1. Boil 'em in Oil
2. Working in the Lab Environment

Activity you are viewing

→ 3. Everyday Chemistry
4. Observing Reactions
5. Energy in Food
6. Boil 'em in Oil Revisited
7. Summative Assessment

IS2: Heat and energy in the earth system

IS3: Atoms, elements, and molecules

IS4: Chemical reactions

IS5: Chemistry of climate change

IS6: The dynamics of chemical reactions and ocean acidification

SEPs: Basic skills for chemistry students

ENGAGE
Chemistry is everywhere
■◀ Time lapse test - Freezing A glass of water

EXPLORE
Heating iced water
■◀ Ice to boiling video

Resources available for this activity. Hyperlink to an external website.

EXPLORE
Patterns of heating
■◀ Cooling and heating curve of naphthalene
■◀ Melting point of an organic compound

Teacher-only resources are identified. These may be scientific papers containing original data or resources to enhance teaching (e.g spreadsheets or simulations).

EXPLAIN
Heating and energy
■◀ Change of state
🔗 Molecules matter

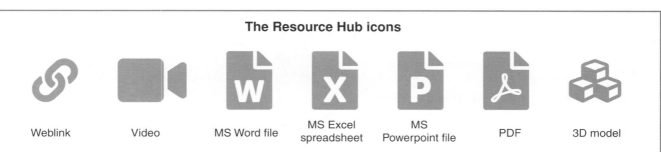

The Resource Hub icons

| Weblink | Video | MS Word file | MS Excel spreadsheet | MS Powerpoint file | PDF | 3D model |

Explore videos

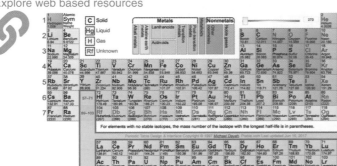

Explore spreadsheet modeling

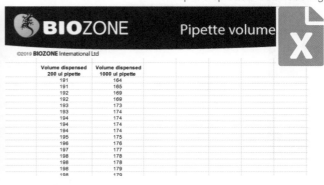

Explore web based resources

Explore 3D models

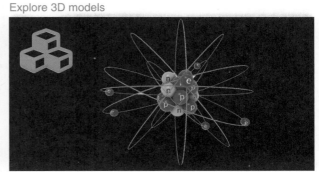

Using the Tab System

The tab system is a useful way to quickly identify the crosscutting concepts, disciplinary core ideas, and science and engineering practices embedded within each activity. The tabs also indicate whether or not the activity is supported online.

The gray hub tab indicates that the activity has online support via the **BIOZONE RESOURCE HUB**. This may include videos, animations, articles, 3D models, and computer models.

The orange disciplinary core idea tabs indicate the core ideas that are covered in the activity. These are covered in the introduction to each chapter, under the guiding questions. The code itself is just a guide for your teacher.

A hub icon in the margin shows which part(s) of the activity have a hub resource.

The **blue** science and engineering practices tabs use picture codes to identify the science and engineering practices (SEPs) relevant to the activity. You will use science and engineering practices in the course of completing the activities.

The **green** crosscutting concepts tabs indicate activities that share the same crosscutting concepts. You will become familiar with the concepts that connect all areas of science.

Science and Engineering Practices

 Asking questions (for science) and defining problems (for engineering)
Asking scientific questions about observations or content in texts helps to define problems and draw valid conclusions.

 Developing and using models
Models can be used to represent a system or a part of a system. Using models can help to visualize a structure, process, or design and understand how it works. Models can also be used to improve a design.

 Planning and carrying out investigations
Planning and carrying out investigations is an important part of independent research. Investigations allow ideas and models to be tested and refined.

 Analyzing and interpreting data
Once data is collected it must be analyzed to reveal any patterns or relationships. Tables and graphs are just two of the many ways to display and analyze data for trends.

 Using mathematics and computational thinking
Mathematics is a tool for understanding scientific data. Converting or transforming data helps to see relationships more easily while statistical analysis can help determine the significance of the results.

 Constructing explanations (for science) and designing solutions (for engineering)
Constructing explanations for observations and phenomena is a dynamic process and may involve drawing on existing knowledge as well as generating new ideas.

 Engaging in argument from evidence
Scientific argument based on evidence is how new ideas gain acceptance in science. Logical reasoning based on evidence is required when considering the merit of new claims or explanations of phenomena.

 Obtaining, evaluating, and communicating information
Evaluating information for scientific accuracy or bias is important in determining its validity and reliability. Communicating information includes reports, graphics, oral presentation, and models.

Cross Cutting Concepts

 Patterns
We see patterns everywhere in science. These guide how we organize and classify events and organisms and prompt us to ask questions about the factors that create and influence them.

 Cause and effect
A major part of science is investigating and explaining causal relationships. The mechanisms by which they occur can be tested in one context and used to explain and predict events in new contexts.

 Scale, proportion, and quantity
Different things are relevant at different scales. Changes in scale, proportion, or quantity affect the structure or performance of a system.

 Systems and system models
Making a model of a system (e.g. physical, mathematical) provides a way to understand and test ideas.

 Energy and matter
Energy flows and matter cycles. Tracking these fluxes helps us understand how systems function.

 Structure and function
The structure of an object or living thing determines many of its properties and functions.

 Stability and change
Science often deals with constructing explanations of how things change or how they remain stable.

Instructional Segment 1

Combustion and Energy Transfer

Activity number

Anchoring Phenomenon

Boil 'em in oil: Cooking in oil produces different results from boiling in water.

1 6

Getting started

☐ 1 Familiarize yourself with the laboratory environment. Identify any potential hazards and recognize and understand how to use personal protection equipment properly. Know what to do in an emergency.

2

☐ 2 Familiarize yourself with the equipment you will use regularly in your exploration of phenomena. Much of the lab work in chemistry involves weighing, measuring, and heating substances so be sure you understand how to use standard equipment correctly.

2

What is energy, how is it measured, and how does it flow within a system?

☐ 3 Examine a glass of iced water. What states does the water exist in? What happens to a measured volume of water when it changes from liquid to solid? What does this tell you about the structure of water and ice?

3

☐ 4 Investigate what happens to the temperature when you heat a beaker of water containing crushed ice. Analyze the results of your investigation. Is this pattern true of other substances? Analyze second-hand data of the melting point of other substances and explain the shape of the curve in terms of temperature and energy in the system.

3

☐ 5 Develop a model (e.g. graph) to show how the temperature of a substance changes as heat energy is added. Use this model to understand what is meant by the latent heat of fusion and latent heat of vaporization. Calculate the energy absorbed by a known mass of a substance during heating. Construct a simple calorimeter and use it to calculate the heat of fusion of ice. How does your result compare with the accepted value?

3 7

What mechanisms allow us to use the energy of foods and fuels?

☐ 6 Use simple investigations to create a model to account for the reactants and products in a chemical reaction, e.g. the reaction of 1.0 M hydrochloric acid and sodium hydrogen carbonate. Calculate the energy released during the reaction. Where has this energy come from? How do the changes you have made to your model system during your investigations demonstrate the laws of conservation of mass and energy?

4 7

☐ 7 Use nutrition labels on some common processed foods to compare their energy value and chemical composition. What do the various ingredients mean and why are they included on the label?

5

☐ 8 Combustion (or burning) is a high temperature, exothermic chemical reaction between a fuel and an oxidant (usually atmospheric oxygen), e.g. $CH_4 + 2O_2 \rightarrow CO_2 + 2H_2O$. You can use combustion to investigate the energy content of food (fuel) and compare it to the values your see on food labels. Use a standard calorimeter to investigate the energy output of a high energy snack food, such as a corn chip. Represent your system with a pictorial model by drawing a diagram of the components and interactions. Use arrows and descriptions to label the energy flows in your system, showing how and why the energy flows from one place to another. Measure the mass of your corn chip before and after combustion and account for any changes in the system. Use your results to calculate the energy in the corn chip and in 100 g of corn chips. How do the results compare to the value of the food label?

5 7

☐ 9 Repeat your investigation with a different medium in your calorimeter instead of water, e.g. oil. How do the results compare? You can repeat the heating curve you made earlier for ice/water using oil. What do the results tell you about the bulk properties (specific heat capacity and thermal conductivity) of different substances?

5 7

☐ 10 Relate the combustion of the snack food in your experiments to the use of combustion in the real world. Make a list of how and where combustion is used. You will revisit these in IS5 when you explore the impact of burning of fossil fuels on global climate.

5 7

1 Boil 'em in Oil

ANCHORING PHENOMENON: Cooking in oil produces different results from boiling in water

Cooking oil and water are two common cooking mediums. Cooking oil is a mixture of fats. Its exact nature depends on the type of oil (e.g. olive oil, canola oil, coconut oil). Water, however, is a pure substance containing only molecules consisting of two hydrogen atoms joined to one oxygen atom (i.e. water molecules). The different nature of these two substances produces two quite different results when they are used for cooking. Look at the photos below of potatoes cooked in oil and in boiling water and the result of each treatment.

   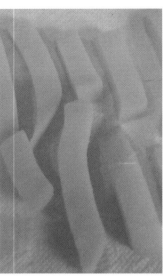

Deep frying in oil   Result   Boiling in water   Result

1. Think of the last time you ate french fries or potato chips. Describe the texture of the fried potato: _____

   _____

   _____

   _____

2. Now think to when you last ate boiled potatoes. Describe the texture of the boiled potato: _____

   _____

   _____

   _____

3. Have you seen potatoes deep frying in oil or boiling in water? What did you notice about the temperature of these two mediums (*hint: think about trying to eat a fresh deep fried potato compared to eating a fresh boiled potato*).

   _____

   _____

4. In groups, discuss why you think oil and water produce different cooking results. Think about the nature of the molecules in the oil and water and how this affects the way they are used for cooking:

   _____

   _____

   _____

   _____

   _____

   _____

   _____

©2019 **BIOZONE** International
ISBN: 978-1-927309-71-1
Photocopying Prohibited

2 Working in the Lab Environment

ENGAGE: Take care!

The chemistry laboratory is an exciting place to be. You will have a chance to carry out or observe many experiments during your course. Some are more spectacular than others! Regardless of the experiment, you need to follow safe laboratory practices to keep yourself and others safe. The cartoon below shows students working in a laboratory.

Drawing by Felix Hicks

1. Identify at least 8 safety hazards in the cartoon above and provide solutions for how you could reduce risk:

_____

_____

_____

_____

_____

_____

_____

_____

_____

_____

_____

_____

_____

_____

_____

EXPLORE: Personal protection equipment

▶ The chemistry laboratory can be a hazardous environment. Strong acids and alkalis are very damaging to the skin. A Bunsen burner is explosive if the gas flowing to it builds up in a confined space and is ignited. However, most risks can be eliminated if proper safety procedures are followed.

▶ Wearing **personal protection equipment** (PPE) and appropriate clothing helps prevent injury from laboratory chemicals. At a minimum, you must wear a lab coat, gloves, and safety goggles. You must also tie back long hair and wear shoes that fully enclose your feet. Depending on the experiment, you may have to wear additional PPE. For example, if you are working with hot objects you should wear heat resistant gloves.

2. Briefly describe the protective role of each item in the photo above: _____

_____

_____

_____

_____

_____

EXPLORE: Safe and sound

In the laboratory you will often be asked to measure, weigh, or heat chemicals and solutions. You must know how to do these things correctly in order to achieve the best possible result in a safe way.

Dangerous laboratory practices

Weighing

Treat all chemicals as potentially hazardous and wear appropriate PPE while working with them.

▶ Choose a balance and weighing vessel suitable for the type and amount of chemical you are weighing out.

▶ Place your balance on an even, stable surface where it will not be bumped and will not move.

▶ Keep the electrical cord safely out of the way.

▶ Never over-fill the weighing vessel.

▶ If spills occur, clean them up immediately.

▶ Make sure your sample is secure when you move from the balance to your work station. Cover it if necessary to stop it falling out of the container.

▶ Some chemicals are very toxic and must be weighed out in a fume hood.

Heating

Wear PPE, use safe laboratory practices and common sense whenever you heat a substance.

▶ Tie long hair back and do not wear loose clothing.

▶ Never reach across a flame.

▶ Keep the area clear, especially of papers and flammable substances. The photo on the left shows what not to do!

▶ Never leave a lit Bunsen burner unattended.

▶ Make sure you never point the open end of a heating vessel at anyone. Never smell or look directly into a heating tube.

▶ Heated materials can stay hot for a long time. Handle them using tongs or thermal gloves so you don't burn yourself. Place them on a hot mat, not directly on to your desk.

©2019 **BIOZONE** International
ISBN: 978-1-927309-71-1
Photocopying Prohibited

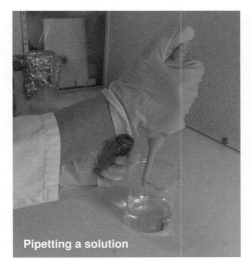

Pipetting a solution

Measuring

Treat all solutions as potentially hazardous and wear appropriate PPE while working with them.

▸ Clearly label your glassware with the name of the solution. Water and concentrated acid look just the same, you don't want to confuse them!

▸ Keep your work space free of clutter. This decreases the chances of accidently knocking things over while you work.

▸ Choose appropriately sized glassware and pipettes to measure the volumes you are working with. This decreases measurement errors.

▸ Measure especially corrosive or noxious chemicals in a fume hood.

DID YOU KNOW?

Until the late 1960s, scientists routinely used mouth pipettes to transfer liquids! The practice was not only dangerous, but could result in sample contamination. Today we use much safer automated and bulb pipettes.

Eyewash station

In the event of an emergency......... do NOT panic!

Good laboratory practices prevent most accidents from happening. But occasionally an accident will occur. Knowing how to deal with it can protect you and your classmates.

▸ Tell your teacher straight away if an accident has occurred.

▸ Listen to their instructions and follow them.

▸ Keep calm. Panicking, yelling, and running can make the situation worse.

▸ Be prepared. Know where the safety stations (eyewash and shower) and fire extinguishers are. Know how to use them.

▸ Know where the exits and fire alarms are located.

EXPLORE: Line it up

Being able to correctly read a liquid level in glassware is critical to obtaining reliable results.

INVESTIGATION 1.1: Reading a meniscus

See appendix for equipment list.

1. Pour 100 mL of water into a 100 mL measuring cylinder.

2. Crouch down until you are looking straight on (eye level) with the 100 mL mark. Using the graduations, record the water volume from this position.

_____

3. What do you notice about the shape of the water's surface?

_____

_____

4. Now move your head slightly so that you are looking at the surface from above and then below eye level.

5. How does changing the viewing position change the position of the surface and therefore the volume readings?

_____

_____

6. Draw a diagram in the space provided to show your observations. Describe how the viewing position affects the volume reading.

©2019 **BIOZONE** International
ISBN: 978-1-927309-71-1
Photocopying Prohibited

3 Everyday Chemistry

ENGAGE: Chemistry is everywhere

Chemistry exists in even the simplest of things. Take a simple glass of iced water for example:

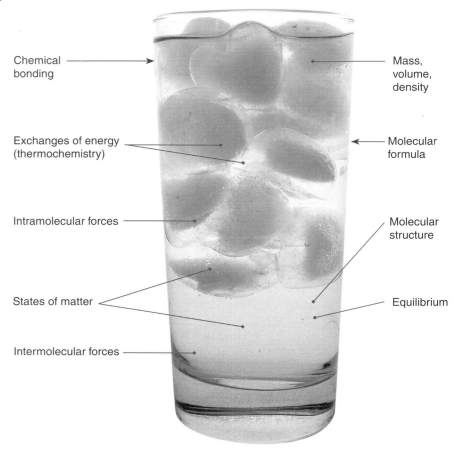

Chemical bonding

Exchanges of energy (thermochemistry)

Intramolecular forces

States of matter

Intermolecular forces

Mass, volume, density

Molecular formula

Molecular structure

Equilibrium

TRY THIS:

▸ Weigh 500 g of water in a beaker or 1 L graduated cylinder (i.e. fill it to the 500 mL mark). Water has mass of 1 g per mL.

▸ Place the cylinder level in a freezer and wait until it has frozen solid.

▸ Check the level of the ice. Is it still at the 500 mL mark?

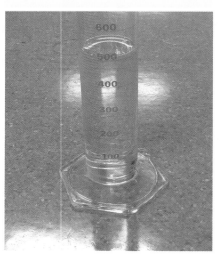

1. (a) Name the three substances shown in the photo above: _____

    (b) How are they different? _____

    _____

    _____

    _____

    _____

2. (a) What do you notice about the position of the ice and the water in the glass? Why do you think this has happened?

    _____

    _____

    (b) Carry out the try this experiment (above right). What happened to the level of the water after it froze to ice? How does this affect the density of the ice compared to the water? Does it tell you anything about the structure of ice compared to water?

    _____

    _____

    _____

3. What kind of energy exchanges do you think are happening here? _____

    _____

    _____

PS1.A   P   CE   EM

©2019 **BIOZONE** International
ISBN: 978-1-927309-71-1
Photocopying Prohibited

EXPLORE: Heating iced water

What happens when you heat a beaker of iced water? There are many changes that take place, some you can see, some you will need instruments to measure.

INVESTIGATION 1.2: Heating iced water

See appendix for equipment list.

1. Place a 100 mL beaker on a balance and add about 50 g of crushed ice. Record the mass of ice here:

   __56.14 grams__

2. Place a thermometer in the ice and wait until the reading has stabilized. This may take a minute with alcohol thermometers.

3. Place the beaker on a tripod over a Bunsen burner.

4. Start a stopwatch. Record the temperature. This is time zero (0 min).

5. Immediately start heating the crushed iced at a constant high heat input (e.g. blue flame).

6. Record the temperature of the ice/water every 30 s for the first 5 minutes then every 1 minute until 3 minutes after the water has begun a rolling boil.

7. Plot your data on the grid provided.

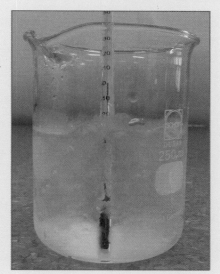

Time (minutes)	Temperature (°C)
0	0.2
.5	0.4
1	2.4
1.5	8.8
2	11
2.5	14
3	17
3.5	22.5
4	26
4.5	35
5	44
5.5	55
6	65
6.5	76
7	85
7.5	95
8	101
9	101
10	101

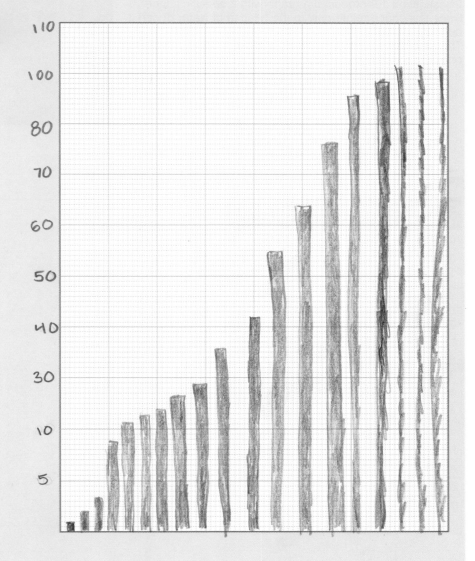

4. Describe three observations during the heating of the crushed ice: _____

   1.) Its started off melting slow

   2.) as the time went on it got hotter faster

   3.) it didn't take long to boil

5. (a) Describe the shape of the graph: A you move to the right it begin an upward slant + at the end it plateau's.

(b) Use your observations to explain the shape of the graph: The graph started off going up gradually + then began to go up more + more.

EXPLORE: Patterns of heating

Investigation 1.2 produced a graph with a specific shape. Does this shape relate only to the heating of water or can it be found elsewhere?

The data below shows the heating of the solid naphthalene, once used in mothballs (right).

Naphthalene was once common in mothballs, but is highly flammable. Today mothballs mostly contain 1,4-dichlorobenzene

6. (a) Plot the data below on the grid:

Time (minutes)	Temperature (°C)	State
0.0	60.0	Solid
0.5	61.0	Solid
1.0	63.0	Solid
1.5	68.0	Solid
2.0	71.0	Solid
2.5	76.0	Solid
3.0	79.0	Solid
3.5	80.0	Solid/liquid
4.0	80.0	Solid/liquid
4.5	80.0	Solid/liquid
5.0	80.0	Solid/liquid
5.5	80.0	Solid/liquid
6.0	80.0	Solid/liquid
6.5	83.0	Liquid
7.0	87.0	Liquid
7.5	90.0	Liquid

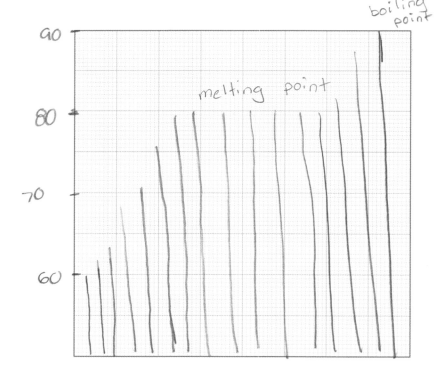

©2019 **BIOZONE** International
ISBN: 978-1-927309-71-1
Photocopying Prohibited

(b) Describe the shape of the graph: It starts of short, then in the middle it plateau's, then it rises again

(c) Why does the temperature not rise between 3.5 and 6.0 minutes? it doesn't rise because its in the middle of trying to melt

(d) What is the significance of the similarity of the naphthalene and ice/water graphs? They both continuously go up.

EXPLAIN: Heating and energy

▶ A molecule is a group of two or more atoms held together by chemical bonds. Molecules are electrically neutral. During heating of a solid, such as ice, energy is being added to the molecules that make up the solid. This energy is stored as vibrations of the molecules. As the vibrations increase, the temperature of the substance increases.

▶ At the melting point, the vibrations become so strong the molecules overcome their attraction to each other and separate, and the solid becomes a liquid. At this point the temperature remains steady. The input in energy instead drives the change of state from solid to liquid. When all the solid has become liquid, the temperature again increases. The energy absorbed by a substance during a change of state is called **latent heat**.

▶ Specifically the energy absorbed when turning from a solid to a liquid is called the **latent heat of fusion**. Latent means hidden and fusion is another word for melting. It is also called the enthalpy of fusion. The energy absorbed when turning from a liquid to a gas is called the **latent heat of vaporization** (or enthalpy of vaporization).

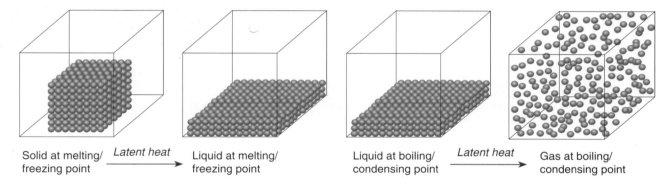

| Solid at melting/ freezing point | *Latent heat* → | Liquid at melting/ freezing point | Liquid at boiling/ condensing point | *Latent heat* → | Gas at boiling/ condensing point |

7. In the space below sketch a graph of the change in temperature of a substance as heat energy is added. Include any relevant labels.

8. Explain what is happening in terms of temperature and energy during the vaporization of a liquid and why this happens:

_____

_____

_____

9. Why does the temperature increase between changes of physical state? _____

_____

_____

_____

ELABORATE: Calculating the energy absorbed during heating

▶ As we have seen when energy is added to a system (e.g. naphthalene or water) the temperature increases steadily until the melting point or boiling point. The rate at which the temperature increases depends on:

- The rate at which the energy is added to the system,
- The mass of the substance being heated
- The specific heat of the substance.

▶ The **specific heat** is the amount of energy required to raise the temperature of 1 g of the substance by 1°C. All substances have different specific heat values. The specific heat of water is 4.186 joules per degree Celsius per gram (4.186 J/°C/g) (equal to one calorie and often rounded to 4.2 J/°C/g).

▶ Knowing the specific heat of a substance (such as water) allows us to determine the amount of heat energy produced by a burning substance (such as natural gas). In our water heating example, the heat released by the burning of the gas in a Bunsen burner can be quantified by measuring the temperature change and the volume of water (1 mL of water = 1 gram).

Energy released = 4.2 x change in temperature (ΔT°C) x mL water
= 4.2 x (50°C – 40°C) x 50
= 4.2 x 10 x 50 = 2100 J
For a 10°C change in the temperature of 50 mL of water.

10. For the heating of water (investigation 1.2) calculate the energy that was produced by the Bunsen burner during the rise in temperature of the water from 10°C to 90°C:

_____

_____

_____

11. Using the specific heat equation for water in the blue box above, calculate the following:

(a) The energy required to heat 100 mL of water by 40°C: _____

_____

(b) The energy required to heat 200 mL of water by 20°C: _____

_____

12. The number you calculated in question 10 above is an underestimate of the energy actually produced by the Bunsen burner. Think about the set up of the investigation with the beaker of ice on a tripod above the Bunsen. Suggest some reasons why the Bunsen produces a lot more energy than you calculated (i.e. where is the energy going?):

_____

_____

_____

_____

©2019 **BIOZONE** International
ISBN: 978-1-927309-71-1

13. Draw a diagram to show the equipment you might use to prevent energy being lost during the heating of the ice/water:

14. How does the heating of water give us a way to calculate the amount of energy in any combustible substance?

_____

_____

_____

_____

_____

ELABORATE: Heat of fusion, heat of vaporization

▶ The table below shows the *melting point, boiling point, latent heat of fusion*, and *latent heat of vaporization* for three common substances at standard atmospheric pressure (1 atm = 101 kPa). This is roughly equivalent to the mean sea-level atmospheric pressure on Earth. Pressure measures force per unit area (1 pascal = 1 newton per m^2). The atm is used as a reference condition for physical and chemical properties, such as the boiling point of water.

Substance	Melting point °C	Boiling point °C	Latent heat of fusion (J/g)	Latent heat of vaporization (J/g)
O_2	-218	-183	12.5	218.8
H_2O	0	100	333.3	2277.8
NaCl	801	1465	478.6	2923.1

▶ In the example of molecular oxygen, to turn one gram of solid oxygen at its melting point to one gram of liquid oxygen at its freezing point requires 12.5 joules. At this point, a graph showing the change in temperature of solid oxygen as heat energy is added would flatten out. The energy being added is not increasing the vibrations of the molecules (kinetic energy). Instead, it is now causing a change in the forces between the molecules (bond energy).

▶ The same principles apply to any changes of state.

15. Using the data table above and the information provided, calculate these:

(a) How much heat energy is required to melt 40 g of sodium chloride (NaCl) at its melting point? _____

_____

_____

(b) How much heat energy is required to raise the temperature of 18 g of liquid water at 70°C to 107°C given that the specific heat of liquid water is 4.2 J/°C/g and the specific heat of steam is 1.9 J/°C/g?

_____

_____

_____

EVALUATE: Heat of fusion of ice

It is accepted that 333 J of heat is needed to melt one gram of ice. But what result do you get when you actually carry out an experiment to test this value?

INVESTIGATION 1.3: Heat of fusion of ice

See appendix for equipment list.

Record your measurements in the table (below right)

1. Weigh the mass of a dry polystyrene cup (your calorimeter).

2. Add 100 mL of hot tap water (>50°C) to the cup. If your water is not hot enough, heat it gently over a Bunsen burner before adding it to your polystyrene cup. Record the mass of the cup and hot water.

3. Using a thermometer, determine the temperature of the hot water.

4. Add two ice cubes into the cup. Gently stir them until they are melted. Record the lowest temperature reached during this stage. This is your final temperature.

5. Determine the mass of the cup, water, and melted ice:

6. Calculate the heat of fusion of ice (show your working in the space below).

Calorimeter mass (g)	
Calorimeter + hot water mass (g)	
Calculated initial mass of hot water (g)	
Initial temperature of hot water (°C)	
Final temperature of hot water and melted ice (°C)	
Temperature change (°C)	
Final mass of calorimeter, hot water and ice (g)	
Calculated mass of ice cubes (g)	

You can determine how close your result is to the accepted (ideal) value by calculating the percentage error. In this instance the ideal value is 333.3 J/g. The equation for measuring percentage error is:

$$\frac{\text{experimental value - ideal value}}{\text{ideal value}} \times 100$$

NEED HELP?
See activity 56

16. Calculate the percentage error for your investigation here (show your working): _____

_____

_____

17. (a) One student obtained a very large percentage error. What could be the possible sources of this? _____

_____

_____

(b) How could they take steps to reduce this? _____

_____

_____

©2019 **BIOZONE** International
ISBN: 978-1-927309-71-1
Photocopying Prohibited

4 Observing Reactions

EXPLORE: Reactions, mass, and energy

▸ An important part of chemistry is accounting for reactants and products in a reaction. Reactants and products are written into equations to show how one forms the other.

▸ Reactions may be written as word equations:

hydrochloric acid + sodium hydrogen carbonate → sodium chloride + carbon dioxide + water

▸ The same reaction may also be written as a chemical equation:

$HCl + NaHCO_3 \rightarrow NaCl + CO_2 + H_2O$

▸ You will often see extra notation in the equation:

$HCl_{(aq)} + NaHCO_{3(s)} \rightarrow NaCl_{(aq)} + CO_{2(g)} + H_2O_{(l)}$

▸ The subscripts $_{(s)}$, $_{(l)}$, $_{(g)}$, and $_{(aq)}$ are important because they tell us what state the substance is in, i.e. solid, liquid, gas, or dissolved in solution (aqueous).

▸ Importantly, a chemical equation shows that the elements on one side of the equation are also on the other side.

INVESTIGATION 1.4 Reacting HCl and NaHCO₃   See appendix for equipment list.

⚠ Caution is required when handling HCl as it is corrosive. Wear protective eyewear, gloves and clothing.

1. Use a measuring cylinder to measure 50 mL of 1.0 M hydrochloric acid (HCl). Add the hydrochloric acid to a 100 mL conical flask. Use a thermometer, record the temperature of the hydrochloric acid here:

_____

2. Place a piece of filter paper on a balance, rezero, and weigh out 2 g of sodium hydrogen carbonate (NaHCO₃).

3. Place the conical flask onto the balance and rezero again. Carefully pour the sodium hydrogen carbonate into the conical flask.

4. Record the mass shown on the balance's display at the beginning and the end of the reaction here:

5. Mass before reaction: _____   Mass after reaction: _____

6. Record the final temperature the solution reached during the reaction: _____

1. What was the mass of the reactants at the start of the reaction? _____

2. What was the mass of the products at the end of reaction, according to the balance? _____

3. (a) Was there a difference? _____

   (b) Can you explain why? _____

   _____

   _____

4 What was the difference in temperature between the start and end of the reaction? _____

5. The mass of the 1.0 M HCl in the reaction (which we can say is mostly water) is effectively 50 g. Calculate the energy gained during the reaction.

NEED HELP?
See page 10

_____

_____

©2019 **BIOZONE** International
ISBN: 978-1-927309-71-1

EM   CE   PS1.B

6. Why is the amount you calculated likely to be an underestimate of the energy gained during the reaction?

_____

_____

7. Where do you think the energy came from? _____

_____

_____

INVESTIGATION 1.5: Production of CO_2 gas

See appendix for equipment list.

⚠ Caution is required when handling HCl as it is corrosive. Wear protective eyewear and gloves. Overproduction of gas could cause the balloon to pop off the conical flask and splash acid.

1. Use a measuring cylinder to measure 50 mL of 1.0 M hydrochloric acid. Add the hydrochloric acid to a 100 mL conical flask.

2. Obtain a balloon with an opening that will fit securely over the opening of the conical flask. Add 2g of sodium bicarbonate into the balloon.

3. Twist the opening of the balloon to ensure the sodium bicarbonate is unable to escape, then stretch the balloon opening over the opening of the conical flask. Ensure the balloon is secure over the conical flask before proceeding.

4. Place the conical flask back on the balance and record the mass here:

_____

5. Now lift the balloon up and untwist it so that the contents mix with the hydrochloric acid. Record any observations:

_____

_____

_____

6. Record the final mass here: _____

8. (a) Was there a difference between the initial and final mass readings? _____

   (b) Explain why: _____

   _____

9. Why did the balloon inflate? _____

_____

10. Was there a difference in the end of reaction mass between investigation 1.4 and 1.5? Explain why: _____

_____

_____

_____

11. From the experiments what can we say about the mass of reactants before a reaction and the mass of products after a reaction?

_____

_____

5 Energy in Food

ENGAGE: Chemistry in food

There are a large variety of chemicals in food. One way to develop an understanding of this is to read the ingredients list and labels on food packages.

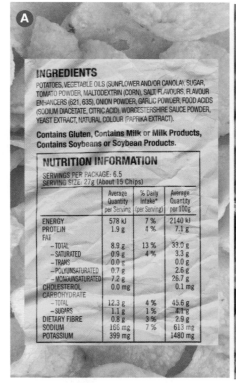

A

INGREDIENTS

POTATOES, VEGETABLE OILS (SUNFLOWER AND/OR CANOLA), SUGAR, TOMATO POWDER, MALTODEXTRIN (CORN), SALT, FLAVOURS, FLAVOUR ENHANCERS (621, 635), ONION POWDER, GARLIC POWDER, FOOD ACIDS (SODIUM DIACETATE, CITRIC ACID), WORCESTERSHIRE SAUCE POWDER, YEAST EXTRACT, NATURAL COLOUR (PAPRIKA EXTRACT).

Contains Gluten, Contains Milk or Milk Products, Contains Soybeans or Soybean Products.

NUTRITION INFORMATION

SERVINGS PER PACKAGE: 6.5
SERVING SIZE: 27g (About 15 Chips)

	Average Quantity per Serving	% Daily Intake* (per Serving)	Average Quantity per 100g
ENERGY	578 kJ	7 %	2140 kJ
PROTEIN	1.9 g	4 %	7.1 g
FAT			
– TOTAL	8.9 g	13 %	33.0 g
– SATURATED	0.9 g	4 %	3.3 g
– TRANS	0.0 g		0.0 g
– POLYUNSATURATED	0.7 g		2.6 g
– MONOUNSATURATED	7.2 g		26.7 g
CHOLESTEROL	0.0 mg		0.1 mg
CARBOHYDRATE			
– TOTAL	12.3 g	4 %	45.6 g
– SUGARS	1.1 g	1 %	4.1 g
DIETARY FIBRE	0.8 g	3 %	2.9 g
SODIUM	166 mg	7 %	613 mg
POTASSIUM	399 mg		1480 mg

B

Nutrition Information
(AVERAGE)
Servings per package: 11
Serving size: 40g (¾ metric cup†)

	quantity per serving	% daily intake Δ per serving	per serve with ½ cup skim milk	quantity per 100g
ENERGY	610 kJ	7%	810 kJ	1530 kJ
PROTEIN	3.0 g	6%	7.7 g	7.5 g
FAT, TOTAL	0.8 g	1%	0.9 g	2.0 g
- SATURATED	0.2 g	1%	0.4 g	0.6 g
CARBOHYDRATE	30.0 g	10%	36.5 g	75.1 g
- SUGARS	10.5 g	12%	17.0 g	26.3 g
DIETARY FIBRE	2.6 g	9%	2.6 g	6.5 g
SODIUM	28 mg	1%	84 mg	70 mg
POTASSIUM	188 mg		393 mg	470 mg
		%RDI*		
THIAMIN (VIT B1)	0.22 mg	20%	0.27 mg	0.55 mg
RIBOFLAVIN (VIT B2)	0.42 mg	25%	0.68 mg	1.06 mg
NIACIN	2.5 mg	25%	2.6 mg	6.2 mg
VITAMIN C	4.0 mg	10%	5.3 mg	10.0 mg
VITAMIN E	1.0 mg	10%	1.0 mg	2.5 mg
FOLATE	100 µg	50%	106 µg	250 µg
IRON	3.0 mg	25%	3.1 mg	7.5 mg

† Cup measurement is approximate and is only to be used as a guide. If you have any specific dietary requirements please weigh your serving.
Δ Percentage daily intakes are based on an average adult diet of 8700 kJ.
* Percentage Recommended Dietary Intake

Ingredients

Whole grains (45%)(wheat, brown rice, rolled oats), fruit (sultanas [15%], sweetened cranberries [sugar, cranberries (1.4%), glycerine, food acid (citric acid), sunflower oil], goji berries [1.5%]), corn, sugar, puffed triticale, invert sugar, barley malt extract, salt, vitamins (vitamin C, vitamin E, niacin, riboflavin, thiamin, folate), flavour, food acid (296), mineral (iron).
CONTAINS CEREALS CONTAINING GLUTEN.
MAY CONTAIN TRACES OF PEANUTS AND/OR TREE NUTS.

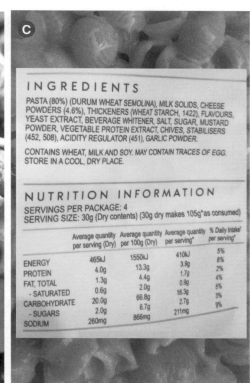

C

INGREDIENTS

PASTA (80%) (DURUM WHEAT SEMOLINA), MILK SOLIDS, CHEESE POWDERS (4.6%), THICKENERS (WHEAT STARCH, 1422), FLAVOURS, YEAST EXTRACT, BEVERAGE WHITENER, SALT, SUGAR, MUSTARD POWDER, VEGETABLE PROTEIN EXTRACT, CHIVES, STABILISERS (452, 508), ACIDITY REGULATOR (451), GARLIC POWDER.

CONTAINS WHEAT, MILK AND SOY. MAY CONTAIN TRACES OF EGG. STORE IN A COOL, DRY PLACE.

NUTRITION INFORMATION

SERVINGS PER PACKAGE: 4
SERVING SIZE: 30g (Dry contents) (30g dry makes 105g* as consumed)

	Average quantity per serving (Dry)	Average quantity per 100g (Dry)	Average quantity per serving*	% Daily Intake† per serving†
ENERGY	465kJ	1550kJ	410kJ	5%
PROTEIN	4.0g	13.3g	3.9g	8%
FAT, TOTAL	1.3g	4.4g	1.7g	2%
- SATURATED	0.6g	2.0g	0.9g	4%
CARBOHYDRATE	20.0g	66.8g	16.3g	5%
- SUGARS	2.0g	6.7g	2.7g	3%
SODIUM	260mg	866mg	211mg	9%

1. Using the food labels above (or you could use your own) list the chemicals in the labels (leave out whole food ingredients e.g. potatoes or wheat).

   A: _____

   _____

   B: _____

   _____

   C: _____

   _____

2. Notice that the labels include the elements sodium, iron, and potassium. In what chemical form would you expect to find these substances in food?

   _____

3. The data below shows the chemical potential energy in 1 g of each of the three food groups:

   Fat: 37 kJ/g   Protein: 17 kJ/g   Carbohydrate: 17 kJ/g

   (a) For food label A how much energy comes from fats per serve? _____

   (b) For food label A how much energy comes from proteins per serve? _____

   (c) For food label A how much energy comes from carbohydrates per serve? _____

   (d) For food label A how much energy in total is there in one serve? _____

4. How might we experimentally verify the chemical potential energy in one serving of any one of these products?

   _____

   _____

SC   EM   SSM   CE   PS3.D   PS1.B

EXPLORE: Carbohydrates, proteins, and fats

Carbohydrates, proteins, and fats, are three important groups of macromolecules (large molecules) in food. They provide us with the essential raw materials we need for building structures in our bodies and make up the bulk of the food we eat.

Carbohydrates are organic molecules made up of carbon, hydrogen, and oxygen atoms. The simplest carbohydrates are single unit sugars, such as glucose and fructose and double-unit sugars such as sucrose. Single unit sugars (monosaccharides) may join together to form polymers called polysaccharides, which include starch and cellulose.

Fats (triglycerides) have a higher proportion of hydrogen than either carbohydrates or protein. This makes them a more concentrated energy source and important as energy storage molecules. When food is short, stored fat can provide energy. Fats are formed from glycerol and three fatty acids. The length of the fatty acids chains and the type of bonding in them affects the melting point of the fat. Longer, straighter (saturated) chains are solid at higher temperatures.

Proteins are macromolecules formed by many amino acid molecules, held together by peptide bonds. The variation in the amino acids in the chain produces the variation in the proteins produced by living organisms. Unlike carbohydrates and fats, proteins contain elements other than carbon, hydrogen and oxygen, including nitrogen and sulfur.

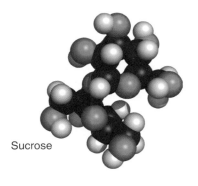

Sucrose

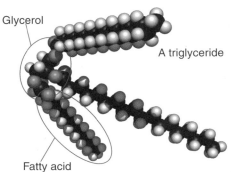

Glycerol

A triglyceride

Fatty acid

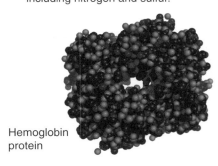

Hemoglobin protein

Sucrose (table sugar)

Vegetable oil is a mixture of triglycerides

Chicken meat has a very high protein content

5. Sugars are often highlighted in food labels. What category of molecule above are sugars? _____

6. Research what each of the molecules do in the body:

   (a) Carbohydrates: _____

   _____

   _____

   (b) Fats: _____

   _____

   _____

   (c) Proteins _____

   _____

   _____

7. Choose a variety of foods and research their carbohydrate, fat, and protein content: _____

   _____

   _____

   _____

©2019 **BIOZONE** International
ISBN: 978-1-927309-71-1

EXPLORE: How much energy is in a corn chip?

▶ Snack foods such as potato or corn chips contain a lot of energy per unit of mass. This is often because they contain a lot of fat or refined carbohydrates (e.g. sugar). The chemical potential energy they contain can be tested experimentally by burning them and using the heat produced to heat a known volume of water. Chemical potential energy is the energy that can be absorbed or released during a chemical reaction or phase transition. Examine the label right from a bag of corn chips:

8. How much energy is there in 100 g of corn chips, according to the label?

_____

9. How would you calculate the energy in one corn chip in the bag? _____

_____

_____

_____

NUTRITION INFORMATION

SERVINGS PER PACKAGE: 6.3
SERVING SIZE: 27g (About 11 Chips)

	Average Quantity per Serving	% Daily Intake* per Serving	Average Quantity per 100g
ENERGY	586 kJ	7%	2170 kJ
PROTEIN	2.4 g	5%	8.9 g
FAT, TOTAL	7.3 g	10%	26.9 g
- SATURATED	3.6 g	15%	13.1 g
CARBOHYDRATE	15.8 g	5%	58.5 g
- SUGARS	0.6 g	1%	2.4 g
DIETARY FIBRE	1.0 g	3%	3.6 g
SODIUM	167 mg	7%	61? g
	51 mg		

10. Work in pairs and using the information presented in this chapter and the knowledge you have acquired so far, design an experimental method to investigate the chemical potential energy in a single corn chip (or other food substance, e.g. a cracker). You should be able to compare your result with the manufacturer's food label on either the image above or from the bag from which you obtained your corn chip. Weigh the corn chip before you start your investigation and after it has burned. As a hint, it is simpler not to let any water boil. Use the prompts below to help you:

(a) Equipment and materials you will need: _____

_____

_____

(b) Sources of error or variables you will need to account for: _____

_____

_____

(c) How will you make sure your results are valid? _____

_____

(d) Write your method here: _____

_____

_____

_____

_____

_____

_____

_____

_____

_____

_____

(e) Carry out a preliminary test and then write any changes you make to your method here: _____

_____

_____

©2019 **BIOZONE** International
ISBN: 978-1-927309-71-1
Photocopying Prohibited

11. Draw your experimental set up here:

EXPLAIN: Energy in a corn chip

12. Carry out your investigation and record your results below. Include initial and final temperatures and any calculations.

13. Weigh any residue corn chip after it has stopped burning. Record the mass here: _____

14. How much energy is there in a single corn chip? _____

15. How energy would there be in 100 g of corn chips? _____

16. (a) How does this compare to the information on the package label? _____

_____

_____

(b) Can you explain any differences? _____

_____

_____

_____

17. (a) What was the difference in mass between the unburned and burned corn chip?_____

(b) Where did this mass go? _____

_____

_____

ELABORATE: Comparing different mediums

▶ Now that you have investigated the energy in a corn chip by heating water, you can compare the result with the heating of other mediums such as vegetable-based cooking oil, which is a common medium used to cook food.

▶ Cooking oil has a specific heat of about 1.2 J/°C/g (this can vary for different blends of cooking oil).

▶ Set up an investigation in the same way as you did for your corn chip investigation (so that the results are comparable) but replace the water with cooking oil. Remember to weigh the corn chip before your start.

 Care should be taken when heating oil. It can become very hot and cause severe burns if not handled carefully. **Do not** let the oil boil or start smoking. Allow the oil to cool before disposing of it. Never pour hot oil down the drain or into the waste.

▶ Record your results here:

Initial oil temperature: _____ Final oil temperature: _____

18. (a) Calculate the energy produced by the corn chip: _____

_____

(b) Calculate the energy in 100 g of corn chips. How does this compare to your energy calculations when you heated water with the corn chip?

_____

_____

ELABORATE: Comparing rate of heating

▶ Earlier you heated ice/water using a Bunsen burner or hot plate and plotted the temperature rise over time. It is worth extending this investigation by heating the same volume of cooking oil and comparing the results:

 INVESTIGATION 1.6: Heating cooking oil   See appendix for equipment list.

1. Add 50 mL of oil (or the equivalent volume to your earlier ice/water investigation) to a 100 mL beaker.

2. Place a thermometer in the oil and wait until the reading has stabilized. This may take a minute with alcohol thermometers.

3. Place the beaker on a tripod over a Bunsen burner or on a hot plate.

4. Start a stopwatch. Record the temperature. This is time zero (0 minutes).

5. Immediately start heating oil at a constant high heat input (e.g. blue flame).

6. Record the temperature of the oil every minute until the oil reaches about 90°C. **Do not** let the oil smoke or boil.

7. Plot your data on the grid below.

Time (minutes)	Temperature (°C)

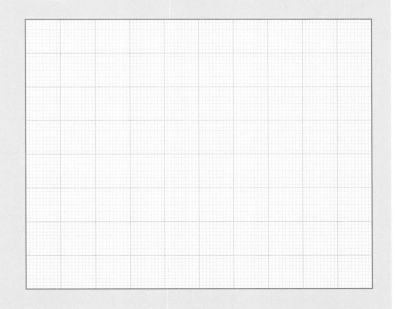

19. Compare and contrast the shape and gradient of the graph with that of the graph for water produced in investigation 1.2:

_____

_____

_____

20. Cooking oil is often a blend of different vegetable oils. Even "pure" oils, such as canola oil extracted from canola seeds, are a mixture of slightly different sized molecules. As a result, cooking oils do not have specific boiling points and often begin smoking before they boil. In general, vegetable-based cooking oils have a smoke point (instead of a boiling point) of about 220°C.

Based on your results on the previous page, how long would you need to heat the oil to reach this temperature?

_____

21. (a) How much energy is required to heat the oil from 30°C to 90°C? _____

(b) Contrast this to heating water from 30°C to 90°C. If you can, explain why there is a difference: _____

_____

_____

_____

ELABORATE: Comparing heat sources

▶ To extend these investigations, it is useful to investigate different heat sources and their effect on the rate of heating of water (or oil). You have investigated the heating of water with a known mass of corn chips. Corn chips are not typically used for heating purposes. It may be helpful to compare the chemical potential energy in a corn chip to that of a useful heating source such as a candle or wood pellets (used in some wood burners for household heating). It may also be useful to compare the energy in the corn chips to the energy in another snack food.

22. Work in pairs to design and carry out an experiment to compare the energy per gram in a candle (or other heat source) to the energy per gram in a corn chip. **Check with your teacher to approve your design before proceeding.**

(a) Equipment and materials: _____

_____

_____

(b) Method: _____

_____

_____

_____

_____

_____

_____

_____

(c) Results:

(d) Conclusion: _____

_____

_____

ELABORATE: Using combustion to do useful work

▸ Combustion is an extremely important process to humans, both in industry and domestically. In the home, it provides the energy for heating and sometimes cooking. In industry, combustion provides the energy needed to produce electricity and to carry out many industrial processes.

▸ One of the most common uses of combustion in the world is the combustion of coal to provide electricity. Although this is not common in California, many other parts of the world still burn coal in thermal power stations. This is because coal is an energy dense, easily transportable and relatively stable substance. In China, for example, two thirds of the electricity generated comes from burning coal, with an installed production capacity of around 1000 gigawatts (GW).

23. The diagram below is a simple model of a combined cycle power station, burning **natural gas**. You will learn more about fossil fuels and combustion chemistry in chapter 5.

    (a) Add labels to the diagram to indicate all the places where you think water changes state and energy is transformed.

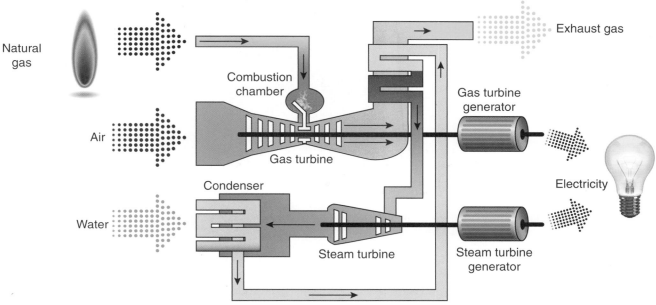

    (b) Use the diagram to come up with a simple explanation of how the gas is used to produce electricity. Why do you think this system is more efficient than a cycle involving just one turbine?

    _____

    _____

    _____

24. Combustion is used in many situations. In groups, discuss how humans use combustion. Summarize your ideas below:

    _____

    _____

25. One common use of combustion is in internal combustion engines. However, in these engines most of the heat produced in the combustion of fuel is a waste product. If a car engine becomes too hot, the engine block can warp and become damaged. How are car engines cooled and how does this relate to the investigations you carried out in this chapter? *Hint: you may need to research antifreeze.*

    _____

    _____

    _____

    _____

    _____

©2019 **BIOZONE** International
ISBN: 978-1-927309-71-1
Photocopying Prohibited

EVALUATE: Food and energy

▸ The measurement of energy in food is often stated in different ways depending on the packaging regulations. In science, energy is measured using joules (J), but a commonly used measurement is the food calorie (sometimes Calorie or large calorie (kcal)). A food calorie is defined as the heat energy required to raise the temperature of one kilogram of water by one degree Celsius. It is a thousand times greater than a small calorie (cal).

26. (a) Convert 1 food calorie into joules: _____

(b) Convert 420 joules into small calories: _____

▸ We have seen that the amount of energy in any kind of food can be determined by burning it and measuring the increase in temperature of a known volume of water. To do this accurately, all the energy in the food item being burned needs to be directed into the water. During this activity you should have realized that a lot of heat is lost if the food item is burned in the open. To prevent the heat loss, the food item should be insulated or surrounded with water. In industry the energy in a burning substance can be measured using a **bomb calorimeter**, shown below.

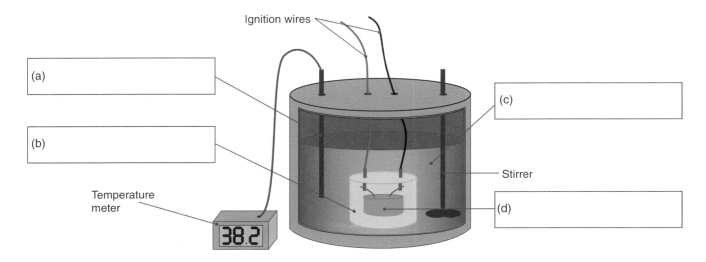

27. Using the knowledge you have gained from this chapter, complete the labeling of the bomb calorimeter using the following word list: combustion chamber, water, food item, temperature probe.

▸ Bomb calorimeters are becoming less common for measuring food energy. A newer way of measuring energy in food is to calculate it directly from the proportions of carbohydrate, fats, and proteins in the food.

28. From the information in the table below calculate the total chemical potential energy content for the specified foods:

Carbohydrate: 17 kJ/g   Fat: 37 kJ/g   Protein: 17 kJ/g

Food	Carbohydrate (g)	Fat (g)	Protein (g)	Total energy (kJ)
Rib eye steak 170 g	0	19.9	47.7	
Lamb rib chops 170 g	0	50.3	37.6	
Chicken breast, 170 g	0	12.7	48.7	
Cod (white fish) 170 g	0	1.5	38.8	
110 g pasta/noodles	28.3	1.2	5.8	
0.5 cup broccoli	3.9	0.3	2.3	
Carrot, medium	7.3	0.1	0.7	
0.5 cup peas, green	9.9	0.3	3.8	
0.5 cup potato, white	15.4	0.1	1.4	
Banana	23.7	0.5	1	
Orange	16.3	0.1	1.4	
Apple, medium	21	0.5	0.3	

29. On average, a healthy person with a reasonable level of physical activity needs 8400 kJ of energy per day. Using the information in the table above, design a meal to provide one third of a person's daily energy needs. Base the energy intake on recommended daily intake of: carbohydrates (45–65% of energy), fat (20–35% of energy), protein (10–35% of energy). Summarize your meal design below and present your findings to the class (or a small group) as a digital presentation with an interactive spreadsheet to show the energy coming from each component:

_____

_____

©2019 **BIOZONE** International
ISBN: 978-1-927309-71-1
Photocopying Prohibited

6 | Boil 'em in Oil Revisited

Boiled or fried?

▶ During this chapter you have been investigating aspects of energy with respect to foods and other substances. From what you have found out you should now be ready to revisit the anchoring phenomenon at the start of the chapter. Why is there a different result when potatoes are placed in hot oil as opposed to being placed in hot water?

 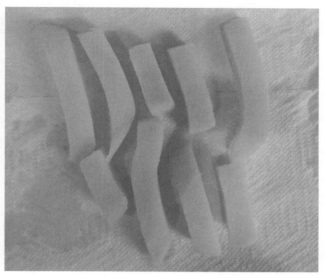

1. Explain why you think the results of deep frying and boiling a potato are so different. Your explanation should include aspects of energy and specific heat:

2. In terms of changes of state, why is it **never** a good idea to put out a fat or oil fire in a pan by pouring water on it?

7 Summative Assessment

1. (a) Using the data in the table below, sketch a graph to show how substance A will increase in temperature over time as heat energy is added at a constant rate. Assume a starting temperature of -5°C:

   (b) Annotate your diagram to explain differences in gradients and line lengths:

Substance	Specific heat (J/°C/g) (solid)	Melting point	Specific heat (J/°C/g) (liquid)	Boiling point	Specific heat (J/°C/g) (gas)
A	4.0	1°C	3.8	80°C	1.9

Heat of fusion: 24 J/g   Heat of vaporization: 246 J/g

2. Study the graph below of the cooling of molten candle wax:

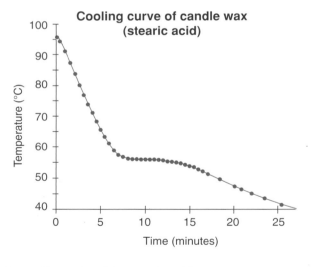

(a) Determine the melting point of the stearic acid: _____

(b) Determine the freezing point of the stearic acid: _____

(c) Explain why the graph flattens out between 6 and 13 minutes: _____

_____

_____

_____

_____

PS1.A   PS1.B   P   EM

©2019 **BIOZONE** International
ISBN: 978-1-927309-71-1
Photocopying Prohibited

3. A farmer uses 2 kilograms of coal in a bricked furnace to heat 200 liters of water in an open steel drum placed on top of the furnace.

(a) Draw a diagram to show the energy flow in this system:

(b) The energy density of coal is 24 MJ/kg. The temperature of the water in the steel drum starts at 19.0°C and the farmer burns all the coal at a steady rate. What is the maximum temperature the water in the drum can reach. Show your working.

_____

_____

_____

_____

_____

(c) At the end of the burn the farmer is left with 100 grams of coal ash and 199.5 liters of water.

i: Explain where the coal has gone to: _____

_____

_____

ii: Explain why there is half a liter of water missing (there is not a leak in the drum): _____

_____

_____

_____

(d) If the farmer were to use dry firewood with an average energy density of 16 MJ/kg, how many kilograms of wood would the farmer need to use to raise the water in the drum by the same amount as in (b)?

_____

_____

_____

_____

Heat and Energy in the Earth System

Anchoring Phenomenon

On the move: The surface of the Earth is constantly moving.

8 16

How is energy transferred and conserved?

☐ 1 What do you understand by energy? Energy is a property of both matter and radiation and is demonstrated as its capacity to do work. Give examples of where energy causes movement on a microscopic and macroscopic scale. As we saw in IS1, energy can be converted in form but neither created nor destroyed. Give examples of both kinetic (moving) and potential (stored) energy and think about how these different forms of energy can be used to perform useful work.

9

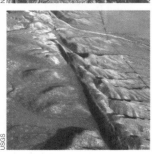

☐ 2 Using models and your own investigations, explain how thermal energy is transferred at the macroscopic scale by convection, conduction, and radiation. Describe what is happening to the individual particles in an isolated system as energy is added. Which way does thermal energy flow? How can these energy flows be used to perform useful work on a larger scale, e.g. in a solar heating or in house heating?

9

☐ 3 Plan and carry out investigations and use a model to provide evidence for the second law of thermodynamics. Use your findings to explain how the energy will flow between the components of a system. Repeat your investigations with different quantities of materials and use your findings to predict temperature changes, equilibrium conditions, and magnitude of energy transferred at other scales.

10 17

☐ 4 Use a physical model of Brownian motion to demonstrate the kinetic theory of matter. Use what you have learned from your model to explain temperature. How does kinetic theory account for the relative movements of gases (e.g. $HCl_{(g)}$ and $NH_{3(g)}$) in a closed system? Calculate the average velocity of particles in a gas and use your calculations to support your explanation for a named system.

11

☐ 5 Use a computational model to investigate heat transfer at the macroscopic scale. Observe convection and/or conduction in a model system and simulate the effects of changing the properties of the system's components, e.g. insulation. You can also revisit your food calorimetry experiment and use the simulation to retrace the flow of heat. Use what you have learned to write a general equation to calculate the change in energy of a substance.

12

How is energy transferred in the Earth's interior?

☐ 6 Based on your prior knowledge, create your own diagram as a model of the Earth's structure. Understand that the drive for thermal equilibrium you have been exploring so far operates on a massive scale inside the Earth. Analyze data from deep mines and boreholes to support the claim that heat is transferred from the hot interior of the Earth outward by convection. Where does this heat come from?

8 13 16

☐ 7 Analyze seismic and other data to map the extent of the Earth's liquid layer and the varying composition of its outer layers. Refine your model to recognize the viscous and elastic behavior of parts of the asthenosphere (the lower part of the upper mantle). Use an analogy to describe how 'solid' rock can behave as a viscous fluid. Recall convection in a lava lamp and use this to explain how density driven flow in the Earth's rocks can account for the movement of the Earth's lithospheric plates (plate tectonics).

14 17

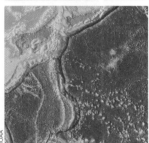

NOAA

☐ 8 Examine the evidence for the motion of the Earth's lithospheric (crustal) plates (e.g. GPS data, age of the seafloor). What patterns can be seen in the data? Use seafloor ages and surface motion rates as evidence for how heat is transferred in the Earth's interior. Draw a labeled diagram of the Earth's interior to communicate your understanding of how heat drives movement within the Earth. Where and why does mantle material melt and what is the effect of this mantle melting on generation of new crust and movement of the crustal plates. Can you now see how the same processes operating on small (laboratory) scales also operate on the scale of the entire Earth?

15 17

8 On the Move

ANCHORING PHENOMENON: The surface of the Earth is constantly moving

| Early Jurassic | Late Cretaceous | Present day Earth |
| 180 mya | 100-66 mya | |

▶ The image on the far right above shows Earth as we know it today. The image on the left shows the Earth as we understand it looked during the early Jurassic period about 180 million years ago, based on a variety of evidence collected over the last hundred years. The continents have separated and rejoined many times over the billions of years of Earth's history. Continental drift describes the movement of the continents over the surface of the Earth. It was not until the 1960s that the theory of plate tectonics, which describes this movement, was confirmed. There is still a lot we do not understand about how this occurs, but clearly it involves massive energy sources beneath the Earth.

1. Write down five things that you know (or think you know) about continental drift in the space below:

   (a) _____

   (b) _____

   (c) _____

   (d) _____

   (e) _____

2. Discuss your ideas with other people in your class. Do they have different ideas to you? Can they add to your current knowledge? Summarize any ideas you had not already thought of:

   _____

   _____

   _____

   _____

3. The circle below represents a cross section of the Earth. Fill in the circle with what you think the Earth looks like in cross section. Add labels to your diagram.

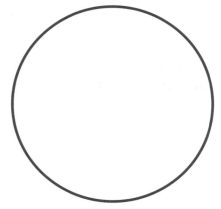

©2019 **BIOZONE** International
ISBN: 978-1-927309-71-1

9 Energy

ENGAGE: There she blows!

The photograph right shows an eruption of lava from Mauna Ulu, a volcanic cone on the island of Hawaii. The lava bubbling from the vent is glowing red hot whereas lava that emerged earlier has cooled and appears black. Where has the energy in the lava (which has a temperature greater than 1000°C) come from? Why does the lava emerge as a fountain? What causes the lava to cool?

1. Have you ever seen volcanic activity of any sort? If so, describe it: _____

   no I have not ever seen volcanic activity.

2. Water boils at 100° C. Think about how long it takes a kettle to boil a liter of water. Compare this to the volume of lava produced during the eruption of Mauna Ulu which covered an area of 44 km², and the energy that must have been required to produce that amount of lava. What does this tell you about the energy stored in the Earth?

   There is an insane amount of energy store in the earth.

EXPLORE: Energy

▶ Energy is a property of an object that allows it to do work. It may be transferred between objects and systems and transformed into different forms but it can not be created or destroyed. The amount of energy in a closed system is the same before and after a transformation. Energy is measured in joules (J).

▶ One simple way of measuring the energy in a system or energy transferred between objects is to measure the temperature or change in temperature. A thermometer measures the average energy of molecular motion in an object or system (average kinetic energy) shown as the temperature of the system. The amount of substance in an object (its mass) is also important in determining the amount of energy in the object.

▶ For example 100 liters of water at 30°C has much more energy stored in it than 1 liter of water at 30°C, even though their temperatures are the same.

3. To develop an understanding of energy and, in particular, how much energy is used or stored by certain objects or systems, research the equivalent use of 10,000 J by the following five objects or substances:

   (a) How long it takes a 100 W light bulb to use 10,000 J of electrical energy: __10 seconds__

   (b) How much 10,000 J will raise the temperature of 1 liter of water by in °C: __4.18__

   (c) What volume of gasoline stores 10,000 J of energy: __8⁄13⁄9⁄1⁄4⁄1 120,276,384⁻¹__

   (d) What mass of table sugar (sucrose) stores 10,000 J of energy: __342.3__

   (e) The speed in meters per second (m/s) of a 145 g baseball that has 10,000 J of kinetic energy __40 m/s__

4. List four different "types" of energy that are commonly used in everyday language: _____

   ~~kinetic~~, hydro, kinetic, wind, solar

5. A cup of hot water cools down over time. Where do you think the energy that was in the water went?_____

   it went out into the air

PS3.A | CE | SPQ | EM | SC

©2019 **BIOZONE** International
ISBN: 978-1-927309-71-1
Photocopying Prohibited

EXPLORE: Forms of energy

▸ As you would have found in your research in question 3-4 on the previous page, energy takes many different "forms". These forms are really just convenient ways for us to categorize and think about energy and how it is being used. If we say "electrical energy" we know that the energy is in the form of charged particles moving around a circuit of wires.

▸ The diagram on the right shows how energy can be categorized as being in one of two forms:
Potential energy = "the energy that is able to do work at some point in the future".
Kinetic energy = "the energy possessed by an object due to its movement".

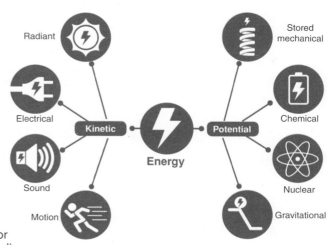

6. Study the images below. Write whether they show potential or kinetic energy and what "form" that energy is in (e.g. chemical).

Ball moving through air — A

Single cell batteries — B

Lightning — C

Compressed springs

Flame from a candle — E

Rocks the at top of a cliff — F

(a) _kinetic_
(b) _potential_
(c) _kinetic_
(d) _kinetic_
(e) _kinetic_
(f) _potential_

EXPLORE: Moving energy

▸ Energy can move from place to place (it can be transferred). For example, light energy released from nuclear reactions in the Sun travels across space to Earth. Plants use some of this energy to carry out photosynthesis and produce sugars, sustaining life on Earth.

▸ There are three ways in which energy is transferred: by convection, by conduction, and by radiation.

Convection

When air or a liquid is heated and then travels away from the source, it carries the thermal energy along.

(a) A boiling electric kettle

(b) An oil-filled electric heater

(c) A hot air balloon

7. In small groups, discuss how you think the electric kettle, the oil-filled heater, and the hot air balloon transfer heat in order to fulfill their function. Summarize your answers below:

(a) Electric kettle: _____

_____

(b) Oil-filled heater: _____

_____

(c) Hot air balloon: _____

_____

▶ The diagram (right) shows a square tube with $KMnO_4$ crystals dissolving at the top and heat from a Bunsen burner being applied at the lower right corner.

▶ Note how the purple color produced by the dissolving $KMnO_4$ crystals has moved from the top of the tube towards the left hand side and down the to the left hand bottom corner.

8. (a) Why do you think the purple color has moved in the direction it has?

_____

_____

_____

_____

_____

(b) Predict what would happen if the experiment was reset and the Bunsen burner moved to the left side of the tube:

_____

_____

_____

(c) Predict what might happen if the Bunsen burner was moved to the middle of the tube and explain your prediction:

_____

_____

9. Use this exploration to come up with your own definition of convection: _____

_____

Conduction

The particles in a substance are constantly moving (kinetic energy). In a solid object, the particles vibrate about a fixed position. The more energy a substance has, the faster and larger the movements of its particles.

10. In terms of heat transfer, what is happening on the grill pictured right?

_____

_____

_____

_____

INVESTIGATION 2.1: Measuring conductivity of different metals   See appendix for equipment list.

1. Place wax dots along a steel rod at 2 cm intervals starting 25 cm from one end. Attach the rod to a clamp stand as pictured so that the first wax dot is 15 cm from the point directly above the Bunsen burner.

2. Set the Bunsen flame to blue and start a timer.

3. Observe the effect on the wax dots. Record the time for each dot to start melting.

4. Let the steel rod cool down, then set the flame to a yellow flame and repeat the procedure.

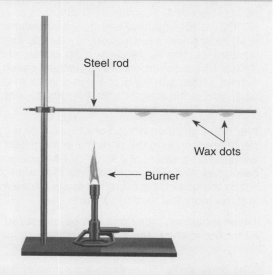

Steel rod

Wax dots

Burner

Wax dot	Time to start melting (blue flame)	Time to start melting (yellow flame)
1		
2		
3		

5. Remove the steel rod and replace it with a copper rod. Carry out the investigation again, this time on the blue flame only.
Record the results in the table right:

6. Repeat step 5 above using an aluminum rod.
Record the result in the table right:

Wax dot	Time to start melting (copper rod)	Time to start melting (aluminum rod)
1		
2		
3		

11. (a) Was there a time difference for each wax dot to start melting when the blue flame was applied? What was it?

_____

(b) Was there a time difference for each wax dot to start melting when the yellow flame was applied? What was it?

_____

(c) Can you explain why there was a difference in time between the first dot melting when a blue flame was applied and when a yellow flame was applied?

_____

_____

_____

_____

(d) Using circles to represent the particles in the metal wire, draw a diagram to represent how you think the energy of the flame is melting the wax dots:

Radiation

▶ All objects above absolute zero (0 Kelvin or -273°C) radiate thermal energy. Electromagnetic (EM) radiation is a form of energy that occurs as waves, including light waves, radio waves, and X-rays. EM radiation occurs as packets called quanta. These can travel through a vacuum such as space. In the case of light, the quantum of energy is called a **photon**.

▶ When EM radiation hits an object, energy is transferred, making the particles in the object vibrate. This transfer of energy by EM waves is called radiation. The more intense the radiation hitting the object, the more energy is transferred and the more the particles vibrate.

▶ These increased vibrations can be measured by a thermometer as a rise in temperature.

12. The photograph above shows a solar water heating unit on the roof of a house. Working in small groups, discuss how you think a solar water heating system might work. In the space below draw a simple diagram to illustrate your ideas.

13. How is heat from the Sun able to reach Earth? _____

_____

_____

_____

14. Why do you feel warm when sitting in the Sun?

_____

_____

_____

Solar energy

Heat

Glass tube

Copper tube

Vacuum

Heating fluid

15. The diagram (right) shows the structure of an evacuated solar tube used in solar water heating. It is made up of an outer tube and a smaller inner tube containing heating fluid. The heating fluid transfers heat to the water cycled past the top of the tube. There is a vacuum between the outer and inner tubes.

Explain how the energy from the Sun is able to heat the heating fluid in the inner tube. What is the significance of the vacuum between the two tubes?

_____

_____

_____

_____

©2019 **BIOZONE** International
ISBN: 978-1-927309-71-1

EXPLAIN: Lava lamp

16. By now you should have an understanding of what energy is and how it is transferred. Use your understanding to explain the behavior and features of the lava lamp shown below in terms of energy and movement of particles. Use diagrams to help with your explanation.

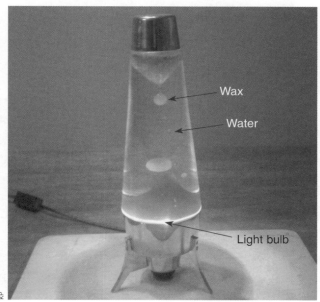

_____

_____

_____

_____

_____

_____

_____

_____

ELABORATE: Wood burners

17. Domestic fireplaces are becoming less common, especially in large cities, but in many places are still an important way of heating the home. The diagram below shows a general layout for the heating of a home using a wood burning fireplace. Using your knowledge of convection, conduction, and radiation, add labels to the diagram to explain how heat energy is moved about the house:

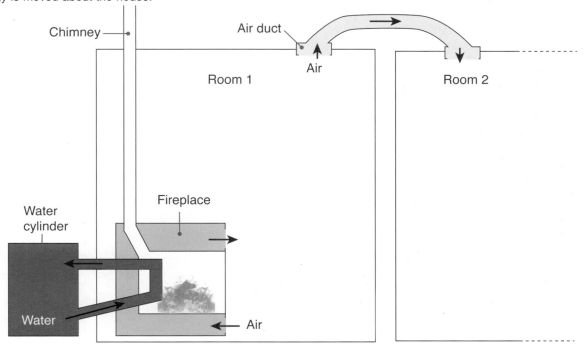

©2019 **BIOZONE** International
ISBN: 978-1-927309-71-1
Photocopying Prohibited

10 Order and Disorder

ENGAGE: A campfire

▶ The photo shows a log of wood burning in a campfire. The wood represents a concentration of energy. The energy is stored in the chemical bonds within the wood (e.g. between the bonds holding atoms together to form cellulose). By burning the wood, the energy is released as heat and becomes spread out (dispersed), heating the air molecules around it and causing them to move faster.

▶ This is an example of increasing **entropy**. Entropy is a measure of how much the energy is spread out in a system. This energy is not available to do work. Entropy in the universe never decreases. It will eventually increase to a point where all energy is evenly dispersed (maximum entropy). The ordered, concentrated energy in wood has low entropy. Burning it increases entropy as the energy in the wood becomes dispersed as heat.

▶ Entropy can be reduced in a closed system, but always by increasing entropy in the wider universe. The energy in the wood was stored as a product of photosynthesis, which is powered by the Sun. The Sun itself is releasing vast amounts of energy every second and thus rapidly increasing the entropy of the universe.

1. Entropy never decreases unless it increases somewhere else by at least an equal amount. Name two everyday devices that reduce entropy somewhere while increasing it somewhere else:

   _____

2. The second law of thermodynamics states that entropy always increases over time. You will sometimes hear it expressed as "order tends to disorder".

   As a class or group discuss what this means and why you think the entropy of the universe will always increase (to a maximum). Summarize your ideas below:

   _____

   _____

   _____

   _____

   _____

EXPLORE: Flow of energy

▶ Place a cup of hot water at 80°C on a bench where the air temperature is around 20°C. Does the cup get hotter or colder over time? Why? The activity below will help illustrate how energy flows.

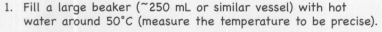

INVESTIGATION 2.2: Measuring heat transfer

See appendix for equipment list.

1. Fill a large beaker (~250 mL or similar vessel) with hot water around 50°C (measure the temperature to be precise).

2. Place a small beaker (~50 mL) filled with water at room temperature into the large beaker. Measure the temperature of the room temperature water to be precise.

3. Place the set up in an insulated box or wrap insulation around the larger beaker to reduce energy loss from the system.

4. Measure and record the temperature of the water in the large and small beaker at two minute intervals and record the temperatures in the table provided on the next page.

5. Do this until the temperatures stabilize. Graph your result on the grid provided on the next page.

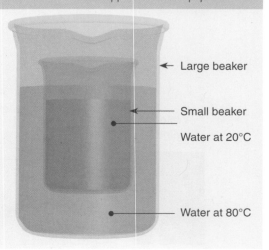

← Large beaker

← Small beaker

Water at 20°C

← Water at 80°C

©2019 **BIOZONE** International
ISBN: 978-1-927309-71-1
Photocopying Prohibited

Time (minutes)	Temperature in large beaker (°C)	Temperature in small beaker (°C)
0 (initial)	50	25
2	42.5	39
4	40.5	42
6	39.3	43
8	38.3	43
10	37.5	43 42.5
12	36.8	42
14	36.3	41
16	36	40
18	35.4	40
20	35	39

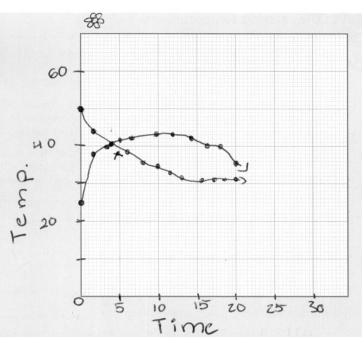

6. Repeat the investigation but this time use cooking oil at 20°C in the small beaker instead of water.

7. Measure and record the temperature of the water in the large beaker and oil in the small beaker at two minute intervals and record the temperatures in the table below.

8. Do this until the temperatures stabilize. Graph your result on the grid provided below.

Time (minutes)	Temperature in large beaker (°C)	Temperature in small beaker (°C)
0 (initial)	50	25
2	54	47
4	53	51
6	50.5	52.5
8	49	52.5
10	47.4	51.5
12	46.1	51
14	45	50
16	44	49
18	43.6	48
20	42.2	47

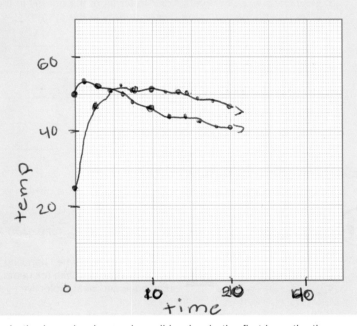

3. (a) Describe the shape of the lines for the temperature in the large beaker and small beaker in the first investigation:

One start of warm + the temp gradually dropped + the other rose in temp peaked + dropped

(b) Why do you think the lines have this shape? (Hint: what is happening to the energy in each beaker?) _____

The energy is transfering from the warmer object to the cooler

(c) Is there a difference between the first and second investigation? Can you explain why? _____

Yes, the temp went a little higher cause it was oil instead of water.

©2019 BIOZONE International
ISBN: 978-1-927309-71-1
Photocopying Prohibited

EXPLORE: Mixing temperatures

INVESTIGATION 2.3: Mixing water of different temperatures   See appendix for equipment list.

1. Set up two 500 mL beakers, each containing 200 mL of water

2. In one beaker, set the water temperature to around 50°C (measure to be precise). In the second beaker, set the temperature to about 20°C (measure to be precise). Record the temperatures in 4(a) below.

3. Predict what will happen when the contents of the two beakers are mixed. Try to predict the precise temperature of the water after mixing based on your initial measurements. Write your prediction in the space provided below.

4. Mix the water in the two beakers together and measure the temperature. How close was your prediction?

4. (a) i. Initial temperature in beaker one: __80__

   ii. Initial temperature in beaker two: __22.7__

   (b) Prediction of temperature after mixing: __I predict that the temp. will be somewhere between the two temps__

   (c) Final temperature after mixing: __42__

   (d) How close was your prediction? In terms of the energy in the system, explain why the temperature changed and what has happened to the overall energy in the system:

   __my prediction was pretty acurate. the temp changed because the energy in the hot water caused the room temp water to rise.__

EXPLAIN: Rate of diffusion

▶ Diffusion is the movement of particles from an area of high concentration to an area of low concentration.

INVESTIGATION 2.4: Temperature and diffusion rate   See appendix for equipment list.

⚠ Caution is required when handling $KMnO_4$ as it is a strong oxidizer. Use with adequate ventilation or in a fume hood and wear protective eyewear and gloves.

1. Fill two 250 mL beakers with 200 mL of water. In one beaker set the water temperature to around 50°C. In the second beaker set the temperature to about 20°C. In this case the temperatures do not need to be precise.

2. Add a few crystals of potassium permanganate ($KMnO_4$) to the 50°C beaker. A few drops of food coloring will also work, as will an M&M (red or blue are easier to see). Observe any changes over the next minute.

3. Repeat the process for the 20°C beaker.

$KMnO_4$ crystals

5. (a) What did you notice about how the $KMnO_4$ diffused in the 80°C water compared to the 20°C water? ____

   __The 80° water got darker + disolved faster than the 20° water.__

©2019 **BIOZONE** International
ISBN: 978-1-927309-71-1
Photocopying Prohibited

(b) In terms of the thermal energy in each beaker, explain why the KMnO$_4$ diffused like this: _____

because there was more thermal energy it mixed in the hot water, there was more energy to react faster.

(c) In water KMnO$_4$ breaks up (dissociates) into K$^+$ and MnO$_4^-$ ions. Draw a diagram or diagrams to show how a crystal of KMnO$_4$ diffuses through water over time:

6. Describe the concept of thermal energy and which direction thermal energy flows. Explain why it behaves like this:

thermal energy flows up + its energy associated with the movements of atoms + molecules

EXPLAIN: Countercurrent exchange

▶ Countercurrent heat exchangers are used to keep heat in one place and prevent it being lost. They work by passing a hotter medium close to a colder one travelling in the opposite direction. Heat is transferred from the hotter to the colder medium. Because the flows are in opposite directions, the gradient for heat transfer is maintained. Countercurrent heat exchangers are common in biological systems where they help to conserve body heat.

7. Complete the diagram below to show how the hot end remains hot while the cold end remains cold:

Hot   Cold

8. Using your knowledge of heat flow, design a countercurrent device that will allow air to reach fuel in a combustion chamber while keeping all the heat produced inside the combustion chamber (i.e heat is not lost due to cold incoming air or loss of heat in hot exhaust gases).

9. In groups, discuss how you might create a physical model of countercurrent heat exchange using flexible PVC piping and thermochromic pigment (a pigment that changes color with temperature changes). Draw a labeled diagram of your model and staple it to this page. Build your model and test how well it works.

11 Kinetic Theory of Matter

ENGAGE: Brownian motion and marbles

▸ In 1827, botanist Robert Brown was observing pollen grains under a microscope. When one of the pollen grains broke open, many small particles were released. Brown noticed that these small particles (later identified as amyloplasts, which store starch) seemed to jiggle about at random. He could not explain the motion but did see it in non-organic particles as well. From this, he concluded that the motion was not to do with living organisms.

▸ Brownian motion was later explained by Albert Einstein as a movement of large particles being bombarded by atoms and molecules. It can be seen under a microscope in fat droplets suspended in water. Brownian motion can be modeled using marbles and a white board duster (right).

Try this:

i.   With 4-6 other classmates sit in a small circle, about 1 m across. This works best on a hard smooth surface, such as concrete.

ii. Each person should have 5-10 marbles.

iii. In the middle of the circle place a white board duster or a small block of wood.

iv. At random, roll the marbles (fast!) at the duster.

v.   Observe the movement of the duster. Carry out the demonstration several times. Is the movement ever the same?

INVESTIGATION 2.5: Observing Brownian motion

See appendix for equipment list.

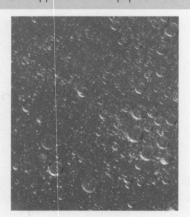

1. Brownian motion can be observed in fat droplets or microbeads suspended in water. To produce a milk suspension, dip the tip of a needle into milk then dip the needle into 1 mL of distilled water (to dilute the milk). The milk needs to be very dilute.

2. Place a drop on a slide using a micropipette and add a coverslip.

3. The microscope needs to be set to maximum magnification (at least 400x). You may need to wait a minute after focusing to ensure there is no bulk flow in the fluid (the water/milk mix moving rather than the particles moving). Bulk flow can be identified when all the particles appear to be moving in the same direction (e.g. sideways).

4. If your microscope has a camera mount, you can try to record this motion and trace it in still images, although each movement will be very small.

1. (a) What is Brownian motion? _____

_____

_____

(b) Carry out the **Try this** again but increase the rate of marble rolling (you may need more helpers to do this). What happens to the duster's motion now? What does the increased frequency of rolling represent?

_____

_____

(c) Carry out the **Try this** again using heavier or larger marbles. Was the resultant motion of the duster any different?

_____

_____

(d) Carry out the **Try this** again using a heavier duster or block of wood but standard sized marble. How does this change the motion of the duster (or block of wood)?

_____

_____

(e) Can you relate the motion of the duster to the motion you observed in the fat droplets in water? What is causing the motion of the fat droplets?

_____

_____

PS3.A   PS3.B   CE   SSM   EM

©2019 **BIOZONE** International
ISBN: 978-1-927309-71-1
Photocopying Prohibited

EXPLORE: There's something in the air

▶ The air (atmosphere) of our planet is made of particles (molecules of gas).

2. In groups, discuss ideas about how to demonstrate that the air around you is actually made up of particles that take up space. Summarize your ideas below. If you have time, try testing them:

_____

_____

_____

_____

_____

_____

▶ Your teacher may be able to do this **demonstration** for you. You would not do it yourself. Hydrogen chloride (HCl) is a highly soluble, colorless gas with a pungent smell (don't ever breathe it in!). It is commonly seen in school as a dissolved and diluted solution of hydrochloric acid (e.g. 1 M HCl is common). Ammonia (NH_3) is also a highly soluble, colorless gas. It also has a very pungent smell (again, don't ever breathe it in!). Ammonia dissolves in water to form ammonium hydroxide (NH_4OH). The image below shows the effect of mixing these gases in a tube.

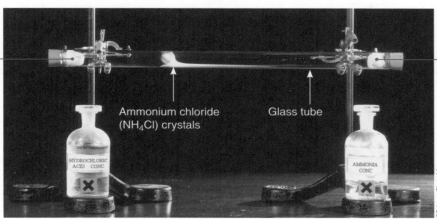

Cotton wool soaked in concentrated HCl

Cotton wool soaked in concentrated NH_4OH

Ammonium chloride (NH_4Cl) crystals

Glass tube

©Science Photo Library

3. (a) The gases HCl and NH_3 are both colorless. How is the formation of ammonium chloride in the tube (NH_4Cl) proof that the gases are composed of particles that are mobile in the air?

_____

_____

_____

(b) Study the image above. What can you say about where in the tube the ammonium chloride crystals have formed:

_____

(c) Can you explain why they have formed at that position? _____

_____

_____

_____

4. What would you expect to happen if you were to reduce the temperature of the experiment above by 10°C? Explain why you would expect this.

_____

_____

_____

©2019 **BIOZONE** International
ISBN: 978-1-927309-71-1
Photocopying Prohibited

EXPLAIN: Temperature

▶ As we noted earlier, a substance's temperature (as measured by a thermometer) is a measure of the average kinetic energy of the particles in it. For any substance at any particular temperature, the particles in it will have range of kinetic energies. This can be shown as a simple diagram:

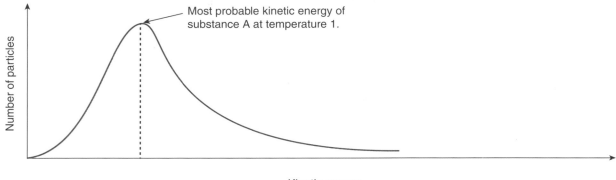

Most probable kinetic energy of substance A at temperature 1.

Number of particles

Kinetic energy

▶ An increase in the energy added to the substance will increase the average kinetic energy of the particles. However an increase in average kinetic energy does not shift the entire graph to the right as there are always some particles that will have zero or close to zero kinetic energy.

5. Sketch a graph below to show the distribution in kinetic energy for substance A (above) if its temperature was increased:

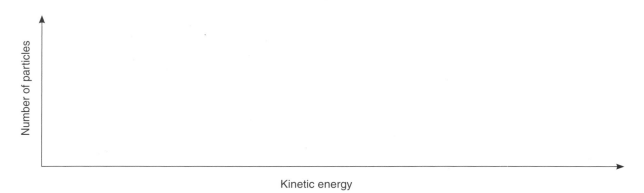

Number of particles

Kinetic energy

6. The graph below shows the kinetic energy distribution of the particles in substance B. Substance B is a liquid at room temperature and normal atmospheric pressure. Use the graph to explain why some of substance B will evaporate (turn into a gas) even though its temperature is not at its boiling point:

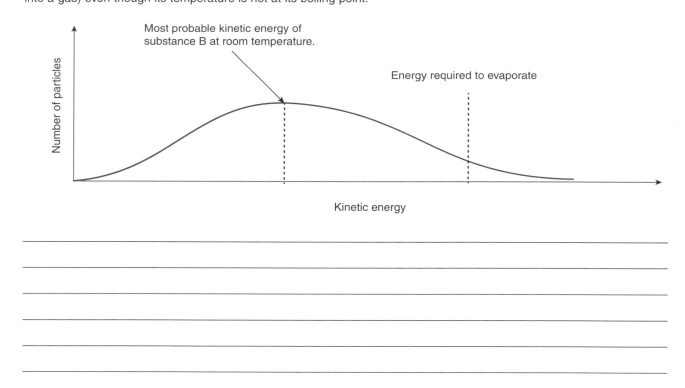

Most probable kinetic energy of substance B at room temperature.

Energy required to evaporate

Number of particles

Kinetic energy

_____

_____

_____

_____

_____

©2019 **BIOZONE** International
ISBN: 978-1-927309-71-1

ELABORATE: Thermometers

▶ You should be familiar with spirit or alcohol thermometers (shown right) and have used them to measure temperature. The spirit thermometer has replaced mercury thermometers in classrooms due to the hazards of mercury escaping from a broken thermometer.

▶ Liquid based thermometers work by having a small reservoir containing the liquid (the bulb). When the temperature of the substance being measured increases, the liquid in the bulb expands into the capillary tube inside. Liquids that expand a lot on heating are useful in thermometers as this makes the reading more precise (because of a greater amount of distance between each mark on the thermometer).

▶ The liquid in the thermometer must also have a lower freezing point and higher boiling point than the range of temperatures being measured.

7. Use diagrams to show how the particles in a spirit thermometer are affected as temperature is increased:

Lower temperature   Higher temperature

8. Discuss how the thermometer works in term of energy transfer between the particles of the substance being measured and the particles in the thermometer:

_____

_____

_____

_____

_____

EVALUATE: Ammonia and hydrogen chloride again

▶ We have seen that an increase in temperature is related to an increase in kinetic energy in the particles of a substance. Kinetic energy is also related to velocity (speed) and mass. An increase in the temperature of a substance will not affect the mass (which will remain constant) so therefore must affect the velocity.

▶ For a gas, we can use these ideas to produce a formula for finding the average velocity of the particles in a gas for any given temperature. The formula is simply:

$$v = \sqrt{\frac{3RT}{M}}$$

Where v = velocity (m/s), R = the gas constant (8.314 J/K/mol), T = absolute temperature (K), and M = the molar mass of the gas in kilograms (kg)

9. Revisit your answer to question 3(c) on page 39. Use the equation to explain why ammonium chloride forms at the position in the tube shown in the photo on page 39.
Note the following: Hydrogen chloride has a mass of 0.0365 kg per mole. Ammonia has a mass of 0.0170 kg per mole (a mole is a specific number in the same way a dozen is a specific number). Room temperature is 298 K.

_____

_____

_____

_____

_____

_____

12 Modeling Energy Flow

EXPLORE: Energy2D

▶ Computer simulations reproduce the behavior of a system using a computer. They provide a way to predict and model changes in a system by altering specific conditions within that system. Computer simulations allow us to examine complex systems and run many simulations in a short space of time without having to experiment with a physical system. The results of simulations are more accurate when the simulation closely models the real system.

▶ During this activity you will explore heat transfer using a simulation program called Energy2D. Energy2D is a free, downloadable simulation software developed by Dr. Charles Xie at the Concord Consortium. The software has many simulations (right) and a workspace where you can build your own thermal experiments.

▶ In this activity, you will use the program to model all three modes of heat transfer (conduction, convection, and radiation).

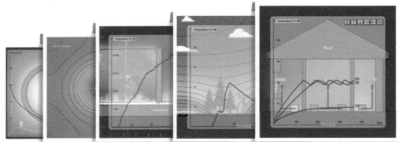

http://energy.concord.org/energy2d/index.html

Energy2D

▶ Download Energy2D via the link on **BIOZONE's Resource Hub** or from http://energy.concord.org/energy2d/index.html

▶ When you open the program you will see the screen on the right. Become familiar with the tools (below).

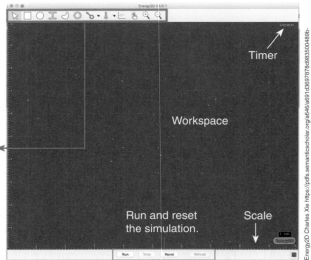

Timer

Workspace

Run and reset the simulation.

Scale

Energy2D Charles Xie https://pdfs.semanticscholar.org/ae646/a691d3b9787d98835004d8bb-761477l06c2d0.pdf

Drawing tools let you draw the object you want to investigate.

You can add thermometers and anemometers to measure temperature and wind speed.

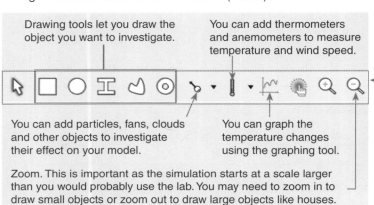

You can add particles, fans, clouds and other objects to investigate their effect on your model.

You can graph the temperature changes using the graphing tool.

Zoom. This is important as the simulation starts at a scale larger than you would probably use the lab. You may need to zoom in to draw small objects or zoom out to draw large objects like houses.

Getting familiar with Energy2D

Follow the instructions below to run a simple simulation looking at heat and temperature and conduction. This will help you to become familiar with using Energy2D.

i. Click on the **Examples** tab at the top of the screen. Select **Heat and Temperature** then **Thermal Equilibrium Between Identical Objects** from the drop down menu (right). You will see the screen shown below right.

ii. Run the simulation for 10 seconds (push stop to end the simulation). You can stop and start the simulation at any time. For this example, the timer has been slowed down. You can do this by right-clicking on the workspace and selecting **Properties**. To set the timer to real-time, set the **Time Steplength** to 0.1. This allows you to easily observe the changes in both thermometers during the simulation period.

iii. You can view the simulation as a graph. After you have run your simulation click the graph icon to view the graph. If you would like to see the data graphed as the simulation runs, simply click on the graph icon *before* you click Run.

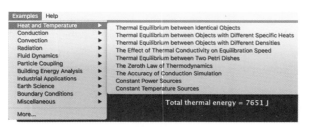

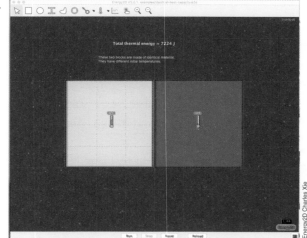

Energy2D Charles Xie

Now you are familiar with the simulation you will carry out some investigations involving conduction, convection, and radiation.

    PS3.A PS3.B ETS1.B CE SPQ SSM EM

©2019 **BIOZONE** International
ISBN: 978-1-927309-71-1

Using Energy 2D to explore conduction

You will rebuild and modify the example simulation to understand how it works. You should get the same outcome as the example on the previous page.

INVESTIGATION 2.6: Exploring conduction using Energy2D

1. Work in pairs if you wish. Click on **File** then select **New**.

2. Reduce the scale by clicking on the **+** zoom tool 3 times.

3. Select the **rectangle** drawing tool and draw a box 2 squares wide by 3 squares high. **Copy** the box and **paste** it into the workspace right next to the original box (box 1). Do not leave any gaps between them.

4. **Right click** box 1 and select **Properties**. Click on the **Source** tab. Set the **Temperature** to 40. Under the **Thermal** tab, set **Thermal Conductivity** to 1, **Specific Heat** to 1000 and **Density** to 1.204. Click **OK**.

5. Repeat for box 2 but set the temperature to 10. Under the **Thermal** tab, set **Thermal Conductivity** to 1, **Specific Heat** to 1000 and **Density** to 1.204. Click **OK**.

6. Click **View** in the menu and select **See through**.

7. Click on the **thermometer icon** and then click on box 1 to add a thermometer. Repeat for box 2.

8. **Right click** on the workspace and select **Properties**. Deselect **Convective** under the **General** tab. This will set the simulation to conductive movement of energy. Set the **Time Steplength** to 0.02. Under the **Medium** tab set **Background Temperature** to 0, **Conductivity** to 0, **Specific Heat** to 1 and **Density** to 1.204. Click **OK**.

9. **Run** the simulation and produce a graph. Print your graphs and staple them to this page if you wish.

1. What happens to the temperature of the boxes over time? _They become the_ _same + stay at 23.8°C_

2. (a) Why is the conductivity of the workspace set to 0 in the simulation? _Cause the atmosphere doesn't affect the temp._

   (b) Set the conductivity of the workspace to 4 and rerun the simulation. Produce a graph. How does this change the way the temperature changes over time? _They both reduce + end at 0°C_

   (c) Why does the temperature change like this? _because the atmosphere's temp is now affecting the temp._

▶ There are many other simulation examples that can be run.

▶ Save your work, then select **Thermal Equilibrium Between Objects with Different Specific Heat** from the examples. Run the simulation and observe the result. You can rebuild this simulation using your previous work, simply change the specific heat of your rectangles to 1000 and 2000.

▶ To see how the energy is flowing click on the **Heat flux** arrows in the **View** menu.

▶ Explore the **Heat and Temperature**, and **Conductive** examples. You will find simulations of some of the investigations your have already carried out in the lab. For example, the **Thermal Equilibria Between Two Petri Dishes** is similar to the beaker inside another beaker experiment you carried out in Investigation 2.2.

3. Carry out the simulation using the conditions you used during the investigation 2.2. Do you get the same results? If not, can you explain the differences? _no the results were a little bit different._

Using Energy2D to explore convection

▶ You will now explore convection using the Energy2D simulations. These will show you how heat flows in a liquid or a gas. You will observe how convection currents can be generated.

INVESTIGATION 2.7: Exploring convection using Energy2D

1. From the **Examples** menu select **Convection** and then **Natural Convection With Different Temperatures** from the pull down menu. Run the simulation and observe how convection currents move.

2. Click on **File** then select new.

3. Select the **rectangle** drawing tool and draw a box 1 square by 1 square. Place this box in the bottom left corner of the workspace.

4. **Right click** box 1 and select **Properties**. Click on the **Source** tab. Set the **Temperature** to 100 and click **Constant Temperature**. Then click **OK**.

5. **Run** the simulation and observe the movement of the convection currents (as areas of heat).

6. Once the simulation is running you may want to add thermometers in the convection flow. Do this by clicking on the **thermometer** icon and then clicking on the workspace to add it. You will need to click on the thermometer each time you want to add a new one.

7. Add some particles to simulation by clicking on the **particle** icon. Place them above the heat source, and in the corners of the workspace (you can change their colors under **Properties**). **Rerun** the simulation and observe their movement.

4. Describe the flow of the convection current about the workspace: _it is flowing_
in a circular motion
_____
_____
_____
_____

5. During the simulation click stop and observe the temperature recorded by the thermometers within the convection current. What do you notice?

The temperature has risen a lot.
_____
_____

6. In step 7 you added particles to the simulation. Describe how the particles move: _____
They move in circles + bounce off
the walls
_____
_____

Using Energy2D to explore radiation

▶ In this activity you will work in pairs or small groups to explore heat transfer through radiation. There are many variables you can investigate, two are provided below but your teacher may ask you to explore others.

▶ **Temperature dependence**: From the **Examples** menu select **radiation** and then **temperature dependence** from the pull down menu. Run the default simulation observing how the temperature of the energy source boxes affect the temperature of the destination boxes. What happens when you change the temperature of the thermal sources higher or lower? You can do this by clicking on the box and selecting properties.

▶ **Angular dependence**: From the **Examples** menu select **radiation** and then **angular dependence** from the pull down menu. Run the default simulation observing how the temperature of the energy source boxes affect the temperature of the destination boxes. What happens when you change the angle of the destination boxes? You can do this by clicking on the box and selecting properties to change its angle relative to the thermal source.

©2019 **BIOZONE** International
ISBN: 978-1-927309-71-1

7. Present your findings to the class as a short oral or digital presentation. If possible use digital media (textual, graphical, audio, visual or interactive) to enhance your presentation and add interest.

Use this page to summarize and organize the findings of your group's exploration of heat transfer through radiation. Present the information in a clear, coherent, and organized manner. This will help you with your digital presentation.

_____

_____

_____

_____

_____

_____

_____

_____

_____

_____

_____

_____

_____

_____

_____

_____

_____

_____

_____

_____

_____

_____

_____

_____

_____

_____

_____

_____

_____

INVESTIGATION 2.8: The Zeroth law of thermodynamics

1. Under examples choose: **Heat and Temperature**, then **The Zeroth Law of Thermodynamics**.

2. Record the temperatures of A and B here: A: _____ B: _____

3. Run the simulation. What are the final temperatures of A and B? _____

4. Reset the simulation. Place a thermometer on C. Record the temperature here: _____

5. Run the simulation again. Record the final temperature of C: _____

6. Reset the simulation and change the temperature of A to 100°C.

   What is the final temperature of all three thermometers now? _____

8. (a) At which point in the simulation do all three substances A, B, and C reach thermal equilibrium?

   _____

   (b) If we know the temperature of A at equilibrium, what can be said about the temperature of B and C at equilibrium?

   _____

   (c) Write an explanation and mathematical expression of the Zeroth Law of thermodynamics: _____

   _____

   _____

9. On a cold morning with an air temperature of 0°C you walk outside and place your hands on the wooden rail of the porch, which feels cool, but not overly so. A bowl of water on the porch has started to freeze. You pick a piece of ice from the water. The water feels very cold. Explain why the wood and the water feel like they are at different temperatures, but in reality are at the same temperature.

   _____

   _____

ELABORATE: Changes in thermal energy

▶ You have seen that thermal energy flows from one object to another in the direction of highest thermal energy to lowest thermal energy (i.e. hot to cold). You have also measured the temperature change in substances as energy is transferred from one to the other.

▶ Thermal energy is given the symbol Q and is measured in joules (J).

▶ Recall the investigation in which a small beaker of cold water was placed into a large beaker of hot water (or the simulation on the previous page). This resulted in the water in the small beaker becoming hotter (gaining energy) and the water in the large beaker becoming cooler (losing energy). Assuming no energy was lost out of the system a simple equation can be written describing the transfer of thermal energy (heat) between the two beakers.

10. Write an equation showing the thermal energy transfer between two masses:

   _____

▶ Recall in chapter 1 you calculated the energy changes when water was heated. You used this calculation to find the amount of chemical energy in a substance (e.g. corn chips). The equation you used was:

   Energy produced = 4.2 x change in temperature (ΔT °C) x mL water

▶ This equation is specifically for calculating the energy in water. You can now produce a more general equation. Energy produced can be replaced by ΔQ, the change in thermal energy. The change in temperature remains the same (ΔT). The mass of the substance (m in grams) can be substituted for mL of water. 4.2 is the specific heat of the water. The symbol for specific heat on any substance is c.

11. Using the information above write an equation to show how to calculate the change in energy in a substance:

   _____

12. We can now explain the thermal transfer between two objects. Study the simple diagram below:

Initial system:

M1.
Temperature: 80 °C
Mass: 200 g
Specific heat: 0.45 J/K/g

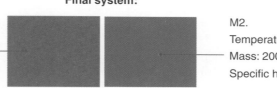

M2.
Temperature: 20 °C
Mass: 200 g
Specific heat: 0.45 J/K/g

Final system:

M1.
Temperature: 48 °C
Mass: 200 g
Specific heat: 0.45 J/K/g

M2.
Temperature: 48 °C
Mass: 200 g
Specific heat: 0.45 J/K/g

(a) What was the total thermal energy of the initial system? _____

(b) Calculate the thermal energy (heat) transferred between the two objects: _____

_____

(c) How much energy was lost from the system? _____

_____

13. (a) A 2.00 kg iron pot was placed on a fire and heated to 140°C. 1.00 kg of water at 20 °C was added to the pot. Assume the pot loses no heat to the environment and negligible water is lost as steam.

Specific heat of water: 4.19 J/K/g
Specific heat of iron: 0.452 J/K/g

Predict the temperature of the system at thermal equilibrium:

_____

(b) The equation for determining the temperature at equilibrium can be derived from your equation in question 10. It is a weighted average of the temperatures (it takes into account mass and specific heat):

$$T_{final} = \frac{m_{iron}c_{iron}T_{iron} + m_{water}c_{water}T_{water}}{m_{iron}c_{iron} + m_{water}c_{water}}$$

Calculate the final temperature of the system: _____

_____

_____

(c) Is the final temperature closer to that of the water's or the iron's original temperature? _____

(d) Explain why: _____

_____

_____

_____

(e) Use the principles above to explain why when cooking food you should only add a small amount of food to be cooked at a time to a hot pan or to a pot of hot water:

_____

_____

_____

_____

©2019 **BIOZONE** International
ISBN: 978-1-927309-71-1

13 Energy in the Earth

ENGAGE: It's hot down there!

▶ Eight of the world's deepest mines (all gold mines) are located in South Africa. Six of these extend more than 3 km below the ground. The deepest is the Mponeng gold mine, which descends 4 km underground (equivalent to 10 Empire State Buildings end on end). The trip from top to bottom takes nearly 90 minutes. At the deepest point in the mine the temperature of the rock is more than 60°C. A slurry of ice is pumped down into the mine to cool the air to below 30°C and fans are used to move the cooled air around. In 2015, the Mponeng mine produced more than 6 tonnes of gold.

▶ The enormous depth of the mine has produced some interesting scientific discoveries. The bacterium *Desulforudis audaxviator* is found only in the Mponeng mine and lives completely independently from the Sun. It is the only organism known to live entirely alone in its ecosystem. It acquires nutrients directly from the radioactive decay of minerals in the surrounding rock and extracts carbon from dissolved carbon dioxide. The hydrogen it needs for its respiration comes from the splitting (decomposition) of water by radioactive decay of uranium and thorium in the rocks.

▶ In comparison to these extremely deep mines, the deepest natural cave system on Earth is the Veryovkina Cave in the country of Georgia. Its deepest known point is 2212 m below the surface.

1. (a) Have you or any of your classmates been in a cave or mine?

   yes I have

   (b) How deep did it go? *very deep*

2. The rock temperature in the Mponeng mine is about 60°C. Discuss with your classmates where you think this heat is coming from. Write your ideas down here:

   the ground + the potential energy stored in the rocks

3. Natural cave systems are often quite cool, rather than hot like deep mines. Can you suggest a reason why?

   mines go down towards the earth core.

4. Temperature increase through the Earth's crust averages about 25°C per km over a 4 km depth, giving 100°C at 4 km *on top of* the surface temperature. However, geothermal heat flows over a continent are not uniform. The Mponeng Gold Mine (and the other deep gold mines in South Africa) are located over a "cold spot", where the increase in temperature with depth is only 9°C per km. Use this information to explain why it has been possible to mine to such depth in this region:

   because its a cold spot + it doesn't get as hot as fast.

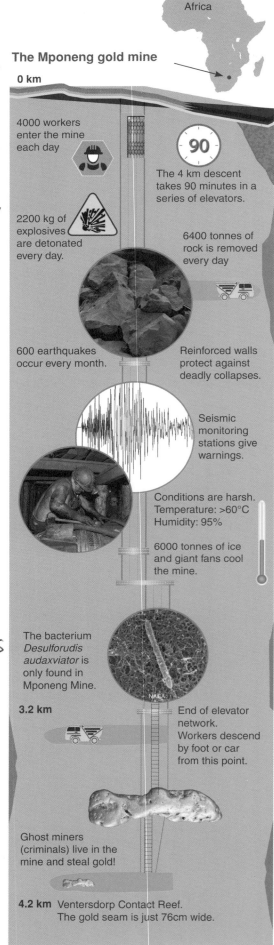

Africa

The Mponeng gold mine

0 km

4000 workers enter the mine each day

90 — The 4 km descent takes 90 minutes in a series of elevators.

2200 kg of explosives are detonated every day.

6400 tonnes of rock is removed every day

600 earthquakes occur every month.

Reinforced walls protect against deadly collapses.

Seismic monitoring stations give warnings.

Conditions are harsh.
Temperature: >60°C
Humidity: 95%

6000 tonnes of ice and giant fans cool the mine.

The bacterium *Desulforudis audaxviator* is only found in Mponeng Mine.

3.2 km

End of elevator network. Workers descend by foot or car from this point.

Ghost miners (criminals) live in the mine and steal gold!

4.2 km Ventersdorp Contact Reef. The gold seam is just 76cm wide.

ESS2.A ESS2.B CE SPQ EM

EXPLORE: A journey to the center of the Earth

▶ There have been many attempts to drill as deep into the Earth as possible. Some of today's oil wells reach 10,000 m below the surface. Drilling to such a depth produces many problems including those due to the effects of the high temperatures at such depths.

▶ Drilling boreholes into the Earth can produce a lot of useful scientific data, including the type of rock encountered and even data about past climates. The most simple but often most interesting is how the temperature changes with depth.

▶ In 1970, a scientific project was started on the Kola peninsula in Russia to drill as far as possible into the Earth's crust. The Kola Superdeep Borehole eventually reached 12,262 m before problems with high temperatures and equipment made it not possible to drill any deeper. At that depth, the temperature measured 180°C.

▶ Drilling was shut down in 1995, but the borehole is still the deepest artificial point on Earth. Some oil drilling projects have drilled longer boreholes but they have not reached as deep into the ground.

▶ One of the most interesting finds of the project was the discovery of water in the rocks nearly 7 km down. Until then no one had thought water would exist at such a depth.

▶ Fossils of microscopic plankton were found 6 km down.

▶ Studies of seismic waves (generated by earthquakes and explosions) indicated a transition between granite above and basalt below ~7 km. Drilling found this was not the case.

The borehole has long been welded shut...

...and the buildings abandoned

5. (a) The data below shows the temperature data for the Kola Superdeep Borehole. Plot the data on the grid provided. When plotting depth data, the depth should be plotted descending on the y axis.

Depth (m)	Temperature (°C)
0	–
200	16.80
400	18.21
600	19.79
800	21.47
1000	23.32
1200	25.24
1400	27.20
1600	30.00
1800	32.46
2000	35.00
2200	37.84
2400	40.24
2600	42.90
2800	45.80
3000	47.91
3200	50.00
3400	54.51
3600	58.00
3800	61.20
4000	62.73
4200	65.10
4400	68.41

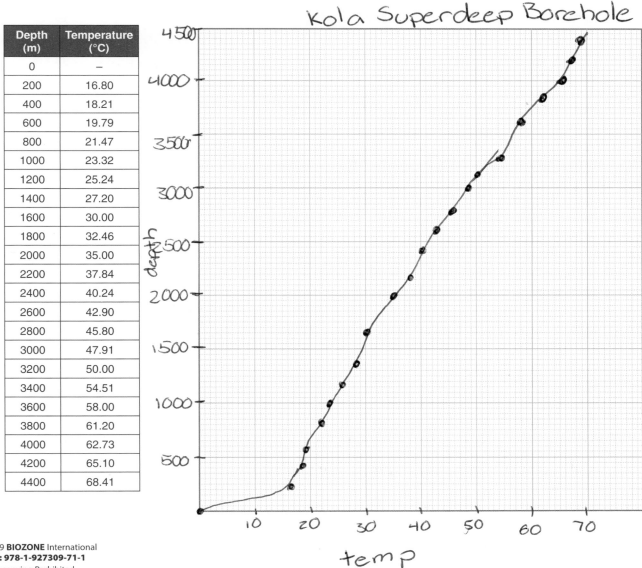

Kola Superdeep Borehole

©2019 **BIOZONE** International
ISBN: 978-1-927309-71-1
Photocopying Prohibited

(b) Describe the shape of the graph and what it shows: _it shows that the deeper you decend the hotter it gets_

(c) Draw a line of best fit through the data and use it to determine the rate of temperature increase per meter:

10°C per 1000 meters

(d) What would you expect to happen to the temperature if depth was increased? _____

it would rise

✖ The limits of the graph stop you from adding the temperature of the of the Kola borehole at 12,262 m (180°C). However this can be done using a spreadsheet such as Microsoft Excel.

(a) Type the data into the spreadsheet in columns as presented on the previous page, then add the final data points to the row underneath. Alternatively you can use the link on **BIOZONE's Resource Hub** to download the data.

(b) Plot the data on a scatter graph (not a line graph). Use the mouse to right click the y axis and select **Format axis**. In the tab that appears tick the box labeled **Values in reverse order**.

(c) Does the shape of the graph change from your original plot? _____

(d) By replotting the data with temperature on the y axis it is possible to obtain an equation for the graph from which we can calculate temperature as depth increases.
Right click on a data point and select **Add trendline**. Then tick **Display equation on chart**.
The equation is $y = 0.0137x + 8.9026$. This means: temperature = 0.0137 x depth (meters) + 8.9026.
On average it is 6,371 km to the center of the Earth.

i. What percentage to the center of the Earth did the Kola Superdeep Borehole reach? _____

ii. Use the equation above to calculate the temperature at the center of the Earth, assuming the temperature keeps rising in the same pattern as your plotted data:

iii. From analysis of various studies and data scientists estimate the temperature at the center of the Earth to be about 6000°C. Does this match with your answer above? What does this mean about how Earth is structured?

7. Scientists were surprised to find water in the rocks more than 6 km deep. Where do you think the water may have come from and why had it stayed at that depth? (HINT: Think of the increase in temperature and pressure at this depth).

I think that it might come from the condensation of the heat

8. Based on the seismic data, scientists thought that there should be a change from granite to basalt at ~7 km below the surface (because the waves travel at different speeds through the different rock types). However, the drilling showed this wasn't the case. As a group, discuss this and suggest what might account for the change in seismic wave velocity:

They underestimated how much it would change per meter.

©2019 **BIOZONE** International
ISBN: 978-1-927309-71-1
Photocopying Prohibited

EXPLAIN: Where does the Earth's internal heat come from?

▶ The Earth's interior contains many different elements. Some have many isotopes (elements with the same atomic numbers but different atomic masses). Some of these isotopes are radioactive and give off heat.

▶ Radioactive elements spontaneously decay. This means their atoms break apart into smaller atoms. This process is called nuclear fission. As the atom decays, a very small amount of mass is lost. This very small amount of mass is turned into a lot of energy. Much of this energy is converted to heat.

▶ The material that formed the Earth included elements such as uranium. Uranium is the heaviest naturally occurring element on Earth. It occurs in numerous isotopes all of which are radioactive. U-238 is the most common and the most stable. It has a half life of about 4.5 billion years (about the current age of the Earth).

▶ When a U-238 atom decays it produces a helium nucleus (an alpha particle) and a thorium atom (Th). The thorium atom itself is unstable and will also decay. There is a decay chain that continues until a stable atom of the elements lead is produced. Heat is released at each stage of the decay and this heats the interior of the planet.

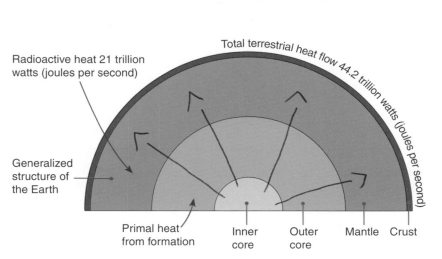

Radioactive heat 21 trillion watts (joules per second)

Total terrestrial heat flow 44.2 trillion watts (joules per second)

Generalized structure of the Earth

Primal heat from formation

Inner core | Outer core | Mantle | Crust

About half the heat radiated by the Earth comes from the decay of radioactive elements. Most of the rest comes from heat left over from the Earth's formation.

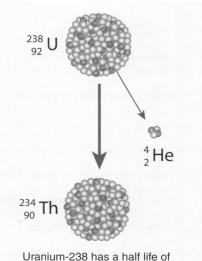

$^{238}_{92}$U

$^{4}_{2}$He

$^{234}_{90}$Th

Uranium-238 has a half life of 4.5 billion years and decays to thorium-234. Thorium-234 has a half life of just 24.5 days.

9. (a) How much heat energy is radiated by the Earth per second? _21 trillion watts per sec_

   (b) Where does the heat in the Earth come from? _the inner + outer core + flows out_

10. Based on your knowledge of the flow of heat add arrows to the diagram of the Earth above to show the direction of the flow of heat we would expect in the Earth:

11. Given that the amount of radioactive isotopes on Earth (or anywhere else) becomes less over time as the isotopes decay what can be said about the heat produced by the Earth in the distant past and in the distant future?

    There was more heat produced long ago + the amount will continuously decrease.

©2019 **BIOZONE** International
ISBN: 978-1-927309-71-1
Photocopying Prohibited

14 Evidence for Earth's Structure

ENGAGE: Earthquakes

▸ Earthquakes occur due to sudden movements in the Earth's crust, usually along fault lines where parts of the crust move in opposite directions.

▸ The release of energy that accompanies this movement moves through the Earth as waves.

▸ The more energy that is released, the larger the waves, the further they travel, and the more damage they can do.

1. When was the last time you experienced an earthquake? _____

2. What did the earthquake feel like? _____

_____

_____

3. (a) Is the area you live in prone to earthquakes? _____

(b) If so, where is the nearest fault line? _____

(c) Is there any evidence of the fault line above ground? If so, describe it: _____

_____

_____

EXPLORE: Seismic waves

▸ Movement of the ground along fault lines in the Earth's crust causes earthquakes. During an earthquake, energy is released as a series of waves. These include compressional, or **P-waves** and shear waves, or **S-waves**. Because these travel through the body of the Earth they are called body waves.

P-waves (Primary waves)

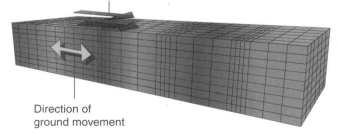

Direction of wave movement

Direction of ground movement

S-waves (Secondary waves)

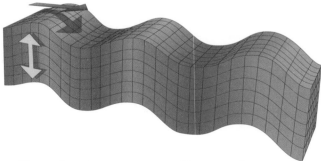

P-waves are compression waves (similar to sound waves in air). P-waves are the fastest moving wave from an earthquake and so are the first to arrive at a seismograph. P-waves can travel through all media whether it is liquid or solid.

S-waves are transverse waves. They move the ground perpendicular to their direction of travel. They are unable to travel through liquids. They move more slowly than P waves, arriving at a seismograph some time after the P wave.

4. Describe two differences between P-waves and S-waves: _____

_____

_____

_____

_____

©2019 **BIOZONE** International
ISBN: 978-1-927309-71-1
Photocopying Prohibited

P-waves are able to travel through both solids and liquids but S-waves can only travel through solids.
This can be demonstrated using the **model of a liquid** below:

Displacement same direction as wave direction

P-waves propagate by compression and expansion of molecules in the direction of the wave's movement. When a **mass of liquid** (right) is displaced, the molecules will bump into neighbors in the direction of the displacement. This produces a compression wave (a P-wave) that moves in the direction of the displacement. Thus P-waves are able to travel in liquids.

Displacement 90° to wave direction

In solids, S-waves move at right angles to a displacement because the molecules in a solid are connected (think of shaking a rope).

If a **mass of liquid** (right) is displaced, the molecules at right angles to the displacement are not connected to the molecules in the displaced volume of liquid and are not in a position to be bumped into by the displaced molecules. This means an S-wave cannot form in liquids.

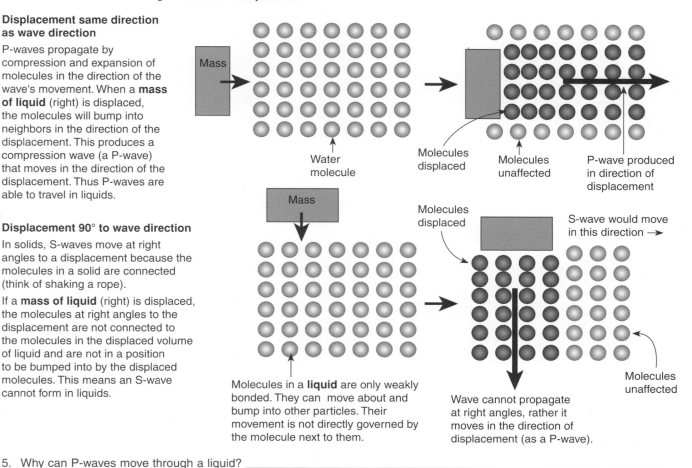

Water molecule

Molecules displaced

Molecules unaffected

P-wave produced in direction of displacement

Molecules displaced

S-wave would move in this direction →

Molecules unaffected

Molecules in a **liquid** are only weakly bonded. They can move about and bump into other particles. Their movement is not directly governed by the molecule next to them.

Wave cannot propagate at right angles, rather it moves in the direction of displacement (as a P-wave).

5. Why can P-waves move through a liquid? _____

_____

_____

6. Draw a model below (similar to the model shown above) to show how an S-wave can move through a solid. Remember in a solid the molecules are more tightly bonded and so are affected by the movement of the molecule next to them:

7. P-waves and S-waves are sent through an object from one side. The make up of the interior of the object is unknown.

(a) If **only** P-waves are recorded on the opposite side of the object, does the object have a solid or liquid interior?

_____

(b) If **both** P-waves and S-waves are recorded, does the object have a solid or liquid interior?

_____

EXPLORE: The deep structure of the Earth

The table right shows the time taken for the first P-waves from an 7.2 magnitude earthquake in Baja California (04 November 2010) to reach seismometers around the world (as determined by a sudden change in the background data).

The locations of the seismometers are given by the degrees from the Earth's center below the origin of the earthquake (the epicenter). There are 360° in a circle, so 180° would be on the other side of the planet from the epicenter (see the next page).

Location (degrees)	Time to reach station (minutes)
2	0.7
15	3.5
25	6.0
38	7.4
50	9.1
65	10.6
77	11.9
89	13.0
101	13.8
113	19.5
122	19.8
140	19.7
151	19.7

8. Graph the data on the grid below as a scatter graph (don't join the points):

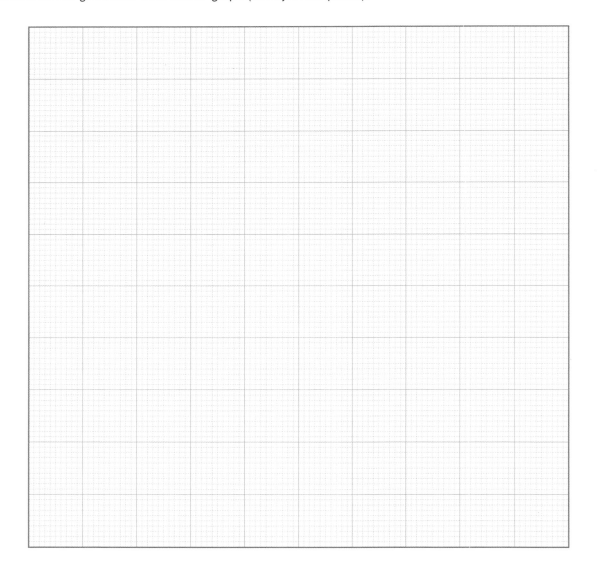

Time

Distance (degrees)

9. There is an anomaly in this data where there appears to be a sudden increase in the time of travel. At what degrees does this anomaly appear?

_____

©2019 **BIOZONE** International
ISBN: 978-1-927309-71-1
Photocopying Prohibited

10. (a) If the interior of the Earth was uniform (all the same) what effect would this have on the travel times of seismic waves as they passed through the Earth?

_____

_____

(b) What does the anomaly we see in the graph tell us? _____

_____

11. (a) The circle below represents a cross section through the interior of the Earth. From the line from the center to the point marked A, use a protractor to measure the angle you wrote in question 9. Mark along the circle's edge where this angle cuts the circle. Do this in both directions from point A.

(b) Draw 2 straight lines from point A to the marks you have made on the circle.

(c) Now rotate point A by 30° along the edge of the circle (shown below for you). Repeat (a) and (b) above measuring and drawing lines from 30°.

(d) Rotate point A another 30°. Repeat this and repeat (a) and (b). Repeat this process until you return to the original point A.

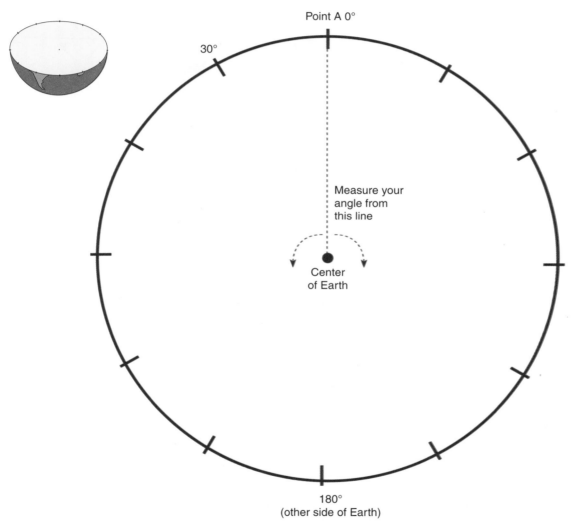

Point A 0°

30°

Measure your
angle from
this line

Center
of Earth

180°
(other side of Earth)

12. (a) What general pattern or shape has been produced on the circle above? _____

(b) What does this tell us above the structure of the Earth? _____

_____

_____

_____

13. (a) Measure the radius (in mm) of the circle representing the Earth on the previous page: _____

    (b) Measure the radius of the inner shape you mapped (in mm): _____

    (c) Given that the radius of the Earth is 6371 km, at what depth (in km) does the structure appear to be?

    _____

    _____

14. The diagram right shows the velocity of P-wave and S-waves at different depths in the Earth.

    (a) What happens to the velocity of the P-wave at 3000 km depth?

    _____

    (b) What happens to the S-wave at 3000 km depth?

    _____

    (c) Relate the diagram right to the diagram of the Earth you mapped on the previous page. In what state (of matter) is the material in the center of the Earth revealed by your mapping? How do you know?

    _____

    _____

    _____

    _____

    _____

    _____

    _____

Wave velocity (km/s)

Depth (km x 1000)

EXPLORE: The outer structure of the Earth - discovering the Moho

▶ In 1909 Andrija Mohorovicic was studying seismic waves from an earthquake in the Kupa Valley (also know as the Kulpa Valley) near Zargreb, Croatia. He plotted the travel times of P-waves and S-waves from the earthquake epicenter to various seismometers on a scatter graph. The fitted trend lines are shown right. Note $\bar{P}$ and P_n are primary waves. The notation reflects the models Mohorovicic used to calculate the lines. $\bar{S}$ and S_n are secondary waves.

▶ Mohorovicic noticed 2 distinct sets of P and S waves and a difference in the travel time of the waves.

▶ His work resulted in the discovery of the Mohorovicic discontinuity.

15. (a) At approximately what distance from the epicenter do the wave travel times of the P waves start to diverge from each other, and the S waves start to diverge from each other?

    _____

    (b) Are the waves slowing down or speeding up after this point (compare $\bar{P}$ to P_n and $\bar{S}$ to S_n)? _____

    (c) What do you think this change in travel time (= change in velocity) might represent? _____

    _____

    _____

    _____

©2019 **BIOZONE** International
ISBN: 978-1-927309-71-1
Photocopying Prohibited

EXPLORE: Experiments reveal more detail about the upper layers of the Earth

In an experiment in New Zealand, geologists exploded charges of TNT to produce seismic waves and recorded their echoes from layers of rock in the Earth. The echoes revealed a jelly-like layer of rock just 10 km thick between the rigid upper layer of the Earth (lithosphere) and the more plastic lower layer (asthenosphere). This research solved the problem of how the lithosphere could move about on the surface of the asthenosphere.

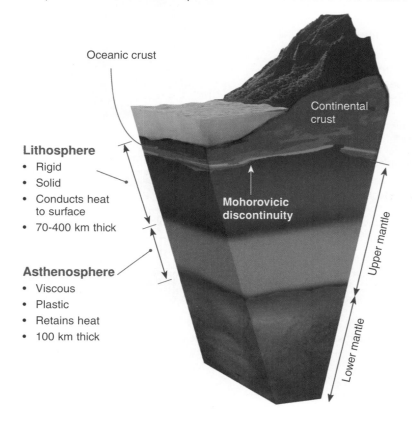

Oceanic crust

Continental crust

Lithosphere
- Rigid
- Solid
- Conducts heat to surface
- 70-400 km thick

Mohorovicic discontinuity

Upper mantle

Asthenosphere
- Viscous
- Plastic
- Retains heat
- 100 km thick

Lower mantle

The lithosphere

▶ The **lithosphere** (*lithos* = "stone") refers to the crust and the very uppermost part of the upper mantle. It is both rigid and solid, and broken up into sections called tectonic plates.

▶ The lithosphere can be divided into continental lithosphere, which contains relatively light minerals, and oceanic lithosphere, which contains much denser minerals. The lithosphere is ~400 km thick over the continents and ~70 km thick in the oceans.

The asthenosphere

▶ The **asthenosphere** *(asthenes* = "weak")* is the upper layer of the Earth's mantle, below the lithosphere. This layer of rock is fluid-like with viscous and elastic behavior. It changes through plastic deformation (much like ®Silly Putty). This means it can slowly move about, allowing for movement of the tectonic plates above.

▶ The asthenosphere is relatively thin (~100 km thick).

16. (a) Describe the structure of the lithosphere: _____

_____

_____

(b) Describe the structure of the asthenosphere: _____

_____

_____

17. Describe the general method that scientists use to study the interior of the Earth: _____

_____

_____

_____

18. Why would exploding charges of TNT be a useful (and convenient) way of exploring the internal structure of the Earth?

_____

_____

19. (a) Studying the diagram above, where is the Mohorovicic discontinuity located? _____

_____

(b) Why would this cause the observation seen in "Discovering the Moho"? _____

_____

_____

EXPLORE: More evidence of what's under our feet

▶ In 1797, Henry Cavendish carried out a simple yet brilliant experiment involving the gravitational attraction of lead balls to measure the density of the Earth. His measurements produced a density of just over 5.4 g/cm. The current revised value is 5.51 g/cm.

▶ This is much denser than the average density of rocks in the crust. This leads us to theorize that the core must contain the majority of the dense material on Earth.

▶ Other evidence of the material in the core comes from laboratory experiments and, somewhat surprisingly, from space.

Meteorites

▶ Certain types of meteorites called carbonaceous chondrites (top right) represent the composition of the early Earth (they are left overs from the formation of the solar system). Their make-up shows that there should be more nickel and iron in the Earth than we see on the surface or in magma welling up from the mantle.

▶ The speed of seismic waves in the mantle do not match what would be expected if it contained more iron and nickel. The missing material must therefore be in the core.

Laboratory experiments

▶ From the size of the Earth and its density, we can begin to estimate the pressures near the core. Using devices called diamond anvils (right) it is possible to reproduce the pressure thought to exist at the core. Experiments have shown how iron behaves at such high pressure and allowed us to construct theories as to how the iron core was formed.

A carbonaceous chondrite meteorite

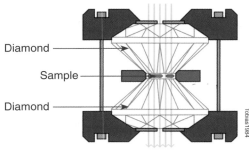

Diamond —

Sample —

Diamond —

20. How does evidence from meteorites help us understand the structure and make-up of the Earth? _____

_____

_____

_____

21. How do laboratory experiments help us understand the structure of the Earth? _____

_____

_____

INVESTIGATION 2.9: Determining properties of rocks

See appendix for equipment list.

1. Gather some examples of different types of rocks. If you can, identify the rock type or its origin, e.g. volcanic or sedimentary.

2. Weigh each rock and record its mass.

3. Measure the volume of each rock by filling a larger graduated cylinder with water to a known volume (e.g 200 mL) and placing the rock into it.

4. Record the increase in volume for each rock.

5. Divide the mass by the volume to find the density of each rock.

Rock sample	Mass (g)	Volume (mL or cm³)	Density (g/mL or g/cm³)
Total			

22. What type of rock had the greatest density? _____

23. Given that the density of Earth's core is though to be 12 g/cm³, how close was this rock to the density of the core?

_____

EXPLAIN: The internal structure of the Earth

▶ Over the course of this activity we have studied various sets of data that can now be used to produce a simple model of the internal structure of the Earth.

▶ We can interpret Mohorovicic's data as representing a fairly shallow boundary between two layers of the Earth. From the earlier seismic data we have determined there is another much deeper boundary between layers.

▶ This leads us to believe there are at least three layers in the Earth, one of which is liquid. Other more refined studies have led scientists to build a model of the Earth as shown below.

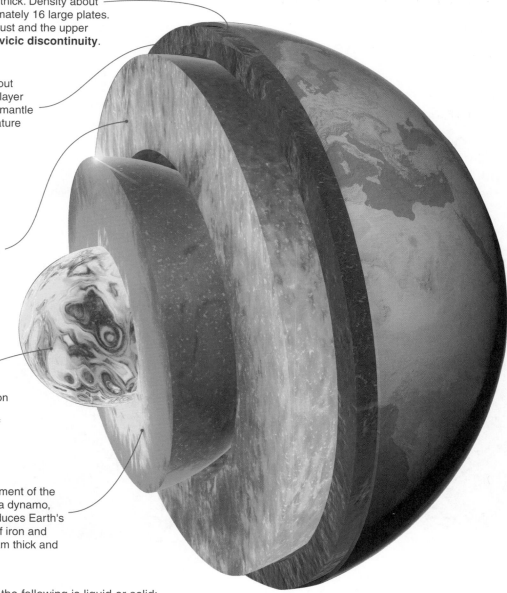

Crust: Between 5 and 70 km thick. Density about 3 g/cm^3. Divided into approximately 16 large plates. The boundary between the crust and the upper mantle produces the **Mohorovicic discontinuity**.

Upper mantle: Solid layer about 400 km thick with a transition layer between the upper and lower mantle of about 300 km. The temperature reaches about 1000°C.

Lower mantle: Approximately 2000 km thick, extending to about 3000 km below the surface. Like the upper mantle it is solid but behaves like a viscous liquid with convection currents slowly moving the mantle about.

Inner core: Solid. The temperature at the core is between 5500°C and 6000°C. The core is made of mostly iron and nickel and is about 1200 km in diameter. The density of the core is about 12 g/cm^3.

Outer core: Liquid. The movement of the outer core produces acts like a dynamo, an electric generator and produces Earth's magnetic field. Made mostly of iron and nickel the outer core is 2200 km thick and reaches 4000°C.

24. Identify whether each of the following is liquid or solid:

   (a) Mantle: _Solid_   (b) Outer core _liquid_   (c) Inner core _Solid_

25. What produces the Earth's magnetic field? _the outer core produces the earths magnetic field_

26. How do we know the mantle and inner core are solids? _because we can measure the density + temp to tell_

27. How do we know the outer core is a liquid? _it acts like dynamo, an electric generator + P waves can go through it_

15 Energy Drives Plate Tectonics

ENGAGE: Earthquakes...again. Oh, and volcanoes

▶ Do you live in a earthquake-prone place? Do you have any volcanoes nearby (with in 200 kilometers)? Or do you live in a place where the ground remains relatively stable and there is little geologic activity?

1. In groups discuss why the area you live in has (or doesn't have) earthquakes. Summarize your ideas below:

orange county has major fauts
running through it so its
earthquake prone. we are
on techtonic plates

2. Think about all the places you have heard of (e.g. on the news or on the internet) that have had earthquakes or volcanic eruptions. In groups, try to place them on a map. Is there any pattern?

the san andreas faut +
on the coast

EXPLORE: Patterns in the Earth

▶ The map below shows the locations of various geological formations and activity including the locations of major earthquakes, volcanoes, mountain ranges, ocean trenches and ocean ridges.

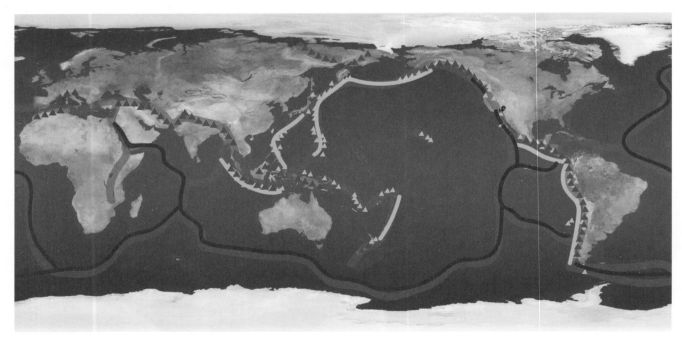

▬▬▬ Ocean ridges	
▬▬▬ Earthquake zones	▲▲▲▲▲▲▲ Mountain chains
▬▬▬ Ocean trenches	▲ ▲ ▲ ▲ Volcanoes

▶ When overlaying these features we see that they produce a pattern. Ocean trenches, oceans ridges, and mountain ranges tend to match up and carry on from one another. Volcanoes are found very near ocean trenches and earthquakes can be felt in all of these places.

▶ From this data scientists have concluded that the surface of the Earth, the crust, is divided up into several large "tectonic plates" and a dozen of so smaller ones.

3. (a) In groups, research tectonic plates. Find the names of the seven major plates and map them. You can download a blank world map from **BIOZONE's Resource Hub**. Staple your map to this page.

(b) There is an area of earthquakes and volcanoes on the map above that isn't like the other areas. Locate and name this unexpected feature:

nawaii island chain

ESS2.B ESS2.C P CE SPQ EM

©2019 **BIOZONE** International
ISBN: 978-1-927309-71-1

EXPLORE: Something's below Hawaii

▶ The Hawaiian islands are well known for their volcanic activity. A fissure of the Kilauea Volcano on Hawai'i (Big Island) erupted on May 3 2018. Huge flows of lava swept towards the coast, destroying many homes along the way. Kilauea has been in an also continuous state of eruption since 1983.

▶ Volcanic activity becomes less on other islands the further away you travel from Big Island.

▶ Images of the islands taken by satellite show a chain of islands and seamounts that are the remains of ancient volcanoes. The oldest are in the north-west, the youngest in the south-east. Only the islands at the south-east end of the chain are still volcanically active.

▶ This leads us to two possible theories:

(1) The volcanic activity under the islands is moving and the volcanic islands form as volcanic activity moves along.

(2) The volcanic activity under the islands is stationary and volcanic islands form as the Earth's surface passes over it.

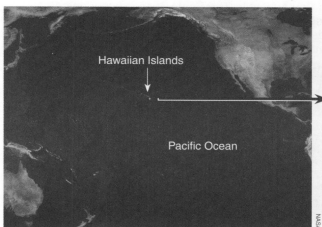

4. In the spaces below draw a simple diagram to show the mechanism of theories 1 and 2 above:

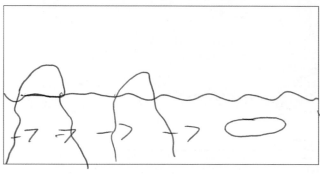

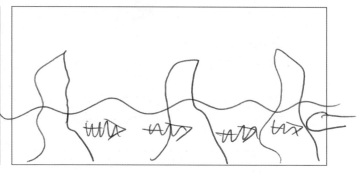

5. (a) Use the information below to produce a graph of the **age of the volcanoes** in the Hawaiian island chain *compared* to their **distance from the Kilauea volcano** on Big island.

Name	Distance from Kilauea (km)	Age (millions of years)
Kilauea	0	0
Mauna Kea	54	0.375
Kohala	100	0.43
East Maui	182	0.75
West Maui	220	1.32
East Molokai	256	1.76
West Molokai	280	1.9
Koolau	339	2.6
Waianae	374	3.7
Kauai	519	5.1
Nihoa	780	7.2
Necker	1058	10.3

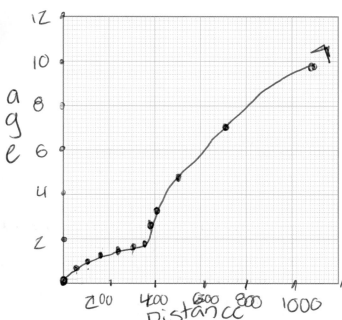

©2019 **BIOZONE** International
ISBN: 978-1-927309-71-1
Photocopying Prohibited

(b) Use the data to calculate the rate of the movement of the volcanic activity below the Hawaiian island chain:

_____

_____

(c) What is the simplest way to find out if the volcanic activity below Hawaii is moving or if the ground above a stationary hot spot is moving? (Hint: think about modern navigation).

_____

_____

EXPLORE: The bottom of the Atlantic Ocean

▶ The Atlantic Ocean is divided into the North Atlantic and South Atlantic. The South Atlantic separates Africa and South America. Rock samples from the South Atlantic sea floor have been dated using radiometric dating (using the decay of radioisotopes). The map below shows the dates of the rocks at various locations on the sea floor. The dark gray areas around the continents indicates continental shelf (see page 64).

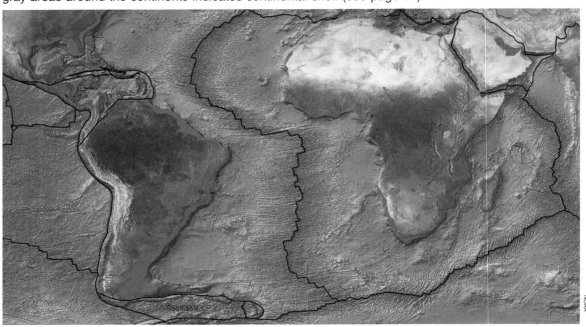

million years

0 20 40 60 80 100 120 140 160 180 200 220 240 260 280

6. What do you notice about the age of the rocks on the sea floor? _____

_____

_____

7. Suggest why areas such as the mid Atlantic ridge are also termed constructive plate boundaries: _____

_____

_____

8. (a) What do you notice about the shape of continental shelves of South America and Africa? What does this suggest?

_____

_____

(b) How does the dating of the rocks in the Atlantic give evidence for your suggestion in (a)? _____

_____

_____

_____

©2019 **BIOZONE** International
ISBN: 978-1-927309-71-1
Photocopying Prohibited

EXPLORE: Ocean trenches

▸ The lowest points on the Earth's surface are in the ocean trenches. The Mariana Trench is the deepest of these trenches at 10,994 meters below sea level, an area called Challenger Deep. The Mariana Trench is located east of Guam in the Western Pacific. Humans have only reached Challenger Deep twice.

▸ Many ocean trenches are found at the edges of plate boundaries where the part of the Earth's crust is sinking down into the mantle. Because of this, these boundaries are also destructive plate boundaries.

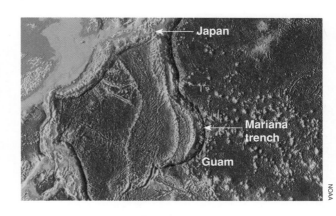

9. The data below shows earthquake depths recorded at the Tonga Trench in the western Pacific Ocean.
   (a) Plot a scatter graph of the data on the grid provided:

Tonga trench	
Longitude (°W)	Depth (km)
176.2	270
175.8	115
175.7	260
175.4	250
176.0	160
173.9	60
174.9	50
179.2	650
173.8	50
177.0	350
178.8	580
177.4	420
178.0	520
177.7	560
177.7	465
179.2	670
175.1	40
176.0	220

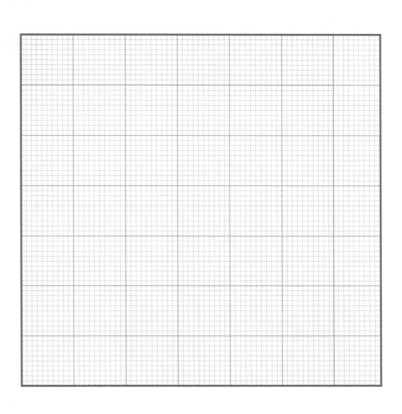

(b) Add a line of best fit through the data points:

(c) Draw a diagram in the space below to show the how the tectonic plates are moving at the Tonga Trench. Include relevant labels:

EXPLORE: Continental shelves

▶ The continents extend out beyond the shorelines many kilometers out to sea. The continental shelf is the part of the continent that is submerged under relatively shallow water (diagram below).

▶ At the edge of the continental shelf, there is a sudden increase in slope (the continental slope). Here the depth of the water suddenly increases from sometimes a few hundred meters to often many thousands of meters. This is the boundary between the continental crust and the oceanic crust.

▶ The continental crust is thicker and less dense than the oceanic crust. As a result it is usually higher than the oceanic crust and much of it sits out of the surrounding oceans.

▶ There are exceptions to this. Most of the continental mass of Zealandia (right) is below the ocean with only the narrow New Zealand archipelago sitting above the water.

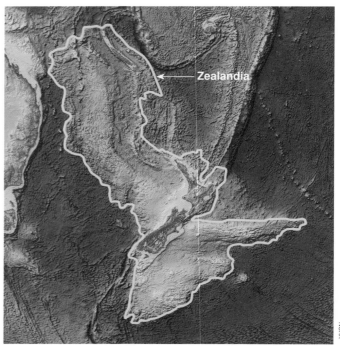

▶ The extent of the continental shelf around a continent varies and some continental areas have very little shelf, especially where the edge of an advancing oceanic plate dives underneath continental crust in an offshore subduction zone such as off the coast of Chile (compare western and eastern coasts of South America opposite).

▶ It is useful to study the shape of the continental shelves rather than the coastlines, because coastlines change over time as ocean levels rise and fall (e.g. when ice sheets expand and retreat). The map opposite shows the continental shelves in **dark gray** at the edges of the continents.

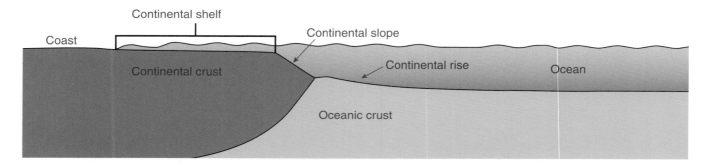

10. From the full page map right we can see that various continental shelves appear to match with other continental shelves. The distortion of the map at the poles makes some of these difficult to see clearly. The age of the rocks on the sea bed are also shown. These can help matching up continental shelves.

(a) Describe the location of continental shelves that match those identified below:

Continental shelf	Matching continental shelf
North eastern coast of North America	
North western coast of Europe	
Eastern coast of South America	
South coast of Australia	

(b) What does the matching of these continental shelves suggest about continents and the tectonic plates?

_____

_____

_____

©2019 **BIOZONE** International
ISBN: 978-1-927309-71-1
Photocopying Prohibited

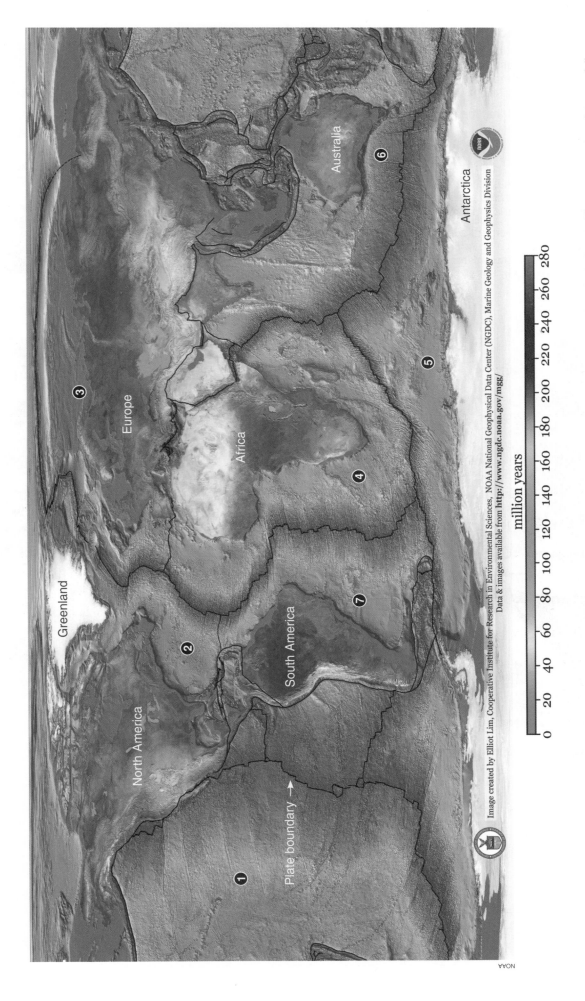

Map of the Earth showing the ages of the sea floor, the boundaries of the plates, the continents, and the continental shelves in dark gray. The seven major plates as follows: **1)** Pacific Plate, **2)** North American Plate, **3)** Eurasian Plate, **4)** African Plate, **5)** Antarctic Plate, **6)** Indo-Australia Plate, **7)** South American Plate.

Image created by Elliot Lim, Cooperative Institute for Research in Environmental Sciences, NOAA National Geophysical Data Center (NGDC), Marine Geology and Geophysics Division
Data & images available from **http://www.ngdc.noaa.gov/mgg/**

million years

EXPLAIN: Plate boundaries

▶ We have seen that the Earth's surface is divided into a series of tectonic plates. These plates appear to be sinking at some plate boundaries e.g. in areas of ocean trenches. In other areas they are spreading apart e.g. in the Atlantic ocean.

▶ We have also seen that the plates move about (such as over the hot spot under Hawaii).

▶ From this evidence, scientists have been able to make a model of the way the tectonic plates move about.

▶ Plate growth occurs at divergent boundaries along sea floor spreading ridges whereas plate attrition (destruction) occurs at convergent boundaries marked by deep ocean trenches.

▶ Divergent and convergent zones make up approximately 80% of plate boundaries. The remaining 20% are called transform boundaries, where two plates slide past one another with no significant change in the size of either plate (right).

The San Andreas fault is a transform boundary running for over 1000 km through California.

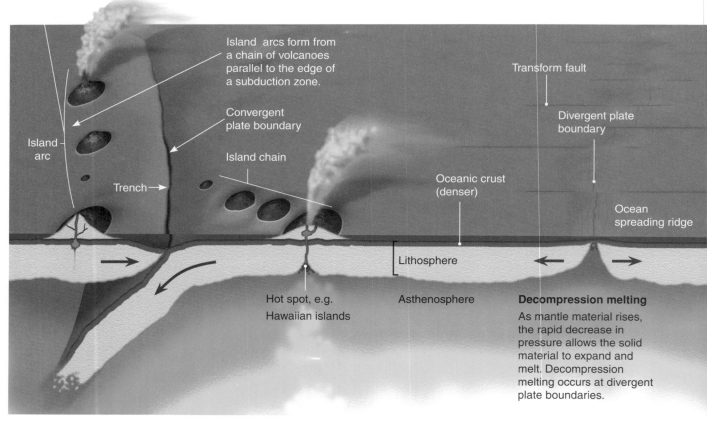

Island arcs form from a chain of volcanoes parallel to the edge of a subduction zone.

Island arc

Convergent plate boundary

Island chain

Trench →

Oceanic crust (denser)

Transform fault

Divergent plate boundary

Ocean spreading ridge

Lithosphere

Hot spot, e.g. Hawaiian islands

Asthenosphere

Decompression melting
As mantle material rises, the rapid decrease in pressure allows the solid material to expand and melt. Decompression melting occurs at divergent plate boundaries.

11. Describe what is happening at each of the following plate boundaries and identify an example in each case:

   (a) Convergent plate boundary: _____

   _____

   _____

   (b) Divergent plate boundary: _____

   _____

   _____

   (c) Transform plate boundary: _____

   _____

   _____

©2019 **BIOZONE** International
ISBN: 978-1-927309-71-1
Photocopying Prohibited

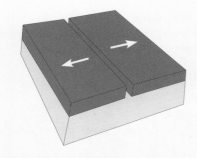

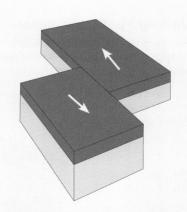

Plate boundaries moving towards each other are called **convergent plate boundaries**. Where oceanic crust and continental crust meet, the denser oceanic crust will travel under the continental crust, creating a subduction zone. Volcanoes form along the continental border of a subduction zone. When continental crusts collide, huge mountain ranges such as the Himalayas can form.

Divergent plate boundaries form where the tectonic plates are moving away from each other. These are commonly found along the mid ocean ridges, but occasionally are seen on land, as in the Great Rift Valley and Iceland. Divergent boundaries are also known as constructive boundaries as they produce new crust from the upwelling of magma.

Transform boundaries are formed when the tectonic plates are moving past each other. Crust is neither formed nor destroyed. Examples include the San Andreas fault in California and the Alpine Fault in New Zealand.

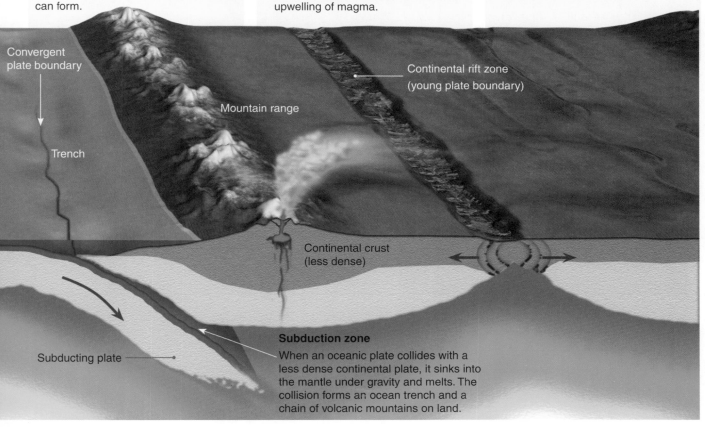

Convergent plate boundary

Trench

Mountain range

Continental rift zone (young plate boundary)

Continental crust (less dense)

Subduction zone
When an oceanic plate collides with a less dense continental plate, it sinks into the mantle under gravity and melts. The collision forms an ocean trench and a chain of volcanic mountains on land.

Subducting plate

12. Identify the type of plate boundary at which each of the following occurs:

(a) Mountain building: _____   (c) Creation of new ocean floor: _____

(b) Subduction: _____   (d) Island arc: _____

13. (a) Explain why the oceanic crust subducts under the continental crust in a subduction zone: _____

_____

_____

(b) What cause volcanoes to form along the continental plate boundary of a subduction zone? _____

_____

_____

_____

©2019 **BIOZONE** International
ISBN: 978-1-927309-71-1
Photocopying Prohibited

ELABORATE: Plates, subduction, and water

▶ The diagram below shows a subduction zone. Hot magma rising above the subducting plate can reach the surface through fissures to form volcanoes. Volcanoes are often found along the edge of a subduction zone, on the plate overriding the plate being subducted.

The rocks of the continental crust have a density of about 2.7 g/cm.

The rocks of the oceanic crust have a density of about 3.0 g/cm.

The oceanic crust sinks under the continental crust and drags the rest of the plate down with it.

The subducting oceanic plate drags down water-laden sediment and rocks. Water vapor rising from the subducting plate meets hotter rocks above, which are close to their melting point. The water vapor enters these rocks, lowering their melting point and producing magma.

The solid mantle deforms under the enormous heat and pressure at depth, moving heat and material by convection. The deformation moves the tectonic plates above.

▶ Water has an important effect on the rocks of the lithosphere and asthenosphere above a subduction zone. Water disrupts the bonds in rocks and lowers their melting point, causing the formation of magma. This can be modeled using ice and salt (NaCl). In this model ice acts as the rock in the mantle and salt as the water held inside the rock.

Sodium chloride and water solution

The data below shows the freezing point (and thus melting point) of several solutions of NaCl. These were made using fresh water and sodium chloride salt to produce concentrations ranging from 0 g/L to 250 g/L:

Solution concentration (g/L)	Freezing/melting point (°C)
0	0
50	-3
100	-6.5
150	-10.9
200	-16.5
250	-24.5

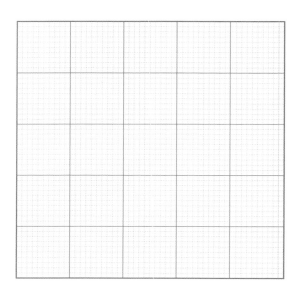

14. Use the tabulated data to graph the melting point of the water/salt solutions:

15. What is the significance of water's effect on rocks below the surface? _____

_____

_____

_____

16 How do the rocks on the mantle move, and why does this appear unusual? _____

_____

_____

_____

©2019 **BIOZONE** International
ISBN: 978-1-927309-71-1
Photocopying Prohibited

16 On the Move Revisited

▶ Throughout this chapter you have studied the way energy flows from hot to cold objects and how energy is transferred by conduction, convection, and radiation.

▶ You have seen that the interior of the Earth is heated by the energy produced by the decay of radioactive isotopes in the mantle and from the heat left over from its formation.

▶ You have also studied the movement of the tectonic plates on the Earth's surface and the way they come together (converge) and move apart (diverge).

▶ You should now have enough information to build a simple model of the interior of the Earth and explain its movements.

1. At the start of this chapter you were shown how Africa and South America were once joined and have now spread apart. You should now be able to explain how this occurs. In your explanation you should draw and explain a model of the Earth to show how convection moves the tectonic plates.

_____

_____

_____

_____

_____

_____

_____

_____

_____

_____

_____

_____

_____

©2019 **BIOZONE** International
ISBN: 978-1-927309-71-1

17 Summative Assessment

1. What do you understand by the term energy? _____

_____

_____

_____

2. Why does a metal rail feel cold on a cold morning? _____

_____

_____

3. Heat energy always flows in a specific direction. What is this direction? Explain how it causes convection currents and at large scales how this drives plate tectonics on Earth. Diagrams will help your explanation.

_____

_____

_____

_____

_____

_____

_____

_____

_____

4. The entropy of the Earth is very slowly increasing. In regard to the interior of the Earth, explain why entropy is increasing and describe the possible effect on plate tectonics of increasing entropy on Earth:

_____

_____

_____

_____

_____

_____

_____

  ESS2.A   EM

©2019 **BIOZONE** International
ISBN: 978-1-927309-71-1
Photocopying Prohibited

▶ This part of this activity uses Google Earth. Google Earth is freely available online at https://www.google.com/earth/ Type Google Earth into your search engine or follow the link on the **BIOZONE Resource Hub** for this activity.

5. Launch Google Earth. On the left hand side of the screen there are menu icons. Click on the **Voyager** icon, the one that looks like a ship's wheel. Find the **Layers** tab and click it. Scroll down until you see the **Seafloor age** globe. Click this. A layer will be added to the globe showing the ages of the seafloor around the globe.Rotate the globe around to the Atlantic Ocean.

    (a) Where are the youngest rocks in the Atlantic found? _____

    _____

    (b) What is their age? _____

    (c) Where are the oldest rocks in the Atlantic found? _____

    _____

    (d) What is their age? _____

    (e) Notice that parts of the continents are shaded blue. How old are these rocks? _____

    (f) Why would these rocks be this age? _____

    _____

    _____

    (g) In general where are the youngest rocks of the Earth's ocean floor found? _____

    _____

    _____

6. Exit the Seafloor age. Google Earth is able to import .kml or .kmz files. These files contain data that adds layers to the globe. First, go to https://earthquake.usgs.gov/learn/kml.php or follow the link at the **BIOZONE Resource Hub**.

    i)   Download the **Tectonic Plate Boundaries** file. Save it where you can find it easily. Return to Google Earth.
    ii) Click on the **My Places** tab, then click **Import KML file**.
    iii) Click **Open file** and navigate to where you have saved the file. You can save the imported file to Google Earth so that it is also available when you open Google Earth.
    iv) Once the file is imported, several layers will appear showing plate boundaries and their direction and speed of movement. Click off the **My Places** tab to hide it and show the map legend.

    (a) Navigate to the edge of the Pacific plate east of Aomori, Japan. Find the point labeled PA-NA. What direction is this point of the plate moving?

    _____

    (b) Click on the point. An information box will appear. How fast is the plate moving? _____

    (c) Navigate to New Zealand, east of Australia. There is an unusual situation regarding the direction of the tectonic plate movements to the north and south of the country and in the middle of the South Island. Describe the direction of the plate movements about New Zealand and predict how this might affect the shape of the country in the distant future.

    _____

    _____

    (d) Navigate to California in the Western United States. The San Andreas fault runs nearly the length of California. What type of fault is it? How can you tell?

    _____

    _____

    (e) Find the point labeled PA-NA just south of Santa Maria. How fast is this point moving? _____

    (f) The distance between Santa Maria and San Jose (on the opposite side of the fault) is about 285 km. How long will it take for these two places to be side by side, based on the speed of movement above?

    _____

    _____

7. (a) Label the layers of the Earth in the diagram below:

   (b) Beside your labels note whether the layer is solid or liquid:

   (c) There was an earthquake at point A on the diagram below. Draw lines to show how the P and S-waves of the earthquake would move through the Earth and identify where they could (or could not) be detected on the surface.

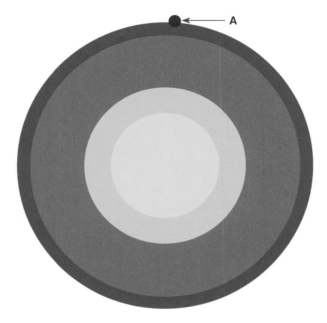

A

   (d) Explain why the waves are detected in this way: _____

   _____

   _____

   _____

   _____

8. Draw a diagram in the space below to show the mechanisms of plate tectonics that shift the plates of the Earth's crust. You should make sure your diagram has divergent and convergent boundaries and the layers of the Earth that are significant in plate tectonics.

©2019 **BIOZONE** International
ISBN: 978-1-927309-71-1
Photocopying Prohibited

9. The data below shows earthquake depths recorded off the coast of Chile with respect to longitude (East/West) position:

(a) Plot a scatter graph of the data on the grid provided:

Chile coast	
Longitude (°W)	Depth (km)
67.5	180
68.3	130
62.3	480
62.0	600
69.8	30
69.8	55
67.7	120
67.9	140
69.2	35
68.6	125
68.1	145
65.2	285
69.7	50
68.2	160
66.2	230
66.3	215
68.5	140
68.1	130

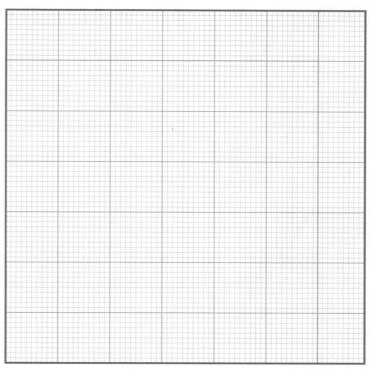

NEED HELP?
See activity 60

(b) Add a line of best fit through the data points:

(c) Draw a diagram below to show the how the tectonic plates are moving near the Chile coast. Include relevant labels:

10. Study the images below. Place them in order of first event to last event. Explain your order of events in terms of entropy:

A   B   C

_____

_____

_____

_____

_____

_____

_____

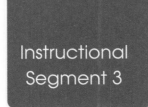

Instructional Segment 3

Atoms, Elements, and Molecules

Anchoring Phenomenon

Burp! Antacid tablets and the stomach.

18 24

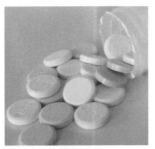

What is inside atoms and how does this affect how they interact?

☐ 1 In the previous chapters, you have analyzed data about the bulk properties of matter (e.g. melting point, boiling point, state at room temperature), and you can now begin to relate these properties to the components that make up atoms. Much of chemistry is about analyzing and explaining patterns and using these explanations to predict unknowns. Try to predict the properties of objects that are missing from a simple pattern. How did you make your decision? In the 1800s, Mendeleev used pattern recognition to arrange the elements known at the time into a table in which elements with similar properties fell into groups. Mendeleev realized that the chemical and physical properties of the elements were related to their atomic mass in a predictable, periodic way. You can model this process yourself using cards representing the first 20 elements of the periodic table. What patterns did you use to organize the elements? How can you use the pattern to predict elements not included?

19

☐ 2 How does atomic structure help to explain the trends and patterns we see in the periodic table? Create a time line to summarize the history of the atomic model showing how models were revised and refined on the basis of new evidence. Examine different models of an atom. How are they similar? How are they different? Use a model of atomic structure based on the number of protons in the nucleus and the number and arrangement of electrons to predict properties of elements in the periodic table and how their atoms will interact.

20

☐ 3 Use a dynamic periodic table and/or second-hand data to investigate the various properties of the first 20 elements in the periodic table, Properties could include atomic radius, first ionization energy, and electronegativity. Describe any patterns revealed by your investigations and explain how they provide evidence for our existing model of atomic structure.

21 25

What models can we use to predict the outcomes of chemical reactions?

☐ 4 Use the periodic patterns of electron configuration to predict the outcome of simple chemical reactions. Explain why atoms of main-group elements tend to combine so that each atom has a filled outer (valence) shell giving it the same electron configuration as a noble gas (octet rule). Use chemical equations as mathematical models to show that matter is conserved as atoms interact in chemical reactions. Use the mole to convert from the atomic to the macroscopic scale (e.g. mass of a substance). Use your knowledge of moles and molar mass to determine the molecular formula of new compounds and investigate the percentage composition of a substance (such as an ore or a hydrated crystal).

22 25

☐ 5 Stoichiometry is a technical word for how we use a balanced chemical equation to calculate the amounts of reactants and products in a chemical reaction. It is based on the *law of conservation of mass* and *law of definite proportions*.

22 25

> *Law of conservation of mass: the mass of an object or objects never changes, no matter how the parts are rearranged.*

> *Law of definite proportions: a chemical compound will always have the same proportions of each element by weight.*

Use mathematics and apply basic principles of stoichiometry to balance equations and determine quantitative values for the reactants and products in your laboratory investigations.

☐ 6 So far we have referred to the amount of a substance using mass in grams. But what about substances that cannot be easily weighed because they are in solution (dissolved)? In these cases, we refer to their concentration, i.e. the amount of the substance per liter. This might be g/L or mol/L. Use a mathematical model to calculate the mass of a substance required to produce a standard solution of a known concentration. Use titration to determine the concentration of an identified analyte for which the concentration is unknown. Show how you would use titration to determine the concentration of an analyte to test claims about the composition of a store-bought product such as vinegar or orange juice. Volume measurements have a key role in titration, so chemical analysis by titration is also called volumetric analysis.

23 25

Borealis

18 Burp!

ANCHORING PHENOMENON: Antacid tablets and the stomach

▶ The stomach naturally produces acid to aid digestion. Indigestion or heartburn are symptoms of damage to the lining of the stomach caused by overproduction of HCl (hydrogen chloride or hydrochloric acid).

▶ The overproduction of acid can be eased by using antacid tablets. These can be easily bought from the local drugstore. There are many types but all work on the principle of neutralizing the acid in the stomach.

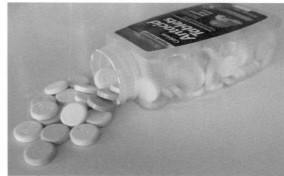

▶ There are many different ways of doing this and some are more effective than others. Some antacids produce carbon dioxide as a product and can make the user burp. Others produce no gas in the reactions.

▶ The various types of antacids generally contain one of three main ingredients to produce the neutralizing effect: calcium carbonate, sodium bicarbonate (sodium hydrogen carbonate), or magnesium hydroxide.

1. Do you know any one who uses antacids? _____

2. Do they make that person burp? _____

3. If you can, find out what the ingredients are in an antacid tablet. Can you figure out why they do or do not make that person burp?

_____

_____

4. What is the pH of stomach acid? _____

5. What is the concentration of stomach acid? _____

▶ The following questions relate to the subject matter you will be learning in this chapter. They may seem difficult now, but by the end of the chapter you should be able to answer them all (and more)!

6. Complete the word equation for each of the following reactions:

(a) Hydrochloric acid + calcium carbonate → _____

(b) Hydrochloric acid + sodium hydrogen carbonate → _____

(c) Hydrochloric acid + magnesium hydroxide → _____

7. Complete and balance the chemical equations for each of the following reactions:

(a)　　HCl +　　$CaCO_3$　→　_____

(b)　　HCl +　　$NaHCO_3$　→　_____

(c)　　HCl +　　$Mg(OH)_2$　→　_____

8. In groups, discuss how you might work out the amount of the active ingredient calcium carbonate in an antacid tablet. (Hint: calcium carbonate doesn't dissolve in water, but it does dissolve in acid). Summarize your ideas here:

_____

_____

_____

_____

_____

_____

©2019 **BIOZONE** International
ISBN: 978-1-927309-71-1

19 Properties and Patterns

ENGAGE: Patterns

▶ Many aspects of science rely on making observations and looking for patterns within a system or its parts.

▶ Once a pattern is identified, possible explanations for it (hypotheses) can be proposed and tested. If the pattern is sufficiently explained, the hypothesis can be used to predict the properties of other parts of the system whether they are known or unknown.

1. Study the simple pattern below. How many sides does the missing object have?

2. Study this simple pattern:

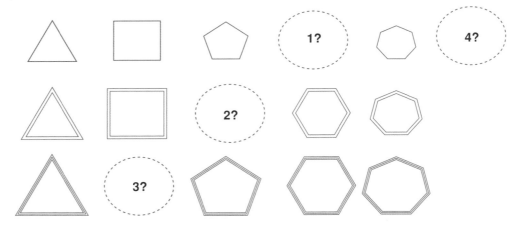

(a) Describe where would you find the largest object with the least sides? _____

(b) What would you expect to find at 3? _____

(c) Is 1? larger or smaller than 2? _____

(d) Patternologists think there may be a shape yet to be discovered at 4. Predict the properties of this shape:

_____

_____

_____

3. Shops often use patterns when displaying items on the shelf. Study the shelves right. Write down the rules by which the display has been made:

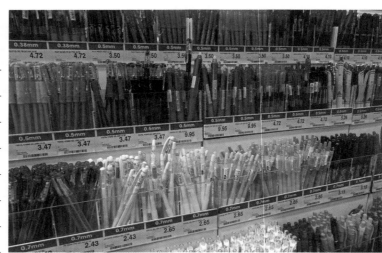

_____

_____

_____

_____

_____

_____

_____

     PS1.A P

©2019 **BIOZONE** International
ISBN: 978-1-927309-71-1
Photocopying Prohibited

EXPLORE: Creating a pattern

▸ Much of chemistry is about analyzing and explaining patterns and using these explanations to predict unknowns.

▸ Patterns could be seen in the way substances react, the heat they give off, or their macroscopic and microscopic structures.

▸ Often patterns may be seen within the group itself. From our example on the right, *a* may be a gas and *e* a solid. Even if we don't have *b*, *c*, or *d*, we can predict that *b* may be a gas or liquid, *c* a liquid and *d* a liquid or solid.

Chemical	Configuration	Energy released on reaction with Y
a		100 kJ
b		80 kJ
c		60 kJ
d		40 kJ
e		20 kJ

4. Study the twenty cards below. They are elements you will come across, some more often than others. Each card has several properties on it. However each card is named only with a letter and these **do not** correspond to any order. Cut the cards out. Use the properties on the cards to place them in some sort of order so that the properties of the cards with missing data can be predicted. You may work in pairs if you wish.

A

State at 293 K: Gas

Common oxidation states: NA

Electronegativity: NA

Valence electrons: 2

Color: Colorless

B

State at 293 K: Solid

Common oxidation states: +3

Electronegativity: 1.61

Valence electrons: 3

Color: Silver

C

State at 293 K: Solid

Common oxidation states: +1

Electronegativity: 0.98

Valence electrons: 1

Color: Silver

D

State at 293 K: Solid

Common oxidation states: +6, +4, −2

Electronegativity: 2.58

Valence electrons: 6

Color: Yellow

E

State at 293 K: Gas

Common oxidation states: −2

Electronegativity: 3.44

Valence electrons: 6

Color: Colorless

F

State at 293 K: Solid

Common oxidation states: +3

Electronegativity: 2.04

Valence electrons: 3

Color: Black

G

State at 293 K: Solid

Common oxidation states: +2

Electronegativity: 1.57

Valence electrons: 2

Color: Slate Gray

H

State at 293 K: Solid

Common oxidation states: +1

Electronegativity: 0.82

Valence electrons: 1

Color: Silver

I

State at 293 K: Gas

Common oxidation states: +1

Electronegativity: 2.20

Valence electrons: 1

Color: Colorless

J

State at 293 K: _____

Common oxidation states: −1

Electronegativity: 3.98

Valence electrons: _____

Color: Pale yellow

K

State at 293 K: Solid

Common oxidation states: +2

Electronegativity: 1.00

Valence electrons: 2

Color: Silver

L

State at 293 K: Gas

Common oxidation states: _____

Electronegativity: _____

Valence electrons: 5

Color: _____

M

State at 293 K: Solid

Common oxidation states: +4

Electronegativity: 1.90

Valence electrons: 4

Color: Gray

N

State at 293 K: Solid

Common oxidation states: +1

Electronegativity: 0.93

Valence electrons: 1

Color: Silver

O

State at 293 K: Solid

Common oxidation states: +4

Electronegativity: 2.55

Valence electrons: 4

Color: Black (commonly)

P

State at 293 K: Solid

Common oxidation states: +2

Electronegativity: _____

Valence electrons: _____

Color: Silver

Q

State at 293 K: Solid

Common oxidation states: +5,−3

Electronegativity: 2.19

Valence electrons: 5

Color: White or red

R

State at 293 K: _____

Common oxidation states: NA

Electronegativity: _____

Valence electrons: 8

Color: _____

S

State at 293 K: Gas

Common oxidation states: NA

Electronegativity: NA

Valence electrons: 8

Color: Colorless

U

State at 293 K: Gas

Common oxidation states: −1

Electronegativity: 3.16

Valence electrons: 7

Color: Yellow

This page has been
deliberately left blank

5. When you are satisfied with your pattern, draw your pattern in the space below (you can draw it in a portrait format or a landscape (sideways) format. Alternatively, glue or tape the cards to a large sheet of paper and attach it to this page. Complete the details for the cards with missing properties.

20 The Atom

ENGAGE: How small is an atom?

▶ If you had a cube of pure carbon measuring 5 cm³ how many times would you have to cut it in half before you reached the smallest possible unit of carbon?

▶ The smallest possible unit of carbon is a single carbon atom. It has a volume of about 2.0 x 10⁻²³ cm³.

Diamonds are pure carbon

▶ One simple way of finding out how may times you would need to cut your sample in half is to enter a simple formula on a spreadsheet. In the cell (A1) type =5/2. In the cell underneath (A2) type =A1/2. Then use the fill down command or click and drag the cell down to copy the formula in A2 into the cells beneath.

▶ Keep copying the formula down until you reach the volume stated above. The number of cells you did this in is the number of times you would have to cut the sample.

▶ Another (more time consuming) way is to enter 5 ÷ 2 into a calculator then continue to divide by 2 until you reach the required volume.

1. (a) How many times did you need to divide the sample in half to reach the volume of a carbon atom?

   7 times

   (b) Given the volume of a single carbon atom (2.0 x 10⁻²³ cm³), how many atoms are there in the 5 cm³ sample of carbon?

   ⋆

▶ The atom is the smallest unit that can be identified in terms of chemical properties. However it is made up of three smaller structures, called protons, neutrons, and electrons. The atom is not solid, it is in fact mostly empty space.

▶ Matter and substance are therefore effectively made up of almost nothing!

▶ If you were to remove all the empty space from yourself, you would have a volume of less than a grain of table salt.

EXPLORE: The history of the atom

▶ Just what the matter of our universe is made up of has been a question that has been asked since the time of the ancient Greek philosophers. The Greek philosophers Leucippus and Democritus believed that matter was made up of indivisible particles. From them we get the word *atom* (from *atomos* meaning uncuttable).

▶ The idea of the atom reached Europe in the late 14th century and was popularized in France in the late 15th century. During the 17th century the idea of atoms began to gain acceptance in scientific communities as research into the make-up of chemicals became more rigorous.

▶ In the 19th century, John Dalton used the concept of atoms to explain why certain elements always reacted together in the same ratios. Dalton's atomic theory was verified by Jean Perrin in the early 20th century using Einstein's explanation of Brownian motion (see the previous chapter).

▶ The theory of indivisible atoms was overturned in 1904 by J.J. Thomson with the discovery of the electron. In 1911, experiments led by Ernest Rutherford (notably the gold foil experiment) discovered that atoms in fact have an extremely dense nucleus around which electrons "orbit".

▶ In 1913, Niels Bohr adapted Rutherford's model of the atom to produce the Bohr model in which electrons are found around the nucleus at specific orbits.

▶ In 1932, James Chadwick discovered the neutron, adding the last subatomic particle to the atomic model.

Ernest Rutherford carried out some of the most important experiments into atomic structure. He was awarded the Nobel prize in 1908 and is sometimes called the father of nuclear physics.

   PS1.A P CE

©2019 **BIOZONE** International
ISBN: 978-1-927309-71-1
Photocopying Prohibited

2. In the space below produce a time line of the development of the atomic model. Research and add any other relevant developments not mentioned in the previous text:

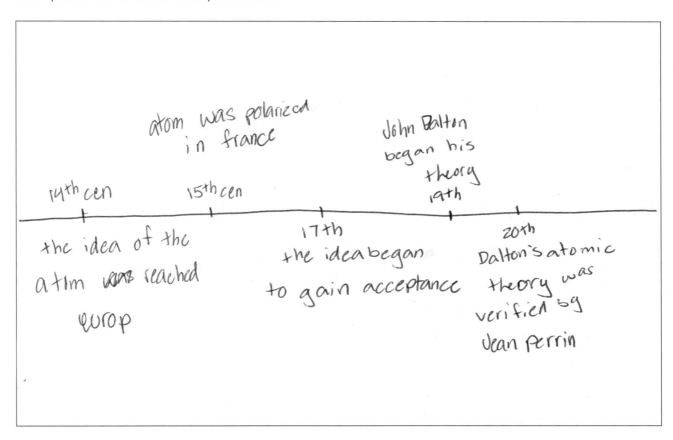

atom was polarized in france

John Dalton began his theory 19th

14th cen   15th cen

the idea of the atm was reached europ

17th the idea began to gain acceptance

20th Dalton's atomic theory was verified by Jean perrin

EXPLORE: Finding the nucleus

▶ Under the direction of Ernest Rutherford, Hans Geiger and Ernest Marsden carried out a series of experiments in which alpha particles (positively charged helium nuclei) were fired at thin gold foil. They observed the pattern produced on a detection screen (below).

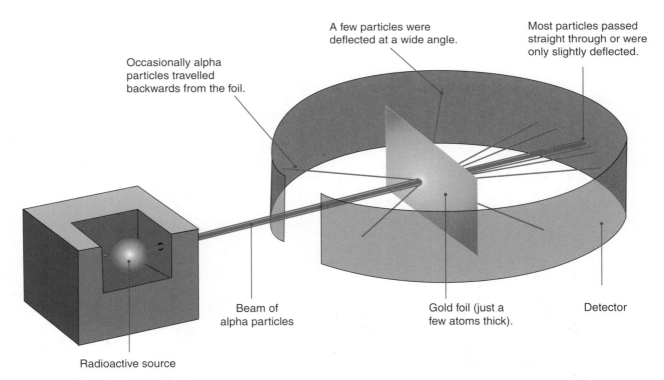

A few particles were deflected at a wide angle.

Most particles passed straight through or were only slightly deflected.

Occasionally alpha particles travelled backwards from the foil.

Beam of alpha particles

Gold foil (just a few atoms thick).

Detector

Radioactive source

▶ Based on calculations from earlier atomic models, it was expected that the alpha particles would pass straight through the gold foil or be only very slightly deflected.

▶ Instead the alpha particles were observed to scatter and occasionally "bounce" back at more than 90°.

Thomson's model of
the atom (1904)

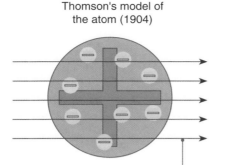

Alpha particles

Rutherford's model of
the atom (1911)

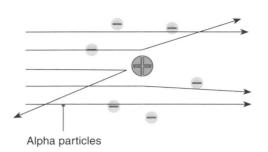

Alpha particles

J.J. Thomson proposed that atoms were a region of positive charge in which electrons were embedded. It is often referred to as the plum pudding model. Under these conditions, alpha particles would pass right through the atom with little deflection.

Rutherford elaborated on an alternative theory proposed by Hantaro Nagaoka known as the Saturn model. Rutherford proposed the atom was in fact made of an incredibly dense nucleus around which the electrons orbited.

3. What were the expected results of the gold foil experiment? _that the alpha particles would pass straight through + very slightly be deflected_

4. Describe the observed results: _they scattered + some bounced back_

5. How did Rutherford explain the observed results? _he said that the atom was very dense nucleus around which the electron orbited_

EXPLORE: Atomic models

▶ Models of the atom are important for being able to explain the behavior of nuclear and chemical reactions. Different models suit different purposes. For example, Rutherford's model of the atom explained the placement of charges and matter in the atom, but it is not suitable for explaining chemical reactions.

▶ Rutherford's model was replaced in 1913 by the Rutherford-Bohr or simply Bohr model. The Bohr model is able to explain the positions of electrons around the nucleus and from that, the behavior of atoms during chemical reactions. Bohr's model has since been replaced by the Schrodinger and Heisenberg model with later modifications (importantly from James Chadwick adding the neutron).

6. The atom is depicted in many ways in books or on the internet. In the space below, choose six models or depictions of the atom you can find in books or on the internet. Draw them or print and paste them into the space below. Describe similarities and differences between them:

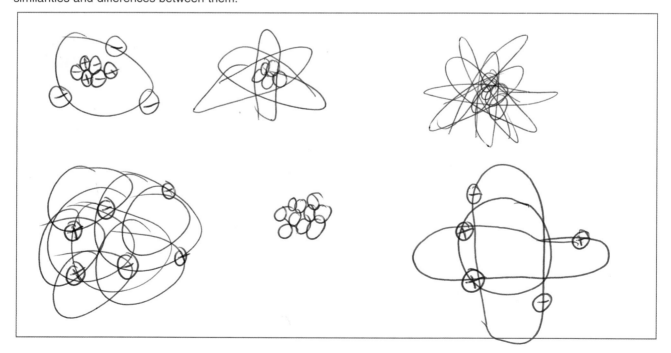

©2019 **BIOZONE** International
ISBN: 978-1-927309-71-1
Photocopying Prohibited

EXPLORE: The structure of the atom

▶ Atoms are the basic unit of an element that can carry out a chemical reaction. Each element (e.g. gold, iron, hydrogen) is made up of only one type of atom.

▶ Atoms have a precise structure. Change it in any way and the behavior or even the type of atom changes. The diagram below shows a stylized representation of the structure of a carbon-12 atom. It is important to remember that at the atomic scale atoms do not look like this, but the model is useful in understanding their behavior.

▶ **Neutral atoms** contain the same number of protons as electrons.

▶ In a neutral carbon-12 atom (right) there are 6 protons and 6 electrons. Electrons orbit the nucleus in shells. Two electrons are found close to the nucleus in the first electron shell. The other four are found orbiting further away from the nucleus in the second electron shell.

▶ Importantly it is the electrons in this outer shell that determine an atom's behavior during a chemical reaction.

▶ The number of protons in the atom determines the element. For example, six protons is carbon, while seven protons is nitrogen.

▶ The nucleus contains protons and neutrons. The number of protons in the nucleus is called the atomic number (symbol Z). The number of protons and neutrons together is called the mass number (symbol A).

▶ A carbon-12 atom has six protons and six neutrons.

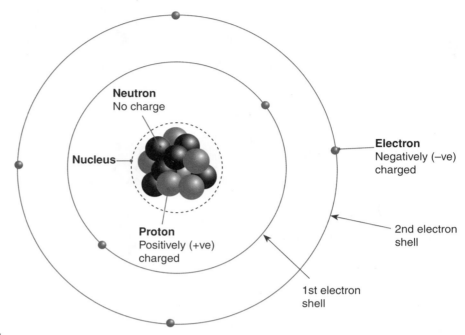

7. (a) What is meant by the term neutral in relation to atoms? _____

_____

_____

(b) If a neutral atom has 18 protons how many electrons would it have? _____

(c) If a neutral atom has 10 protons how many electrons would it have? _____

8. Use the periodic table on page 250 to answer the following questions:

(a) If a carbon atom spontaneously lost a proton what element would be formed? _____

(b) If a sulfur atom gained 3 protons what atom would be formed? _____

(c) Name the element that has atoms with 4 protons in the nucleus: _____

(d) Name the element that has atoms with 20 protons in the nucleus: _____

(e) Name the element with an atomic number of 12: _____

(f) Name the element with an atomic number of 1: _____

9. (a) How many neutrons are there in an atom with an atomic number of 14 and a mass number of 29? _____

(b) How many neutrons are there in an atom with an atomic number of 8 and a mass number of 16? _____

(c) Does the number of neutrons in the nucleus affect the type of atom? _____

10. (a) If an atom had 3 protons but only 2 electrons how would this atom be affected? _____

_____

(b) If an atom had 17 protons but 18 electrons how would this atom be affected? _____

_____

EXPLORE: The placement of electrons

▶ The electron is many times smaller than the proton or neutron. Protons have a mass of 1.67×10^{-24} grams. Neutrons are fractionally heavier. Elections have a mass of several orders of magnitude less at 9.11×10^{-28} grams.

▶ It is the electrons that dictate the chemical behavior of an atom, and most importantly it is the electrons in the outer shell (the **valence shell**) that take part in a chemical reaction.

▶ Electrons are arranged around an atom's nucleus in specific ways. For the **first twenty atoms** of the periodic table (see next activity) electrons are added to the electron shells in the following way:

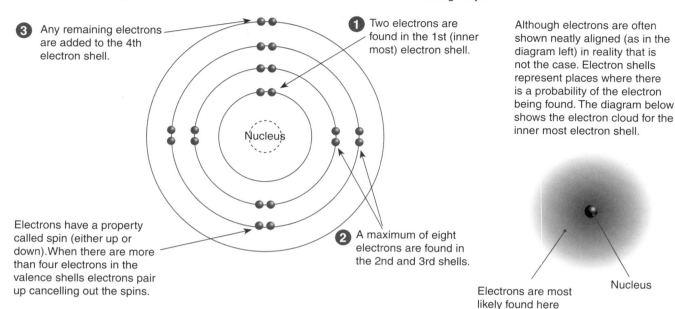

3 Any remaining electrons are added to the 4th electron shell.

1 Two electrons are found in the 1st (inner most) electron shell.

Although electrons are often shown neatly aligned (as in the diagram left) in reality that is not the case. Electron shells represent places where there is a probability of the electron being found. The diagram below shows the electron cloud for the inner most electron shell.

Electrons have a property called spin (either up or down). When there are more than four electrons in the valence shells electrons pair up cancelling out the spins.

2 A maximum of eight electrons are found in the 2nd and 3rd shells.

Electrons are most likely found here

Nucleus

▶ The arrangement of electrons around an atom is called its electron configuration. For an atom of calcium (Z = 20) the electron configuration can be written as 2,8,8,2. This shows the first three electron shells are full and two electrons are in the valence shell.

11. What are the electron configurations for:

(a) Oxygen (Z = 8): _____

(b) Magnesium (Z = 12) _____

12. (a) Draw a diagram (as shown above) of the electrons around oxygen:

(b) Draw a diagram of the electrons around magnesium:

▶ Atoms with full valence shells are chemically stable. They do not undergo chemical reactions. An atom without a full valence shell will undergo a chemical reaction in order to obtain a full valence shell. During the reaction electrons may be gained or lost or shared between atoms depending on the number of electrons in the valence shell.

13. Predict the following:

(a) Will lithium gain or lose electrons in a reaction? _____

(b) Will chlorine lose or gain electrons in a reaction? _____

(c) How reactive would you expect neon to be? _____

©2019 **BIOZONE** International
ISBN: 978-1-927309-71-1
Photocopying Prohibited

EXPLAIN: Gaining and losing electrons

▶ Apart from a small group of elements called the "noble gases", elements are never found in nature as singular free floating atoms. They are always found bonded to other atoms. These can be either the same kind of atom (as in hydrogen gas) or they can be different atoms (as in carbon dioxide).

In its pure form, the element sodium is a silvery metal. Its atoms share their mobile electrons and are held together by **metallic bonds**. It is a very reactive metal.

Chlorine is a gaseous element with a yellow tinge. In its pure form, the atoms are found **covalently** bonded together in pairs. Chlorine is highly toxic and reactive.

Sodium chloride (table salt) is a highly stable crystal made of sodium and chloride ions held together by **ionic** bonds.

▶ Atoms without full valence shells are reactive because having unpaired electrons and vacant orbitals is energetically unfavorable. Vacant orbitals can be filled by either sharing electrons (e.g. covalent bonding) or by gaining or losing electrons. When an atom gains or loses an electron (or electrons) it becomes an **ion**.

▶ In the example above of sodium and chlorine, both elements are highly reactive in their pure form. Although their atoms are sharing electrons it is energetically more favorable for sodium atoms to lose an electron and chlorine atoms to gain an electron and form ions. When sodium and chlorine react a large amount of thermal energy is released and the resulting product, sodium chloride, is stable and unreactive.

Sodium reacting with chlorine in the presence of water (which "kick starts" the reaction).

Forming ions

▶ What happens during a reaction between sodium and chlorine? It helps to look at the electron configurations of each. In the diagram below, we see that sodium has a single electron in the valence shell and chlorine has seven.

▶ Earlier you were asked to predict if chlorine would lose or gain an electron in a reaction. We have to ask the question: Is it easier (does it take less energy) to gain one electron to fill chlorine's valence shell or to lose seven electrons and thus lose a shell entirely?

▶ A similar question must be asked of sodium. Is it easier to lose one electron (and thus the shell) or gain seven electrons to fill the valence shell?

▶ Of course it is easier for chlorine to gain one electron and sodium to lose one electron (we shall look at the why later). The atoms then form ions. Ions are atoms that have gained or lost electrons and thus have positive or negative charges.

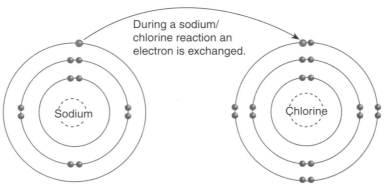

During a sodium/chlorine reaction an electron is exchanged.

Sodium

Chlorine

14. (a) Write the electron configuration of the sodium ion: _____

   (b) Write the electron configuration of the chloride ion: _____

15. (a) What charge does the sodium ion have? _____

   (b) What charge does the chloride ion have? _____

©2019 **BIOZONE** International
ISBN: 978-1-927309-71-1
Photocopying Prohibited

16. Explain why sodium loses an electron during a reaction: _____

_____

_____

17. Explain why chlorine gains an electron during a reaction _____

_____

_____

18. Explain why sodium chloride is a highly stable substance in comparison to sodium and chlorine: _____

_____

_____

_____

19. (a) Draw a diagram showing the magnesium ion: (b) Draw a diagram showing the oxide ion:

20. Complete the table below (you may need to use the periodic table on page 250):

	Element	Atomic number (Z)	Mass number (A)	Number of neutrons	Number of electrons	Possible charge of ion
(a)	Hydrogen		1		1	
(b)		13		14		
(c)	Potassium					
(d)	Argon		40		18	
(e)		20				
(f)	Fluorine	9		10		

21. (a) Would you expect elements to become more or less likely to form ions as you move from left to right along a row of the periodic table?

_____

_____

(b) What do you notice about the charges on ions formed when moving left to right along a row of the periodic table?

_____

_____

ELABORATE: Grouping together

▶ An important part of chemistry is the distinction between atoms, ions, compounds, molecules, and mixtures. Some of these terms we have already come across and it is now useful to see how they relate to each other. Examine the diagrams below:

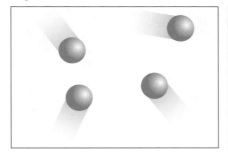

Atoms of an element

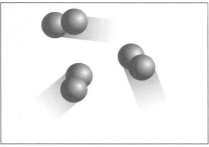

Molecules of an element

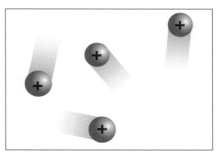

Ions have a postive or negative charge

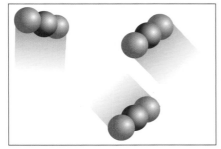

Molecules of a pure compound

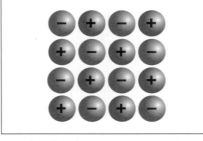

Ions forming a pure compound

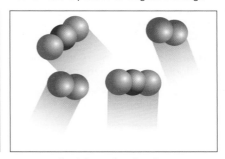

A mixture of molecules

22. Define the following:

(a) Atom: _____

_____

(b) Compound: _____

_____

(c) Ion: _____

(d) Mixture: _____

_____

(e) Molecule: _____

_____

(f) Pure: _____

_____

▶ Ions may be singular such as Na^+. These are called monoatomic ions. Sometimes ions can be found as groups. These are called polyatomic ions.

▶ Polyatomic ions you will commonly come across include the sulfate ion (SO_4^{2-}), the hydrogen carbonate (bicarbonate) ion HCO_3^-, the carbonate ion (CO_3^{2-}), the hydroxide ion (OH^-), the nitrate ion (NO_3^-), and the ammonium ion (NH_4^+).

▶ You may have also noticed that when an atom turns into an ion in some cases there is a name change. Metal atoms do not change their name when they form an ion. Non metal atoms, however, use the -ide suffix, e.g. chlorine becomes chloride.

23. Name the following:

(a) The ion that forms from the fluorine atom: _____

(b) The ion that forms from the sulfur atom: _____

(c) The compound that forms from the reaction between lithium and chlorine: _____

(d) The compound that forms when a potassium ion and a sulfate ion combine: _____

©2019 **BIOZONE** International
ISBN: 978-1-927309-71-1
Photocopying Prohibited

21 The Periodic Table

ENGAGE: Periodic tables

▶ A period is a length of time. Something that happens periodically happens once and then again and again after a certain time interval. Periodic can therefore also be used to describe a repeating pattern.

▶ Run you finger over a piano keyboard and hit all the keys and you will of course hear a repeating pattern of octaves. Every key plays a note one octave higher or lower than the key eight keys before or after. The set of seven keys A-G plays the set of notes within one octave.

▶ During the development of the periodic table, chemists noticed this "law of octaves". Every eighth element seemed to have similar properties. However this pattern broke down as more elements were discovered and added to the table. The periodic table itself is called periodic simply because it displays repeating patterns.

▶ However there is more than one type of periodic table. The one printed in this book is the standard Mendeleev periodic table seen in many texts.

1. There are many versions of the periodic table. Try typing "alternative versions of the periodic table" into an internet search engine and explore that numerous different versions. Print some out and paste them into the space below:

©2019 **BIOZONE** International
ISBN: 978-1-927309-71-1
Photocopying Prohibited

EXPLORE: Getting to know the periodic table

▶ The periodic table as we use it today in chemistry was first formulated by the Russian chemist Dmitri Mendeleev (right) in 1869. Not only did he organise the then known elements into the table, but he predicted the properties of eight unknown elements and left spaces in the table for when they were discovered.

▶ It was not until 1913 that it was proved that the order Mendeleev placed the elements was in fact the same as ordering the elements by their atomic number.

▶ Before you start looking at the finer details of the periodic table it is worth getting to know the large scale structure of the table.

▶ The periodic table is organized into columns called groups and rows called periods.

▶ The periodic table below shows the different groups of elements in the periodic table. Different groups of elements are given different names for easier reference:

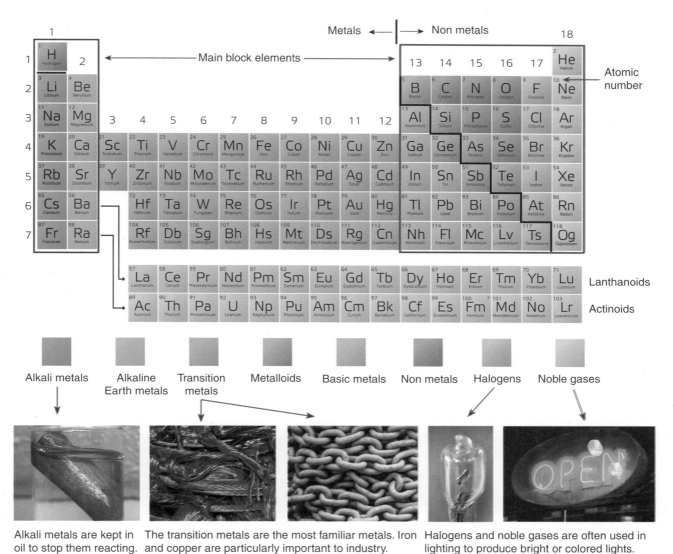

Alkali metals are kept in oil to stop them reacting.

The transition metals are the most familiar metals. Iron and copper are particularly important to industry.

Halogens and noble gases are often used in lighting to produce bright or colored lights.

2. Which side of the periodic table are the metals on? _____

3. Which group number are the noble gases in? _____

4. Which group number are the halogens in? _____

5. What is the name given to the metals that includes copper and gold? _____

6. Why are the actinoids and lanthanoids placed on a table below the rest of the periodic table? _____

_____

7. How does the atomic number (number of protons) change along a period? _____

90

EXPLORE: Trends in the periodic table

▸ It is useful to now explore more subtle details in the periodic table. The table below shows the atomic radius of the atoms from atomic number 1 (hydrogen) to 36 (krypton). This includes the first four rows of the periodic table (three short rows and one long row).

▸ The atomic radius at its simplest definition is the distance from the nucleus to the edge of the electron cloud. Since the electron cloud has no fixed edge, a more definitive measure of the atomic radius is half the distance between two identical atoms in a covalent bond (the covalent radius).

Atomic number	Atomic radius (pm)
1	53
2	31
3	167
4	112
5	87
6	67
7	56
8	48
9	42
10	38
11	190
12	145
13	118
14	111
15	98
16	88
17	79
18	71
19	243
20	194
21	184
22	176
23	171
24	166
25	161
26	156
27	152
28	149
29	145
30	142
31	136
32	125
33	114
34	103
35	94
36	88

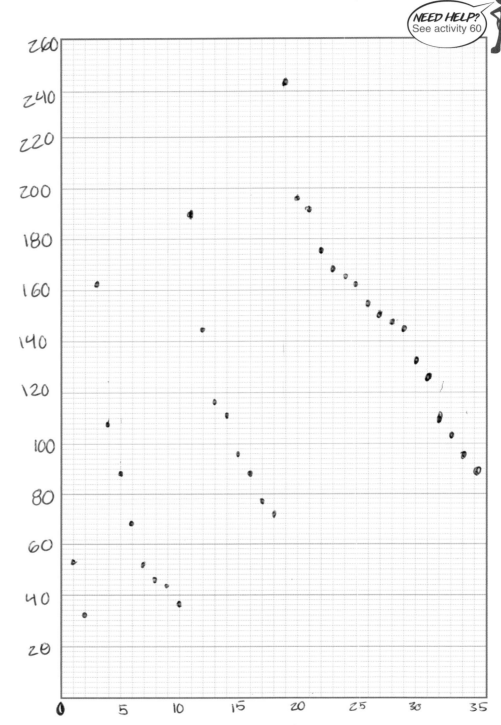

NEED HELP? See activity 60

8. Plot the data on the grid provided:

9. Describe any trends or patterns you can see in the data: It starts low & begins to sudenly ris + fall rapidly a few times

©2019 **BIOZONE** International
ISBN: 978-1-927309-71-1
Photocopying Prohibited

10. Predict the trend in atomic radius across row five of the periodic table: _It'll do the same as the last one, rise + the fall_

11. Can you explain why this trend in occurring? (Hint think about the effect of the increasing positive charge in the nucleus).

because the charges are always changing which causes the others to change quickly

▶ There are many other trends and patterns that can be seen in the periodic table. The data below shows the first ionization energy of the first 20 atoms.

▶ The first ionization energy is the energy required to remove one mole of the mostly loosely held electrons from one mole of neutral atoms in a gas state to produce one mole of ions each with a charge of +1. Similarly there can be second and third ionization energies for atoms.

Atomic number	1st ionization energy (kJ/mol)
1	1312
2	2372
3	520
4	899
5	801
6	1086
7	1402
8	1314
9	1681
10	2081
11	496
12	738
13	578
14	786
15	1012
16	1000
17	1251
18	1521
19	419
20	590

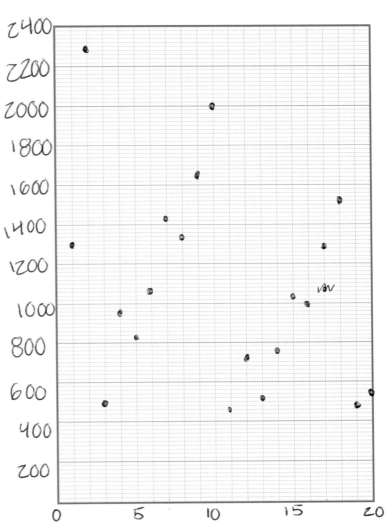

12. What is the trend in ionization energy across the first twenty atoms? _its scattered with rises + falls_

13. How does the atomic number and the electron configuration help to explain the pattern in 1st ionization energy?

the atomic # stays but the # of electrons very

▶ An important property of atoms is their electronegativity. This is the ability to attract a pair of bonding electrons in a chemical bond. The electronegativity of atoms affects how they share electrons when forming a chemical bond and this in turn affects the properties of the product produced in a reaction.

▶ The graph below shows how the electronegativity changes for the first twenty atoms.

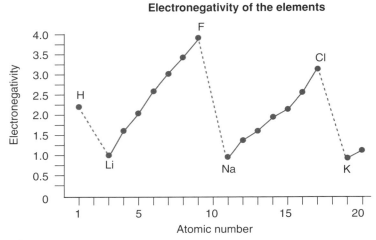

Electronegativity of the elements

14. (a) If a reaction occurs between an element with a high electronegativity and one with a low electronegativity (e.g. lithium and fluorine) what do you think will happen in terms of the sharing of electrons in the product (e.g. lithium fluoride)?

flooride will take it, lithium doesn't want it that much

(b) If a reaction occurs between two elements with similar electronegativities what do you think will happen in terms of the sharing of electrons in the product?

they will fight over the electron

15. Suggest why the electronegativity of the noble gases can not be calculated: _because it alters_

16. How does electronegativity change down a group and across a period (left to right)? _it grows + needs more electrons left → right_

▶ While it is informative to plot trends right across a number of periods, it is also informative to plot trends down a group. The graphs below show the boiling point and density of the halogens (group 17).

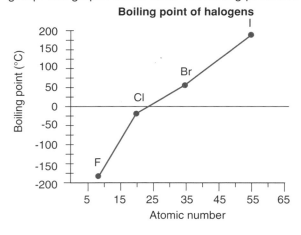

Boiling point of halogens

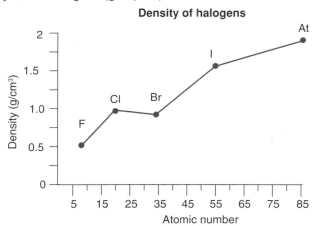

Density of halogens

17. What can be said about the trends in boiling point and density of the halogens? _they are both increasing but the right plateaus for a little_

©2019 **BIOZONE** International
ISBN: 978-1-927309-71-1

▶ You have so far explored a number of trends across the periodic table and attempted to explain some of them. By finding more data than is presented here many other trends in the table can be seen. These include **ionic radius** and **electron affinity** (the energy change that occurs when an electron is accepted by an atom in the gaseous state to form an ion with a charge of −1).

▶ You have also been asked to suggest reasons for the trends. You may have realized that the trends are a result of (1) the charge inside the nucleus and (2) the number of electrons in the valence shell.

▶ A third reason you may not have realized is called shielding. As the number of electron shells increases, they have the effect of shielding the attractive charge from the nucleus and reducing the electrostatic attraction between the positive protons and negative electrons.

▶ The combination of these three effects can account for the trends we see in the periodic table. We can summarize these trends on the diagram below:

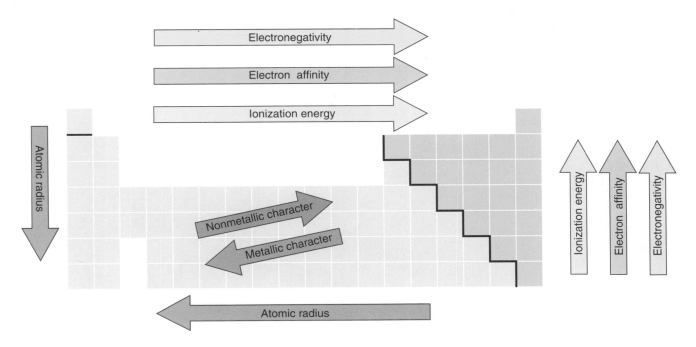

18. Using the information in this and the previous activity answer the following questions:

(a) Complete the table:

Element	Electron configuration	Electronegativity	Metal / nonmetal
A	1	2.20	nonmetal
B	2,8,2	1.31	metal
C	2,8,3	1.63	metal
D	2,4	2.55	nonmetal
E	2,8,6	2.58	nonmetal

(b) Complete the following statements:

i. When a halogen reacts with a metal it will form an ion that will have a charge of _____8_____ .

ii. When an alkali metal reacts it will form ions with a charge of _____4_____ .

iii. Alkaline earth metals form ions with a charge of _____4_____ .

iv. Noble gases are unreactive because they have _____3_____ valence shells.

v. When a halogen reacts with an alkali metal the ratio of metal ions to halogen ions is _____5_____ .

vi. When an alkali metal reacts with oxygen the ratio of metal ions to oxide ions is _____4_____ .

ELABORATE: Important ions

▶ You should realize by now that metals form positive ions and non metals form negative ions. Positive and negative ions are also referred to as cations and anions respectively.

Cations are positive

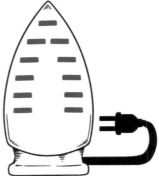

Anions are negative

▶ Important monoatomic ions you should know are shown below:

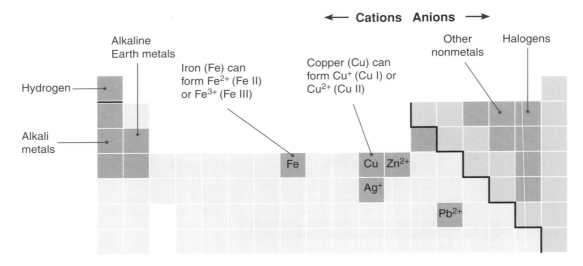

19. Explain why first group elements always form an ion with a single positive charge: _____

_____

_____

_____

20. Would you expect the element carbon to form a cation or an anion? Explain your reasoning:

_____

_____

_____

21. Explain why nonmetals do not form cations: _____

_____

_____

_____

22. What can be said about any elements that are in the same group number of the periodic table?

_____

_____

_____

©2019 **BIOZONE** International
ISBN: 978-1-927309-71-1
Photocopying Prohibited

22 The Mole

ENGAGE: Numbers

▶ Sometimes names are given to certain amounts or numbers of objects. We are all familiar with the term "dozen". One dozen is of course equal to twelve. There are many other names used for particular amounts:

1. Write down the ways you can think of to express a number. Check with your classmates. What can they come up with?

_____

_____

_____

▶ One number in particular is used in chemistry: **the mole**. This is a number that all measurement in chemistry is based upon. When we say "one mole of sodium" we mean an exact number of sodium atoms. It is like saying "one dozen sodium atoms" except that a mole is several billion times larger.

EXPLORE: Relative atomic mass (A_r)

▶ The first table of relative atomic masses was published by John Dalton in 1805. These were based on relative masses of the elements obtained by experiment.

▶ Water can be broken into hydrogen and oxygen by passing an electric current through it. When we do this we find that we collect twice the volume of hydrogen gas as we do oxygen gas. We can therefore conclude that water contains 2 hydrogen atoms for every 1 oxygen atom per unit of water.

▶ However the mass of oxygen gas obtained (the mass of a gas can be determined from its volume) is 8 times more than the mass of the hydrogen gas. We can therefore calculate that 1 hydrogen atom must be 16 times lighter than 1 oxygen atom.

▶ Using experiments such as this, early chemists arbitrarily gave hydrogen a mass of 1. They could therefore say that oxygen had a relative mass of 16. From this, other "relative" atomic masses could be calculated.

▶ Until the 1960s, relative atomic masses were based on the mass of oxygen. It was later decided that the relative atomic masses should be based on the carbon-12 atom (carbon atoms with 6 protons and 6 neutrons).

▶ On your periodic table on page 250 you may have noticed that the atomic mass is not always a whole number. For example the atomic mass of lithium is given as 6.94.

▶ It was discussed earlier that the atomic mass is equal to the number of protons and neutrons in an atom. Lithium has 3 protons which means according to the periodic table it has 3.94 neutrons. How is this possible?

▶ The answer is that not all lithium atoms have the same number of neutrons. Some have three, most have four. These are called **isotopes**.

▶ The number given is the **relative atomic mass**. It is defined as "*the average mass of all the atoms of an element compared to 1/12 the mass of the carbon-12 atom*".

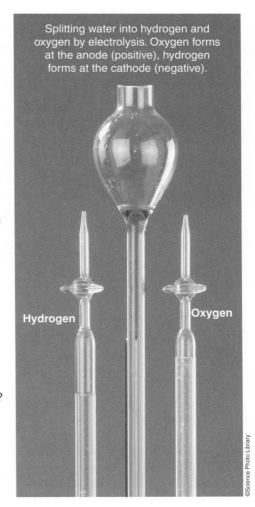

Splitting water into hydrogen and oxygen by electrolysis. Oxygen forms at the anode (positive), hydrogen forms at the cathode (negative).

Hydrogen   Oxygen

©Science Photo Library

2. What does relative atomic mass mean? _____

_____

_____

3. Use the periodic table on page 250 to find the A_r of the following:

(a) Na: _____   (d) Ca: _____

(b) N: _____   (e) Al: _____

(c) Au: _____   (f) I: _____

EM   SPQ   P   PS1.B   PS1.A

EXPLORE: Relative molecular mass (M$_r$)

▶ Just as elements have a mass relative to carbon-12, so do compounds. This is called the **relative molecular mass (M$_r$)**.

▶ The relative molecular mass can be calculated by adding together all the relative atomic masses of the individual atoms in one unit of the compound.

▶ For example the relative molecular mass of sulfur dioxide (SO_2) is equal to the relative atomic mass of sulfur plus twice the atomic mass of oxygen: $32.1 + (16.00 \times 2) = 64.1$

4. Use the following A$_r$ values to calculate the M$_r$ values for the compounds listed below:
   $A_r(H) = 1.0$, $A_r(C) = 12.0$, $A_r(O) = 16.0$, $A_r(Fe) = 55.8$, $A_r(Cu) = 63.5$

   (a) H_2: _____

   (d) H_2O: _____

   (b) CuO: _____

   (e) Fe_2O_3: _____

   (c) CH_4: _____

   (f) C_3H_8: _____

EXPLORE: Avogadro's constant and the mole

▶ Making the relative atomic mass of all elements relative to carbon-12 gives us a way to measure equal numbers of atoms of different elements.

▶ In 12 grams of carbon-12 there is a certain number of atoms. We call this number of atoms the mole. But how many atoms are there in a mole?

▶ In 2011, the International Bureau of Weights and Measures stated that "The mole is the amount of substance of a system which contains as many elementary entities as there are atoms in 0.012 kg of carbon-12". This number, 6.02×10^{23} (to 2 significant figures), is also called Avogadro's constant (named after Amedeo Avogadro).

▶ The figure of 6.02×10^{23} is directly linked to the mass of carbon-12 (the standard for the measurement of relative atomic masses).

▶ You can easily find the mass of one mole (1 mol) of atoms in any element because it is the relative atomic mass in grams.

5. Why would being able to measure precise numbers of atoms be important in chemistry? _____

_____

_____

6. How is the weighed mass of an element linked to the number of atoms in that mass? _____

_____

_____

_____

EXPLAIN: The mole and chemical formulae

▶ One of the most important aspects of chemistry is understanding chemical formulae. Every compound can be written as a chemical formula, based on the number and type of atoms present in the compound. We have already come across some simple formula earlier and is it is now useful to fully explain what they mean. Consider the formula for sulfuric acid:

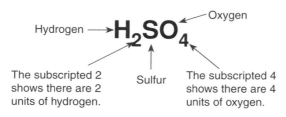

▶ From this formula we can tell that in one unit of sulfuric acid there are two hydrogen atoms, one sulfur atom and four oxygen atoms, making a total of seven atoms. The same is true for the number of moles in one mole of sulfuric acid (there are two moles of hydrogen, one mole of sulfur, and four moles of oxygen).

©2019 **BIOZONE** International
ISBN: 978-1-927309-71-1
Photocopying Prohibited

▶ Now consider the formula for 2 units of aluminum sulfate:

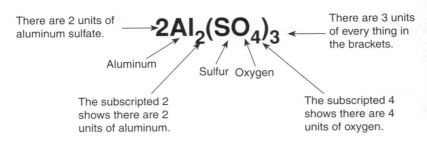

There are 2 units of aluminum sulfate. → **2Al₂(SO₄)₃** ← There are 3 units of every thing in the brackets.

Aluminum

Sulfur   Oxygen

The subscripted 2 shows there are 2 units of aluminum.

The subscripted 4 shows there are 4 units of oxygen.

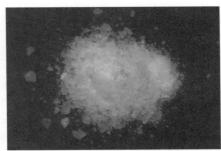

Aluminium sulfate is used as a flocculent in water purification.

▶ From this formula we can see that there are two moles of aluminum sulfate. In total there are four moles of aluminum, six moles of sulfur, and twenty four moles of oxygen, a total of thirty four moles of atoms.

7. The mineral dawsonite has the formula $NaAlCO_3(OH)_2$. Explain what this formula means:

_____

_____

_____

_____

8. Write out the full name of the following chemicals:

   (a) MgO: _____

   (b) Li_2S: _____

   (c) $CaCO_3$: _____

9. Calculate the number of moles of atoms in the following :

   (a) NaOH: _____   (c) $2CaCl_2$: _____

   (b) Al_2O_3: _____   (d) $2Al(OH)_3$: _____

▶ Finally you need to be able to interpret chemical equations in terms of moles of products and reactants. Consider the equation below:

$$C_2H_5OH + 3O_2 \rightarrow 2CO_2 + 3H_2O$$

10. The arrow in the equation means "goes to form". Explain the meaning of the equation in terms of moles of products and reactants:

_____

_____

_____

_____

EXPLAIN: Molar mass (M) and the mole

▶ The molar mass links the relative atomic and relative molecular masses to the mole. The molar mass is the mass of one mole of a substance in grams. So if the relative atomic mass of lithium is 6.94, then the molar mass is 6.94 g/mol. Similarly if the relative molecular mass of sulfur dioxide is 64.1 then its molar mass is 64.1 g/mol.

▶ In this text molar mass is rounded to 1 d.p. for ease of calculation.

11. Calculate the molar mass of the following compounds. Show your working:
    M(H) = 1.0 g/mol, M(C) = 12.0 g/mol, M(N) = 14.0 g/mol, M(O) = 16.0 g/mol,

   (a) CH_3COOH: _____

   (b) C_2H_5OH: _____

   (c) HNO_3: _____

   (d) $(NH_4)_2CO_3$: _____

▶ It is now useful to compare moles of substances in real terms. The investigation below is a simple observation task that may be set up by your teacher or you may weigh out the substances yourself.

INVESTIGATION 3.1: Comparing one mole of various substances   See appendix for equipment list.

⚠ Caution is required when handling chemicals in the lab. Avoid contact with skin. Wear protective eyewear and gloves.

M(H) = 1.0 g/mol, M(C) = 12.0 g/mol, M(O) = 16.0 g/mol, M(Na) = 23.0 g/mol, M(S) = 32.1 g/mol, M(Cl) = 35.5 g/mol, M(Fe) = 55.8 g/mol, M(Cu) = 63.5 g/mol,

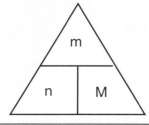

1. Here, you will compare one mole of the following substances: sodium chloride (NaCl), sulfur (S), hydrated copper II chloride ($CuCl_2.2H_2O$), iron II oxide (FeO), carbon (C), and glucose ($C_6H_{12}O_6$).

2. To begin, calculate the molar masses (M) of the six substances:

   (a) NaCl: _____

   (b) S: _____

   (c) $CuCl_2.2H_2O$: _____

   (d) FeO: _____

   (e) C: _____

   (f) $C_6H_{12}O_6$ _____

3. Obtain six clean petri dishes or 6 sheets of filter paper.

4. Weigh 1 mole of sodium chloride onto the first petri dish or filter paper.

5. Continue weighing out the other five substances onto separate petri dishes or filter paper.

6. Observe the differences in mass and volume of one mole of the different substances. Remember there is the same number of atoms in each of the samples you have weighed out.

By now you may have noticed a relationship between the number of moles of a substance, the mass, and the molar mass.

If we have a sample of one mole of sodium chloride, its mass is 58.5 g. If we have a sample of two moles of sodium chloride its mass is 2 x 58.5 = 117 g.

The mass of a sample in grams (**m**) equals the number of moles (**n**) multiplied by the molar mass of the substance (**M**).

This is also written as: **n = m ÷ M**

Learn how to use the equation n = m/M to find the different variables. The pictogram below is a simple tool to help you. Cover the variable you want to know and you are left with how to calculate it, e.g. cover m and you are left with n x M.

```
      ╱ ╲
     ╱ m ╲
    ╱─────╲
   ╱ n │ M ╲
  ╱────┴────╲
```

12. Calculate (a)-(e) using the following molar masses: M(H) = 1.0 g/mol, M(Li) = 6.9 g/mol, M(O) = 16.0 g/mol, M(Cl) = 35.5 g/mol, M(Al) = 27.0 g/mol, M(Fe) = 55.8 g/mol, M(Zn) = 65.4 g/mol

   (a) The number of moles in 29.8 grams of Li_2O: _____

   _____

   _____

   (b) The mass of 1.5 moles of ZnO: _____

   _____

   _____

   (c) The molar mass of 1.5 moles of an element with a sample mass of 40.5 grams (name the element):

   _____

   _____

   (d) The number of moles in 40 grams of $FeCl_3$: _____

   _____

   _____

   (e) The mass Al^{3+} in 2 moles of Al_2O_3:

   _____

   _____

   _____

©2019 **BIOZONE** International
ISBN: 978-1-927309-71-1

ELABORATE: Finding the formula

▶ A working knowledge of molar mass and moles can help us determine the molecular formula of new compounds.

▶ In the investigation below you will determine the formula for magnesium oxide:

INVESTIGATION 3.2: Determining the molecular formula of magnesium oxide

See appendix for equipment list.

 Magnesium is a flammable metal. If ignited it produces a bright and extremely hot flame that can cause severe burns. Do not look directly at the flame. Wear protective eyewear and use tongs to handle the crucible.

▶ M(O) = 16.0 g/mol, M(Mg) = 24.3 g/mol

1. Weigh a crucible and lid on a balance. Record the mass: _____

2. Coil a 10 cm length of magnesium ribbon and place it in the crucible. Replace the lid and reweigh. Record the mass of the crucible, lid, and magnesium ribbon here:

_____

3. Place a clay triangle onto a tripod and put the crucible, magnesium ribbon, and lid on top. Heat the crucible with a blue Bunsen flame. Using tongs, open the lid to allow air into the crucible.

4. Watch for the magnesium to ignite (this may take a minute or so). When it does, immediately place the lid back on the crucible.

5. Continue heating the crucible for several minutes, using tongs to lift the crucible lid slightly once or twice to allow air into the crucible.

6. After several minutes, check to see if the reaction is complete. You will be able to tell as a white powder (magnesium oxide) will form and no flame or "smoke" will be seen.

7. Leaving the crucible lid on, turn the Bunsen off and allow the crucible to cool. Check to make sure all the magnesium has reacted. If there is still some metal in the crucible, you will need to continue heating.

8. When the crucible is cool, reweigh the crucible, magnesium oxide, and lid. Record the mass here:

_____

13. (a) Calculate the mass of magnesium at the start of the reaction: _____

(b) Calculate the mass of magnesium oxide formed: _____

(c) Calculate the mass of oxygen that has reacted with the magnesium: _____

(d) Calculate the moles (n(Mg)) of magnesium used in the reaction: _____

(e) Calculate the moles (n(O)) of oxygen in the reaction: _____

(f) What is the ratio of n(Mg) to n(O) (in whole numbers)? _____

(g) What is the formula for magnesium oxide? _____

(h) Write a balanced equation for the reaction of magnesium metal (Mg) with oxygen gas (O_2).

_____

(i) Using your knowledge of the periodic table and ion formation explain why magnesium oxide has the formula you determined:

_____

_____

_____

©2019 **BIOZONE** International
ISBN: 978-1-927309-71-1
Photocopying Prohibited

‣ Let us now compare the formula of magnesium oxide to the formula of sodium oxide. Burning sodium in air is too dangerous in a lab situation because sodium is highly reactive. The reaction does not form pure sodium oxide in any case (some sodium peroxide is formed).

‣ Sodium oxide can be formed by the thermal decomposition of sodium carbonate (Na_2CO_3). When sodium carbonate is heated to above 800°C under one atmosphere of pressure it decomposes to sodium oxide and carbon dioxide (CO_2).

14. 3.00 grams of sodium carbonate was thermally decomposed. The remaining sodium oxide powder was weighed and had a mass of 1.75 grams. M(C) = 12.0 g/mol, M(O) = 16.0 g/mol, M(Na) = 23.0 g/mol.

(a) Write a word equation for the reaction: _____

(b) Calculate M(Na_2CO_3): _____

(c) Calculate n(Na_2CO_3) that were heated: _____

(d) Calculate n(Na) in the sample of Na_2CO_3: _____

(e) How many moles of sodium must therefore be in the sodium oxide? _____

(f) How many grams of sodium must therefore be in the sodium oxide? _____

(g) How many grams of oxygen must therefore be in the sodium oxide? _____

(h) Calculate n(O) in sodium oxide: _____

(i) What is the ratio of sodium to oxygen atoms in the sodium oxide (in whole numbers)? _____

_____

(j) What is the formula of sodium oxide? _____

(k) Use your understanding of the periodic table and ion formation to explain why sodium oxide has the formula you determined.

_____

_____

_____

Empirical and molecular formulae

‣ Finding the formula for chemical compounds is an important part of chemistry. The formulae you have determined for magnesium oxide and sodium oxide are **empirical** formulae. An empirical formula is the simplest whole number ratio of atoms in a compound. For ionic compounds such as magnesium oxide, the formula is always given in the simplest ratio.

‣ However discrete molecules can have both an empirical and a **molecular** formula. For example, the molecule hydrogen peroxide has the molecular formula H_2O_2. The empirical formula is the simplest ratio and is therefore HO.

‣ The diagram below shows a method for determining the products of combustion of cyclohexane and therefore its composition and empirical formula:

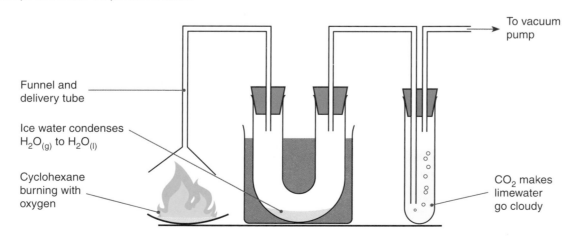

©2019 **BIOZONE** International
ISBN: 978-1-927309-71-1
Photocopying Prohibited

▶ Cyclohexane is a hydrocarbon and therefore contains only hydrogen and carbon atoms.

▶ From the diagram we can see that only the only products of the reaction are water (H_2O) and carbon dioxide (CO_2).

▶ It is possible to calculate the percentage composition of C and H in cyclohexane by weighing the cyclohexane before combustion in plentiful oxygen (to prevent the formation of soot or carbon monoxide) then condensing and weighing the mass of water produced. We can then determine the empirical and molecular formulae.

15. 5.6 grams of cyclohexane was completely combusted and the products passed through a condenser. The mass of water obtained was 7.2 grams. M(H) = 1.0, M(C)= 12.0, M(O) = 16.0.

(a) Calculate n(H_2O): _____

(b) Calculate n(H) in the cyclohexane that was combusted: _____

(c) Calculate the mass of hydrogen in cyclohexane: _____

(d) Calculate the mass of carbon in cyclohexane: _____

(e) Calculate n(C) in the cyclohexane that was combusted: _____

(f) What is the ratio of C to H to cyclohexane (in whole numbers)? _____

(g) The molar mass of cyclohexane is known to be 84 g/mol. What is the molecular formula of cyclohexane?

_____

_____

ELABORATE: Percentage composition

▶ Percentage composition is commonly used in industry. The label on the right shows the percentage composition of the various components in cat food.

▶ Percentage composition can be calculated from the mass of a component ÷ the total mass of the substance x 100 or:

$$\% \text{ composition} = \frac{\text{Mass of component}}{\text{Total mass}} \times 100$$

GUARANTEED ANALYSIS:
Crude Protein (Min) 34.0%
Crude Fat (Min) 14.0%
Crude Fiber (Max) 4.0%
Moisture (Max) 12.0%
Linoleic Acid (Min) 2.3%
Calcium (Ca) (Min) 1.0%
Phosphorus (P) (Min) 0.9%
Zinc (Zn) (Min) . . . . 150 mg/kg
Selenium (Se) (Min) . . . . 0.35 mg/kg
Vitamin A (Min) . . . . 14,000 IU/kg
Vitamin E (Min) .450 IU/kg
Taurine (Min) 0.15%

▶ Percentage composition is also important in mining. Minerals and ores are a mixture of elements. Determining whether or not to mine somewhere may depend on the percentage composition of the elements in the ores found at the site. For example, the copper ore chalcocite (right) has the formula Cu_2S. The percentage composition can be calculated from the formula and the molar mass:

$$M(Cu_2S) = (63.5 \times 2) + 32 = 159$$

$$\% \text{ Cu} = \frac{(63.5 \times 2)}{159} \times 100 = 79.9\%$$

▶ Empirical formula can also be calculated from the percentage composition. For example a substance contains 20% hydrogen and 80% carbon by mass. By assuming that there is 100 grams of the sample we can turn the percentages into grams, i.e. 20 g of H and 80 g of C. It is then a simple matter of calculating the moles of each component and obtaining the ratio. If the molar mass is known, the molecular formula can also be calculated.

16. Using the percentages of C and H given above:

(a) Calculate n(C) and n(H): _____

_____

(b) Determine the ratio of C to H: _____

(c) Write the empirical formula of the compound: _____

(d) If the molar mass is of the compound is 30 g/mol what is its molecular formula? _____

_____

©2019 **BIOZONE** International
ISBN: 978-1-927309-71-1
Photocopying Prohibited

ELABORATE: Determining the ratio of water to copper sulfate in hydrated copper sulfate

▶ Many ionic compounds contain water bound into the crystal structure. This must be taken into account when weighing out the substance. Different compounds contain different ratios of water in their crystal structures. The formula for a hydrated compound is *ionic formula*.xH$_2$O, where x is the number of water molecules incorporated into the crystal. It is important to realize that the water is not part of the compound, it is simply bound inside the crystal structure.

▶ In the investigation below you will determine the ratio of copper sulfate to water in hydrated copper sulfate and hence the value of x in $CuSO_4.xH_2O$. M(H) = 1.0 g/mol, M(O) = 16.0 g/mol, M(S)= 32.1 g/mol, M(Cu) = 63.5 g/mol.

INVESTIGATION 3.3: Determining the ratio of water to copper sulfate in hydrated copper sulfate

See appendix for equipment list.

⚠ Be careful when handling copper sulfate. It can irritate the skin and ingestion and inhalation of the dust is harmful. The crucible will become extremely hot. Wear eyewear and gloves, and use tongs to lift the crucible lid.

1. Weigh a crucible and lid on a balance. Record the mass here: _____

2. Add about 6 grams of hydrated copper sulfate to the crucible. Reweigh:

   _____

3. Record the color of the hydrated copper sulfate: _____

4. Place the crucible on a clay triangle. Tilt the lid slightly to allow water to escape. Heat gently for a minute or so over a Bunsen burner then heat strongly for about 5 minutes.

5. Close and lid and allow the crucible to cool. Reweigh the crucible when it is cool enough to touch. Any hotter than this and it could damage the balance. Record the mass of the first heating:

   _____

6. Reheat the crucible and copper sulfate for 2 more minutes, tilting the lid to let any water escape. Close the lid, cool, and reweigh. Record the mass of the second heating:

   _____

7. Repeat if the mass is not constant (to within 0.02 g depending on the accuracy of your balance). Final mass:

   _____

8. Record the color of the dehydrated copper sulfate: _____

17. (a) Calculate the mass of $CuSO_4.xH_2O$ in the crucible before heating: _____

    (b) Calculate the mass of $CuSO_4$ in the crucible after heating: _____

    (c) Calculate the molar mass of anhydrous $CuSO_4$: _____

    (d) Calculate the moles of $CuSO_4$ left: _____

    (e) Calculate the mass of water lost: _____

    (f) Calculate the molar mass of water: _____

    (g) Calculate the moles of water lost: _____

    (h) Determine the ratio of $CuSO_4$ to H_2O: _____

    _____

    (i) What is the formula of hydrated copper sulfate? _____

18. Why is it important to include the number of bound waters when weighing out a compound? _____

_____

©2019 **BIOZONE** International
ISBN: 978-1-927309-71-1
Photocopying Prohibited

ELABORATE: Ionic formula

▸ So far we have investigated the ratios of ions in ionic compounds (MgO, Na_2O, and $CuSO_4.5H_2O$) and we have explained why these ratios appear.

▸ In a reaction, Mg forms a 2+ ion and oxygen forms a 2− ion. The electrostatic forces of each ion attract each other in a 1:1 ratio, and form MgO. Because Na forms a 1+ ion two Na^+ ions are needed to balance the charge on O^{2-}.

▸ It is important to be able to write ionic formula so that the charges on the ions balance. For example, aluminum oxide has the formula Al_2O_3. Al forms a 3+ ion, while O forms a 2− ion. To balance these charges we need to find a common multiple. This can be done by multiplying the charges: 3 x 2 = 6. So there must be enough of each ion to add up to either 6+ or 6−.

▸ Therefore 2 x 3+ = 6+ and 3 x 2− = 6−. So 2 Al react with 3 O to form Al_2O_3.

▸ This can be looked at as a model of jigsaw pieces:

1 We can line up the pieces and join them. The pieces do not form a regular rectangle.

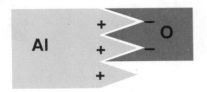

2 Let's add another O to fill up the space. The pieces still do not form a regular rectangle:

3 Let's add an Al to fill up the space. Not quite there.

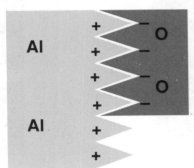

4 Let's add another O. Perfect! To make a rectangle we need 2 Al and 3 O. So we get Al_2O_3.

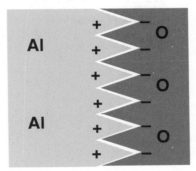

▸ Another method is called the "swap and drop" as shown below:

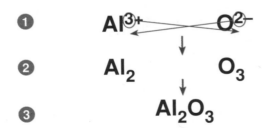

1 Take the numbers (not the charge) and place it behind and below the opposite ion.

2 Al_2 O_3

3 Al_2O_3 Place the ions together

19. (a) In the space draw a jigsaw diagram to show the formula of lithium sulfide:

NEED HELP? See activities 20 & 62

Write balanced ionic formula for each of the following:

(b) Calcium hydroxide: _____   (d) Sodium sulfide: _____

(c) Iron III chloride: _____   (e) Potassium sulfate: _____

©2019 **BIOZONE** International
ISBN: 978-1-927309-71-1
Photocopying Prohibited

ELABORATE: Balancing equations

▸ You will hopefully have noticed in the previous example that oxygen was referred to as O (the singular atom) as opposed to O_2 (molecular oxygen as it is found in the gas state). If we were to write an equation for the reaction of aluminum with oxygen to form aluminum oxide we would need to write oxygen as O_2 (as this is the oxygen in the air that is reacting with the aluminum).

▸ So our equation is $Al + O_2 \rightarrow Al_2O_3$.

▸ But we can see the number of atoms on each side of the equation are not equal. There is one Al and two O on the left but 2 Al and three O on the right. We need to write a number in front of the Al and O_2 to increase the number of atoms and balance in the equation.

▸ Let's set out the units of Al, O_2, and Al_2O_3:

1 We need 1 Al, 1 O_2, and 1 Al_2O_3

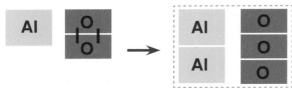

2 We can increase the amount of Al by adding another Al:

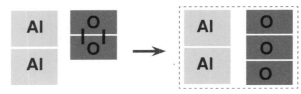

3 This balances the Als but the O_2s are still not balanced. Lets add another O_2 to the left side of the equation. To do that we also need another unit of Al_2O_3 to the right side of the equation:

4 There are now 4 Als and 6 Os on the right. We can balance those by adding 2 more Als and 1 O_2 to the left.

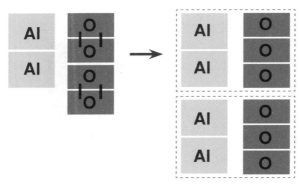

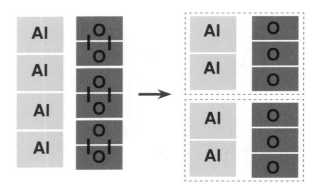

5 We now have equal numbers of Al and O on the left and right sides of the equations. The final equation for the reaction is:

$$4Al + 3O_2 \rightarrow 2Al_2O_3$$

20. Balance and rewrite the following equations:

(a) $ZnO + HCl \rightarrow ZnCl_2 + H_2O$: $ZnO + 2HCl \rightarrow ZnCl_2 + H_2O$

(b) $Al + Cl_2 \rightarrow AlCl_3$: $2Al + 3Cl_2 \rightarrow 2AlCl_3$

(c) $Na_2O + H_2O \rightarrow NaOH$: $Na_2O + H_2O \rightarrow 2NaOH$

(d) $H_2SO_4 + NaOH \rightarrow NaSO_4 + H_2O$: $H_2SO_4 + 2NaOH \rightarrow Na_2SO_4 + 2H(OH)$

(e) $HCl + CaCO_3 \rightarrow CaCl_2 + CO_3 + H_2O$: $2HCl + CaCO_3 \rightarrow CaCl_2 + CO_2 + H_2O$

(f) $Fe_2(SO_4)_3 + BaCl_2 \rightarrow BaSO_4 + FeCl_3$: $Fe_2(SO_4)_3 + 3BaCl_2 \rightarrow 3BaSO_4 + 2FeCl_3$

21. The equations you have balanced above all involve the movement of ions. Not all reactions involve ions, but the principles of balancing the equations remains the same. The combustion of simple organic compounds (e.g. methane) usually produces just CO_2 and H_2O as the products. Try balancing these:

(a) $CH_4 + O_2 \rightarrow CO_2 + H_2O$: $CH_4 + O_2 \rightarrow CO_2 + 2H_2O$

(b) $C_3H_8 + O_2 \rightarrow CO_2 + H_2O$: $C_3H_8 + 6O_2 \rightarrow 3CO_2 + 6H_2O$

(c) $C_2H_5OH + O_2 \rightarrow CO_2 + H_2O$: $2C_3H_5OH + 2O_2 \rightarrow 4CO_2 + 6H(OH)$

(d) $C_3H_6 + O_2 \rightarrow CO_2 + H_2O$: $2C_3H_6 + 7O_2 \rightarrow 6CO_2 + 6H_2O$

(e) $C_6H_{12} + O_2 \rightarrow CO_2 + H_2O$: $C_6H_{12} + 9O_2 \rightarrow 6CO_2 + 6H_2O$

ELABORATE: Stoichiometry

▸ Stoichiometry studies the amount of each substance in a reaction. You have already been doing this to some extent by using mole ratios to calculate an empirical or molecular formula. A balanced equation will show the stoichiometric ratios of the reactants and products.

▸ From the stoichiometry of a reaction it is possible to calculate the expected **yield** of a product from a set of reactants.

▸ For example consider the production of ammonium nitrate, an important part of fertilizer. The reaction for its production is $HNO_3 + NH_3 \rightarrow NH_4NO_3$.

▸ From the equation we can see the stoichiometric ratios or stoichiometry is $1:1 \rightarrow 1$. That is, 1 mole of nitric acid + 1 mole of ammonia reacts to form 1 mole of ammonium nitrate.

▸ Suppose we use 1.00 kg (1000 g) of ammonia to make ammonium nitrate. Using the stoichiometry, we can calculate the mass of ammonium nitrate that we can expect to produce (the yield).

22. (a) Using the following molar masses calculate the moles of ammonia in 1 kg of ammonia: M(O) = 16.0 g/mol, M(N) = 14.0 g/mol, M(H) = 1.0 g/mol.

_____

(b) How many moles of ammonium nitrate would be produced?

_____

(c) What is the mass of ammonium nitrate that could be expected to be produced?

_____

▸ How much product is expected compared to how much is actually produced can be expressed as the **percentage yield** (% yield). This simply the mass of the product produced ÷ the expected mass of the product x 100.

$$\% \text{ yield} = \frac{\text{Mass product produced}}{\text{Expected mass of product}} \times 100$$

23. Suppose for the production of ammonium nitrate above, the reaction only produced 3500 g. What was the percentage yield of ammonium nitrate?

_____

▸ Barium sulfate ($BaSO_4$) is an insoluble ionic compound. It has many uses in industry including oil well drilling fluid, paper brightener, as part of white pigments in paint, and as a radiocontrast agent for X-ray imaging.

24. Barium sulfate can be produced by mixing together solutions of sodium sulfate (Na_2SO_4) and barium chloride ($BaCl_2$). This produces a precipitate (a solid forming out of solution) of solid barium sulfate.
M(O) = 16.0 g/mol , M(S) = 32.1 g/mol, M(Na) = 23.0 g/mol, M(Cl) = 35.5 g/mol, M(Ba) = 137.3 g/mol,

(a) Balance the equation: $BaCl_{2(aq)} + Na_2SO_{4\ (aq)} \rightarrow BaSO_{4(s)} + NaCl_{(aq)}$

(b) If there was 2.0 grams of $BaCl_2$ in solution, what yield of barium sulfate (in grams) would you expect?

_____

_____

(c) Determine the percentage yield if the realized yield was only 1.5 grams: _____

_____

(d) If the solution was filtered to remove the $BaSO_4$, then evaporated to produce NaCl, what mass of NaCl would be expected if all the $BaCl_2$ and Na_2SO_4 reacted?

_____

_____

©2019 **BIOZONE** International
ISBN: 978-1-927309-71-1
Photocopying Prohibited

EVALUATE: Cycling matter in chemical reactions

▶ You should have realized by now that matter is not lost in a chemical reaction. All the atoms or ions in the reactants are present in the products.

▶ In the investigation below you will investigate the movement of cycling a group of copper ions through a series of reactions.

INVESTIGATION 3.4: The cycling of copper ions through a series of reactions

See appendix for equipment list.

Buchner funnel

⚠ Copper carbonate can irritate the skin and ingestion and inhalation of dust is harmful. H_2SO_4 is corrosive. Wear eyewear and gloves.

1. Weigh precisely about 2 g of copper II carbonate ($CuCO_3$) on to a piece of filter paper. Record the mass here:

   _____

2. What color is the copper carbonate? _____

3. Weigh a clean and dry test tube and record the mass: _____

4. Carefully place all the copper II carbonate into the test tube (don't leave any behind!). Attach the test tube to a clamp stand. Place a rubber cork and delivery tube on the end of the test tube and place the delivery tube in a beaker of limewater.

5. Place a Bunsen burner under the test tube and carefully heat the copper carbonate. Observe the change in the limewater. What gas is being produced?

   _____

6. Note the color change in the copper carbonate as it is heated. What color does the copper carbonate turn? What is this new powder?

   _____

   _____

7. When the color change is complete (the powder is all the same color) turn off the Bunsen and let the test tube and powder cool.

8. Reweigh the test tube and powder. Calculate the mass of the powder: _____

9. Weigh and record the mass of a clean, dry 100 mL beaker and place all the powder from the test tube into the beaker. Reweigh the beaker and powder and record the mass:

   _____

10. Add 80 mL of 1 mol/L H_2SO_4 to the beaker. Stir the solution with a clean glass stirring rod. Record the color change in the solution. What is this new solution?

    _____

11. Use steel wool or sandpaper to clean any coating from a large iron nail. Record the mass of the nail:

    _____

12. Add the cleaned nail to the solution and leave the solution overnight.

13. Record the color change of the solution and any other observations of the reaction:

    _____

    _____

14. Filter the solution to recover the new powder that has formed on the iron nail. Rinse the filtered powder with distilled water. The powder will need to be dried. Place the powder and filter paper onto a Buchner funnel to remove any remaining distilled water. If you have a drying oven, place the powder and filter paper into the oven just long enough to dry the powder completely.

15. Record the mass of the powder. What is this new powder? _____

    _____

©2019 **BIOZONE** International
ISBN: 978-1-927309-71-1

16. Record the mass of a test tube: _____

17. Place all the powder into the test tube. Hold the test tube with tongs and heat it strongly over a Bunsen burner. When all the powder has changed color let the test cool and weigh the test tube and power (if possible try to weigh the powder on it own). This new powder is the same as the powder you produced in step 6.

_____

▶ You must now try to explain the changes in the series of reactions you carried out. If everything has worked correctly and you have been very careful to collect all the powder at the different stages the powder you weighed in step 8 should have the same mass as the powder in step 17. It is unlikely the masses will be identical, but you should be close.

▶ For the calculations below use the following molar masses M(Cu) = 63.5 g/mol, M(Fe) = 55.9 g/mol, M(S) = 32.1 g/mol, M(O) = 16.0 g/mol, M(C) = 12.0 g/mol, M(H) = 1.0 g/mol.

25. (a) From the mass of copper carbonate calculate $n(CuCO_3)$: _____

(b) Heating the $CuCO_3$ produced a **decomposition reaction**. Carbon dioxide (CO_2) was lost from the $CuCO_3$ and black CuO remained. Write an equation for the decomposition of $CuCO_3$.

_____

(c) What mass of CuO would you have expected to be yielded from the $CuCO_3$? _____

_____

(d) What mass of CuO did you actually produce?: _____

(e) Write an equation for the reaction of the CuO with the H_2SO_4: _____

(f) When the iron nail was placed in the solution a **displacement reaction** occurred. The iron in the nail displaces the copper ions in solution causing them to form red copper metal (although it is powdery). From the original mass of $CuCO_3$ calculate the expected yield of Cu:

_____

_____

(g) What was the actual mass of Cu you produced? _____

(h) Heating the powdered copper caused it to oxidize (react with oxygen) producing the same black powder as you produced after heating the $CuCO_3$. What was this powder?

_____

(i) What mass of this powder should you have yielded and what was your actual yield? _____

_____

26. Explain the reactions above and the cycling of copper through the reactions in terms of ions present, stoichiometry of the reactions, and conservation of mass. Include balanced equations for all the reactions.

_____

_____

_____

_____

_____

_____

_____

_____

_____

_____

23 Aqueous Reactions

ENGAGE: Solutions

▸ Have you ever made a flavored drink by adding powder from a sachet to a liter of water?

▸ In doing this you have produced a solution. It will have had a certain concentration, perhaps 100 grams of powder per litre or 100 g/L.

▸ Sometimes you may have added a concentrate to water to form a diluted solution. This might be adding a cordial or house hold ammonium solution to water.

1. In groups come up with a list of other solutions about the house that need diluting or making into a solution before they are used. Write your list here:

_____

_____

_____

_____

EXPLORE: Concentration

▸ So far in chemistry when we have referred to the amount of a substance we have used its mass in grams. In reality many substances you will come across will not be able to be easily weighed out because they are dissolved in solution. We must refer to their concentration, the amount of substance per liter. This might be as grams per liter (g/L) or, specifically in chemistry, moles per liter (mol/L). Consider the label on the right from a bottle of orange juice:

NUTRITION INFORMATION			
SERVINGS PER PACKAGE: 4			
SERVING SIZE: 250mL			
	AVERAGE QUANTITY PER SERVING	% DAILY INTAKE* PER SERVING	AVERAGE QUANTITY PER 100mL
ENERGY	479kJ	6%	191kJ
PROTEIN	2.3g	5%	<1g
FAT, TOTAL	<1g	1%	<1g
-SATURATED	0g	0%	0g
CARBOHYDRATE	22.3g	7%	8.9g
-SUGARS	22.1g	25%	8.8g
DIETARY FIBRE	<1g	2%	<1g
SODIUM	7.9mg	0%	3.2mg
POTASSIUM	415mg	-	165mg

2. (a) What volume is a serving of orange juice? _____

(b) How many servings in 1 L (1000 mL) of orange juice? _____

(c) What is the concentration of potassium in g/L (1 g = 1000 mg)?

_____

(d) What is the concentration of sugars per liter in g/L? _____

EXPLORE: Salt from the sea

▸ Sodium chloride is one of the most common chemicals used by humans. It is used to enhance flavor in food, in medicine (e.g. saline solution), thousands of tonnes are spread on roads every year to prevent ice forming, and it is an important ingredient in many industrial reactions. Approximately 280 million tonnes are produced every year.

▸ Much of this comes from the sea or salt lakes by evaporating seawater in huge shallow ponds (shown right). Seawater has a concentration of sodium chloride of about 35 g/L. Different seas and oceans have very slightly different salinities due to their position. For example the Mediterranean Sea is mostly enclosed and has a concentration of 38 g/L.

▸ Some lakes have very high salt concentration. The Great Salt Lake in Utah has a salt concentration of up to 317 g/L (right).

Jeff Kubina CC 2.0

3. (a) Sodium chloride has a molar mass of 58.5 g/mol. How many moles of sodium chloride are in one liter of sea water?

_____

(b) How many times more concentrated than seawater is the Great Salt Lake? _____

(c) What is the concentration of the Great Salt Lake in moles per liter? _____

▸ Many metals can be found in seawater. Gold has a concentration of 1×10^{-11} grams per liter of seawater. That's 1 gram per 100 million tonnes of seawater.

4. Gold has a molar mass of 197.0 g/mol. What is the concentration of gold in seawater in moles per liter? _____

_____

 PS1.A PS1.B SPQ EM

©2019 **BIOZONE** International
ISBN: 978-1-927309-71-1
Photocopying Prohibited

EXPLAIN: Creating standards

▶ Standards are important in everyday life. We use standards for measuring other things against. Standards can be anything and people have come up with some interesting ones over time.

▶ Examples include standards in height: e.g. storeys, as in "it was 5 storeys tall!". We don't know exactly how high that is, but we get the idea. Other odd standards include jumbo jets ("the Wright brothers first flight was less than the wingspan of a jumbo jet"), or football fields, or elephants.

5. Write down some everyday standards you measure things against (they don't have to be strange): _____

_____

_____

_____

▶ When trying to find out the concentration of a solution we first need a standard to measure the unknown concentration against. This is called a **standard solution**. Standard solutions are made up in volumetric flasks. Placing a known mass of a compound in the flask and then filling up to the mark with distilled water will produce a volume with a known and precise concentration against which other solutions can be measured.

▶ This can be demonstrated by making a standard solution of anhydrous sodium carbonate (Na_2CO_3) and using it to standardize a solution of hydrochloric acid.

6. (a) The molar mass of Na_2CO_3 is 106 g/mol. How many moles of Na_2CO_3 are needed to make up a 250 mL solution of 0.05 mol/L Na_2CO_3?

_____

_____

(b) What mass of Na_2CO_3 is your answer in (a) equal to?

_____

_____

_____

In chemistry, it is the number of atoms or ions involved in a reaction that matters. To know this, we must know the number of moles of reactants. In a solution, the number of moles is expressed as moles per liter (mol/L). When we refer to the concentration of a solution we are referring to mol/L. To calculate a solution's concentration we can use a simple equation:

$$c = n/V$$

Or concentration (in mol/L) = number of moles ÷ volume (in liters).

Learn how to use the equation $c = n/V$ to calculate concentrations. You will be able to solve for any variable in the equation if you know the other two. Cover the variable you want to know and you are left with how to calculate it.

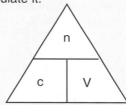

INVESTIGATION 3.5: Making a primary standard (Na_2CO_3)

See appendix for equipment list.

1. Add about 1.3 grams of anhydrous Na_2CO_3 to a clean, dry beaker. Record the precise mass you have weighed:

_____

2. Dissolve the powder in distilled water.

3. Clean and rinse a 250 mL volumetric flask with distilled water. Using a funnel, transfer the Na_2CO_3 solution to the volumetric flask, rinsing the beaker with distilled water to ensure all the Na_2CO_3 is transferred.

4. Add distilled water to the flask until it is about half full. Stopper the flask and invert several times to ensure the Na_2CO_3 solution is thoroughly mixed.

5. Fill the flask almost to the mark. Then use a wash bottle or dropper to fill the flask to the mark so that the meniscus sits on the mark. Do not overfill or you will not be able to calculate a precise concentration.

6. Stopper the flask and mix again.

7. This is your primary standard. You will use it to standardize other solutions.

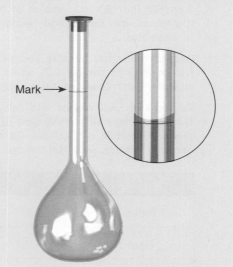

Mark →

A volumetric flask is designed to have an exact volume (to within +/– 1%) when filled to the mark.

7. Calculate the exact concentration of your standard flask from the mass you weighed at the start:

_____

8. (a) Why should distilled water be used to make up a standard solution instead of tap water?

_____

_____

   (b) What should you do if you overfill your volumetric flask? _____

_____

9. Primary standards should be made from solid compounds with a high molar mass. This reduces measuring errors. Explain why measuring out a high mass solid such as sodium carbonate is a more accurate way of making a standard than weighing out a low molar mass solid like sodium hydroxide:

_____

_____

_____

_____

ELABORATE: Standardizing HCl

▶ The sodium carbonate solution can now be used to standardize other solutions that are more suitable for testing unknown solutions against. This is done by **titration**.

▶ Your lab supply of hydrochloric acid (HCl) may be 1 mol/L. This is too concentrated for the volumetric analysis of many solutions. You must produce a 0.1 mol/L solution and standardize it using your sodium carbonate solution.

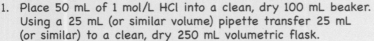

INVESTIGATION 3.6: Volumetric analysis of HCl   See appendix for equipment list.

1. Place 50 mL of 1 mol/L HCl into a clean, dry 100 mL beaker. Using a 25 mL (or similar volume) pipette transfer 25 mL (or similar) to a clean, dry 250 mL volumetric flask.

2. Add distilled water to the flask until it is about half full. Stopper the flask and invert several times to ensure the HCl solution is thoroughly mixed.

3. Fill the flask almost to the mark. Then use a wash bottle or dropper to fill the flask to the mark.

4. Rinse a 50 mL burette with the HCl solution, then place the burette in a clamp stand and fill it with the HCl solution.

5. Transfer four 20 mL samples of Na_2CO_3 solution into four clean 100 mL conical flasks. Add two drops of methyl orange indicator to each flask.

6. Record the initial burette volume. Add the HCl solution from the burette to the Na_2CO_3 while swirling the flask until the indicator **just changes color** (the **equivalence** point).

7. Record the final volume and calculate the difference. This is the **titre** (the minimum volume of a solution needed to reach the end point in a titration). Do not use this volume in your final calculations (it is a just trial to become familiar with the volume of HCl solution required).

Burette containing HCl

Conical flask containing Na_2CO_3 solution

Burette reading	Trial titration	First titration	Second titration	Third titration
Initial reading				
Final reading				
Difference (titre)				

8. Carry out the titration at least three more times and record the volume added for each in the table.

©2019 **BIOZONE** International
ISBN: 978-1-927309-71-1

10. Balance the equation for sodium carbonate and hydrochloric acid: $Na_2CO_3 +$ ___ $HCl \rightarrow$ ___ $NaCl +$ ___ $CO_2 +$ ___ H_2O

11. (a) Calculate $n(Na_2CO_3)$ in the conical flask: _____

    (b) Calculate $n(HCl)$ used: _____

    (c) Calculate the average (mean) volume of HCl solution used: _____

    (d) Calculate the concentration of HCl in the volumetric flask: _____

    _____

EVALUATE: Finding the concentration of ethanoic acid in vinegar

▶ A standard sodium hydroxide solution is useful for testing the acid concentration of various solutions. It must be standardized whenever it is used as it tends to absorbs carbon dioxide from the air, which can change the concentration.

▶ In the following investigations, you will standardize a solution of NaOH from the lab supply then immediately use it to calculate the concentration of ethanoic (acetic) acid in a store bought white vinegar.

INVESTIGATION 3.7: Volumetric analysis of ethanoic acid

See appendix for equipment list.

1. Add 50 mL of 1 mol/L NaOH solution to a clean, dry 100 mL beaker. Transfer 25 mL to a 250 mL volumetric flask using a 25 mL pipette.

2. Alternatively weigh 1 gram of solid NaOH in a 100 mL beaker and dissolve with distilled water before transferring to a volumetric flask.

3. Following the same procedure as to produce the HCl earlier, dilute the NaOH by filling the volumetric flask up to the mark with distilled water.

4. Rinse a burette with the dilute NaOH solution. Then fill the burette with the solution.

5. Rinse a pipette with your standardized HCl solution then pipette four 20 mL samples into four clean, dry 100 mL conical flasks.

6. Add two drops of phenolphthalein indicator to the conical flasks. This will turn pink when the HCl/NaOH reaction is complete.

7. Again, you will need to carry out at least three titrations plus a trial run. Use the table at the bottom of the page to record your results:

8. Record the initial burette volume. Add the NaOH solution from the burette to the HCl while swirling the flask until the indicator just changes color. Record the final volume and calculate the difference (the titre).

9. Carry out the titration at least three more times and record the volume added for each.

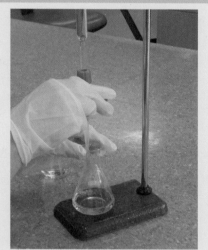

The titration is complete when the phenolphthalein turns a slight pink.

Burette reading	Trial titration	First titration	Second titration	Third titration
Initial reading				
Final reading				
Difference (titre)				

12. Balance the equation for sodium hydroxide and hydrochloric acid: ___ $NaOH +$ ___ $HCl \rightarrow$ ___ $NaCl +$ ___ H_2O

13. (a) Calculate $n(HCl)$ in the conical flasks: _____

    _____

    (b) Calculate the average (mean) volume of NaOH solution used: _____

    (c) Calculate $n(NaOH)$ used: _____

    (d) Calculate the concentration of NaOH in volumetric flask: _____

    _____

▶ You can now use the standardized NaOH to investigate the concentration of ethanoic acid in vinegar.

INVESTIGATION 3.8: Volumetric analysis of vinegar

See appendix for equipment list.

1. Refill the burette with your standardized NaOH solution.

2. Rinse a 25 mL pipette with vinegar. Transfer 25 mL of vinegar to a 100 mL volumetric flask and fill to the mark with distilled water (to dilute the vinegar).

3. Rinse a 10 mL pipette with distilled water then use it to transfer 10 mL of vinegar solution into each of four 100 mL conical flasks.

4. Add two drops of phenolphthalein indicator to the conical flasks.

5. Again, you will need to carry out at least three titrations plus a trial run. Use the table below to record your results:

Burette reading	Trial titration	First titration	Second titration	Third titration
Initial reading				
Final reading				
Difference (titre)				

Record the initial burette volume. Add the NaOH solution from the burette to the vinegar while swirling the flask until the indicator just changes color. Record the final volume and calculate the difference.

6. Carry out the titration at least three more times and record the volume added for each.

14. Balance the equation for sodium hydroxide and ethanoic acid: $NaOH + CH_3COOH \rightarrow CH_3COONa + H_2O$

15. (a) Calculate the average (mean) volume of NaOH solution used: _____

_____

(b) Calculate n(NaOH) used: _____

(c) Calculate n(CH_3COOH) in the conical flasks: _____

_____

(d) Calculate the concentration of CH_3COOH in the conical flask: _____

_____

(e) The CH_3COOH in the vinegar was diluted by how many times in the volumetric flask? _____

_____

(f) What was the original concentration of ethanoic acid in the vinegar? _____

_____

16. What are some errors that may have arisen in your analysis of the vinegar? _____

_____

_____

17. Check your results with others in your class. How close were you to their results? _____

_____

18. How close were you to the actual concentration of acid in the vinegar (as stated on the bottle)?

_____

19. Your NaOH solution could now be used analyze the concentration of other solutions: On a separate sheet write a method for analyzing the total acid concentration in fresh squeezed orange juice. Staple your method to this page.

©2019 **BIOZONE** International
ISBN: 978-1-927309-71-1
Photocopying Prohibited

24 Burp! Revisited

▶ At the beginning of this chapter you were introduced to some chemical equations relating to the neutralizing of stomach acid by antacid tablets.

▶ With the concepts you have learned throughout this chapter you should now be able to answer questions posed about these tablets and devise a way of finding out the mass of the active ingredient in a particular tablet.

1. At the start of the chapter you were asked to complete the word equations below. Redo them now, then check them against your original answers:

(a) Hydrochloric acid + calcium carbonate → _____

(b) Hydrochloric acid + sodium hydrogen carbonate → _____

(c) Hydrochloric acid + magnesium hydroxide → _____

2. Complete and balance the chemical equations for each of the following reactions:

(a) $HCl +$ $CaCO_3$ →   _____

(b) $HCl +$ $NaHCO_3$ →   _____

(c) $HCl +$ $Mg(OH)_2$ →   _____

3. For question 2(c) explain the balancing of the reaction in terms of the atoms and ions present. You may wish to draw a diagram to help you:

_____

_____

_____

_____

_____

4. At the start of the chapter you were asked to develop a method for working out the amount of active ingredient in an antacid tablet. You may now want to modify your method. How would you find out the amount (the mass) of calcium carbonate in an antacid tablet with calcium carbonate as the active ingredient? Calcium carbonate doesn't dissolve in water, but it does dissolve in acid.

_____

_____

_____

_____

_____

_____

_____

_____

_____

_____

©2019 **BIOZONE** International
ISBN: 978-1-927309-71-1

25 Summative Assessment

For the following summative assessment you may refer to your periodic table on page 250 of this book.

1. Study the diagram of the atom labelled X below:

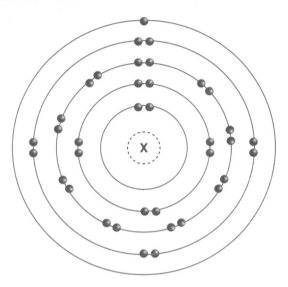

Based on the diagram of the atom predict the following:

(a) Its position in the periodic table (which group and period): _____

(b) Its reactivity relative to other elements in its group and period: _____

_____

(c) The formula of the chloride it will produce: _____

(d) The formula of the oxide it will produce: _____

(e) Whether it is a metal or nonmetal: _____

(f) Its electronegativity relative to other atoms on the periodic table: _____

(g) Its ionization energy relative to other atoms in its group: _____

2. (a) The graph below shows the atomic radii of the alkali metals. Sketch a line on the graph to show where you think **ionic radii** for these metals would go.

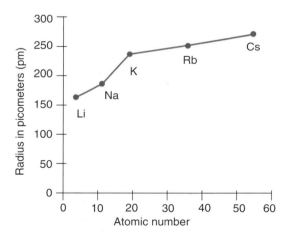

(b) Explain the placement of your sketch: _____

_____

_____

_____

©2019 **BIOZONE** International
ISBN: 978-1-927309-71-1
Photocopying Prohibited

3. (a) An atom has 17 electrons. Write down its electron configuration: _____

   (b) Will the atom form a positive or negative ion? _____

   (c) What would the charge on the ion be? _____

   (d) Is this atom a metal or nonmetal? _____

4. An element has atoms with 20 protons, 20 neutrons, and 20 electrons:

   (a) What is the atomic number of this element? _____

   (b) What is the mass number of the element? _____

   (c) In the boxes draw the electron arrangement of the atom and its ion:

   Atom

   Ion

5. During a reaction metal X and nonmetal Y react to form the compound XY_2.

   (a) Write a balanced equation for the reaction of X and Y: _____

   (b) Which group of the periodic table would you expect X to be in? _____

   (c) Which group of the periodic table when your expect Y to be in? _____

   (d) Explain your answer: _____

   _____

   _____

   _____

6. Balance the following equations:

   (a)   Ca +   HCl $\rightarrow$ $CaCl_2$ + H_2

   (b)   Li + H_2O $\rightarrow$ LiOH + H_2

   (c) C_2H_6 + O_2 $\rightarrow$ CO_2 + H_2O

   (d) C_2H_5OH + O_2 $\rightarrow$ CO + H_2O

7. A chemist accidently mislabeled a container holding a silvery metal element. To find out what the metal was, the chemist carried out a series of tests. The results are stated below:

   The density of the metal lay between sodium and sulfur
   When reacted with acid, the reaction was relatively fast, much faster than iron in the same concentration of acid.
   When reacted with water the reaction was relatively slow, much slower than adding sodium to water.
   When burned in oxygen, a one gram piece of metal reacted with 0.66 grams of oxygen (M(O)=16 g/mol).

   What do you think this metal was? Explain your answer: _____

   _____

   _____

   _____

For the remaining questions in this summative activity use the molar masses given: M(H) = 1.0 g/mol, M(C) = 12.0 g/mol, M(N) = 14.0 g/mol, M(O) = 16.0 g/mol, M(Na) = 23.0 g/mol, M(S) = 32.1 g/mol, M(Cl) = 35.5 g/mol, M(Fe) = 55.8 g/mol, M(Cu) = 63.5 g/mol, M(Ba) = 137.3 g/mol

8. Calculate the following:

   (a) n(NaCl) in 10 grams of NaCl: _____

   (b) n(Cu) in 20 grams of $CuSO_4$: _____

   (c) n(H) in 20 grams of H_2O: _____

9. The oxygen fuel tank for NASA's new SLS (Space Launch System) holds about 740,000 L of liquid oxygen. Liquid oxygen has a density of 1141 g/L. The oxygen will react with liquid hydrogen to provide the rocket's thrust.

   Oxygen fuel tank for the SLS

   (a) Calculate the mass of hydrogen needed to completely react all the oxygen:

   _____

   _____

   _____

   (b) Liquid hydrogen has a density of 71 g/L. What is the minimum volume of liquid hydrogen needed to completely react all the liquid oxygen?

   _____

   (c) What is the volume (in liters) of the combined fuel tanks? _____

   _____

10. (a) A mining company wanted to mine iron ore. They had the choice of two sites. Site 1 contained ore with approximately 80% hematite (Fe_2O_3). The second site contained ore with approximately 70% magnetite (Fe_3O_4). Determine which site will produce the greatest amount of iron.

    _____

    _____

    _____

    _____

    (b) To refine the iron, the iron oxides are reacted with carbon monoxide (CO). The reactions occur in up to three stages:

    Stage One: $3\ Fe_2O_3 + CO \rightarrow 2\ Fe_3O_4 + CO_2$
    Stage Two: $Fe_3O_4 + CO \rightarrow 3\ FeO + CO_2$
    Stage Three: $FeO + CO \rightarrow Fe + CO_2$

    i.   At which stage would the extraction of iron begin at the site with the hematite ore? _____

    ii. At which stage would the extraction of iron begin at the site with the magnetite ore? _____

    iii. How many moles CO are need to form 1 mole of Fe from hematite? _____

    iv. How many moles CO are need to form 1 mole of Fe from magnetite? _____

    v.   Carbon monoxide is produced by reacting coke (C) with oxygen (O_2): $2C + O_2 \rightarrow 2CO$. Coke costs approximately US$200 per tonne ($10^6$ g). Calculate the amount of coke required to refine 1 tonne of iron (Fe) from magnetite and hematite.

    _____

    _____

    _____

    _____

    vi. Which ore would cost less to refine in terms of the cost of coke? _____

    _____

©2019 **BIOZONE** International
ISBN: 978-1-927309-71-1
Photocopying Prohibited

11. Fertilizers show the different percentage of components in the fertilizer by printing an NPK rating on the bag. This stands for nitrogen – phosphorus – potassium. A rating of 13 – 10 – 10 contains 13% nitrogen by mass, 10% phosphorus (actually P_2O_5), and 10% potassium (actually K_2O) by mass.

A fertilizer company made a fertilizer claiming a rating 15 – 0 – 0. The nitrogen was contained as ammonium sulfate (($NH_4)_2SO_4$).

A student tested the percentage of N in the fertilizer by dissolving 100 grams of fertilizer in 1 L of distilled water. 50 mL of the solution was then reacted with excess 1 mol/L barium chloride ($BaCl_2$) solution.

The equation for the reaction is $BaCl_{2(aq)} + (NH_4)_2SO_{4(aq)} \rightarrow BaSO_{4(s)} + 2NH_4Cl_{(aq)}$.

The solid barium sulfate was then filtered, dried and weighed. Its mass was 6.3 grams.

(a) Calculate the mass of $(NH_4)_2SO_4$ in 100 grams of fertilizer: _____

_____

_____

(b) Calculate the concentration of the $(NH_4)_2SO_4$ solution: _____

_____

_____

(c) How many moles of SO_4 are in 50 mL of the $(NH_4)_2SO_4$ solution? _____

_____

_____

(d) What mass of $BaSO_4$ would be expected to be produced in the reaction? _____

_____

_____

(e) Was the fertilizer company correct in saying its fertilizer contained 15%N? Give reasons for your answer:

_____

_____

_____

12. Lactic acid (abbreviated to HLac) is the acid found in sour milk products such as sour cream, cottage cheese, and yoghurt. Lactic acid has a molar mass of 90 g/mol. It is water soluble and as an acid will react with NaOH solution in the following way:

$$HLac_{(aq)} + NaOH_{(aq)} \rightarrow NaLac_{(aq)} + H_2O_{(aq)}$$

A student decided to test the amount of lactic acid in a sample of unsweetened yoghurt. She dissolved 100 grams of yoghurt in distilled water in a 250 mL volumetric flask. She then titrated 25 mL samples of the solution with 0.025 mol/L NaOH. The volumes of NaOH used (excluding the initial) were 20.1 mL, 20.2 mL, 20.0 mL, 20.0 mL, and 20.2 mL.

(a) Calculate the moles (n(HLac)) of lactic acid in the 250 mL flask:

_____

_____

_____

_____

(b) Calculate the mass and percentage of lactic acid in the 100 g sample of yoghurt: _____

_____

_____

_____

©2019 **BIOZONE** International
ISBN: 978-1-927309-71-1

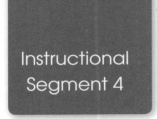

Instructional Segment 4

Chemical Reactions

Anchoring Phenomenon

Hot! Too hot! Instant heat and instant cold.   26 32

What holds atoms together in molecules?

☐ 1 You will know that chemical reactions can store and release energy, but what are the   27 33
mechanisms of these energy changes? You can begin to answer this question by making
a simple balloon model to show how molecules will orientate spontaneously into shapes
with the least potential energy. You can extend this model by using Lewis diagrams to
show how the valence electrons of atoms combine during a reaction to fill the valence
shells of each atom in the reaction. You can then use your Lewis diagrams to explain the
different shapes of molecules or compounds.

☐ 2 Observe how different materials behave on their own and with other substances.   28 33
Investigate the properties of different materials (e.g. state at room temperature, boiling
point, melting point, conductivity) and organize the materials into groups based on the
similarities and differences of the properties you have observed. Use your findings to
support a model of different types of chemical bonds and attractions.

☐ 3 Analyze patterns in the electronegativities of some of the substances you have   28 33
encountered and use these patterns to explain the polarity of molecules and the bonds
that hold molecules and compounds together. Use the equation for Coulomb's law as
a mathematical model to support your explanation. Analyze data on the properties of
a simple series of hydrocarbons (the alkanes) and relate patterns in the data to the
intermolecular forces involved in those molecules.

How do chemical reactions absorb and release energy?

☐ 4 In IS1 you explored some aspects of changes of state including the energy required to   29 33
change state (e.g. the heat of fusion). Analyze data about changes of state to develop
a model of how energy is absorbed and released during different types of chemical
reactions. Identify changes of state as either exothermic or endothermic depending on
whether the molecules in the substance are being attracted by intermolecular forces or
must overcome them.

☐ 5 You will now know that chemical reactions involve breaking and forming chemical bonds.   30
Separating atoms (breaking chemical bonds) requires energy and bringing them closer
together in different combinations (forming chemical bonds) releases energy. Recall how
you measured the energy in a corn chip in IS1. Use the same techniques to determine the
energy released during burning an alcohol such as methanol (the enthalpy of combustion).
Compare your values to reported values and explain any differences. Next, investigate
energy changes in some common chemical reactions. Classify them as endothermic or
exothermic and explain the thermal changes you observe in each reaction.

☐ 6 In chemistry, bond enthalpy (H) is the measure of the strength of a chemical bond.   30 33
Enthalpy change (ΔH) is the name given to the amount of heat released or absorbed in
a reaction. Investigate and calculate the change in enthalpy for some common reactions,
including combustion ($\Delta_c H$) and product formation ($\Delta_f H$).

☐ 7 Compare the bond energies of products and reactants to construct mathematical models   30
of the energy in different chemical systems and to predict whether or not energy will be
absorbed or released. Develop your mathematical model to incorporate the activation
energy into graphs showing changes in bond energy during photosynthesis and cellular
respiration.

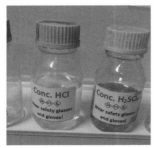

☐ 8 You have seen from your investigations that there are differences in the relative   30
strength of different types of bonds and attractions. Are these differences related to
the energy stored in the bonds? Analyze data for bond enthalpies, e.g. for the alcohols
you investigated earlier, and look for patterns. As an extension activity, use calculations
of total average bond enthalpies to predict the temperature change when you react a
certain mass of reactants.

☐ 9 Investigate the rate of a chemical reaction under different conditions of temperature and   31 33
concentration of reactants. Analyze and interpret your data and explain any patterns you
see. What effect do catalysts (chemical or biological catalysts) have on reaction rates?
Can you modify your mathematical model to show how activation energy is changed by
the addition of a catalyst?

Ben Mills

26 | Hot! Too Hot!

ANCHORING PHENOMENON: Instant heat and instant cold

▶ Have you ever been out on a cold morning and felt as if you needed something to warm your hands? Or been caught out in the open and needed an emergency heat supply?

▶ Have you ever had a sports injury and had a cold pack applied to it that the coach had in the kit bag? It wasn't ice, or in a chiller, so how did it get cold?

▶ Study the images below:

Reusable heat pack

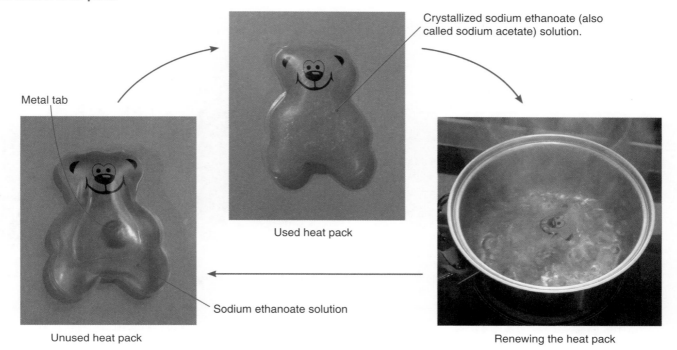

Metal tab

Crystallized sodium ethanoate (also called sodium acetate) solution.

Used heat pack

Sodium ethanoate solution

Unused heat pack

Renewing the heat pack

Nonreusable hot and cold packs

The heat pack (right) contains the active ingredient, iron powder, which reacts with air when the pack is opened.

Instant cold packs contain solid ammonium nitrate and water in separate bags. Squeezing or squashing the outer bag ruptures the inner bags and mixes the contents together.

1. In groups, discuss how you think these hot and cold packs work. Where is the heat in the heat pack coming from? Why does the cold pack feel cold? Why can the heat pack at the top be renewed by placing it in boiling water? Summarize you ideas below:

_____
_____
_____
_____
_____
_____

©2019 **BIOZONE** International
ISBN: 978-1-927309-71-1
Photocopying Prohibited

27 Molecular Structure

ENGAGE: Spontaneous orientations

▸ Sometimes objects orientate themselves into certain shapes without any apparent input of energy. In fact by orientating themselves in such shapes, the objects are losing energy and becoming more stable.

▸ For example, take a laminated aluminum foil bag from a potato chip pack. Scrunch it up (not too tightly) and then let it go and it will return to its original shape. Why?

1. What other objects can you think of that return to shape when bent or compressed? _____

_____

_____

2. (a) Observe the spring being bent in the photo. The spring has been placed under tension. What will happen if the tension is removed from the spring?

    _____

    _____

   (b) Which configuration has less potential (stored) energy?

    _____

   (c) Which configuration is more stable, the bent or unbent spring?

    _____

3. (a) Think about the foil bag again. Which configuration has the least potential energy, scrunched or unscrunched?

    _____

   (b) The laminate that covers the bag is made of a large network molecule. How does scrunching the bag affect the shape of this molecule?

    _____

   (c) In terms of energy why does the bag return to shape (mostly) when let go after being scrunched?

    _____

    _____

EXPLORE: More spontaneous orientations

INVESTIGATION 4.1: Modeling bond orientations with balloons   See appendix for equipment list.

1. Inflate a balloon and tie it closed. Use a marker pen to draw a dot at each end of the balloon (top and bottom).

2. Imagine a line connecting the dots you have drawn. Box 1 on the next page shows a simple drawing of the two dots and the line connecting them.

3. Inflate a second balloon and tie it closed. Draw a dot on the top. Tie the end of the second balloon to the end of the first balloon.

4. In box 2 draw a diagram (similar to box 1) to show how the three dots are connected.

5. Bend the balloons at the point where they are joined. What happens when you let them go?

6. Inflate a third balloon and tie it closed. Again draw a dot on the top and tie it to the join of the first and second balloons.

7. In box 3 draw a diagram to show how the four dots (the top of three balloons and the one at the bottom of the first balloon) are connected.

8. Repeat this procedure with a fourth balloon and draw the diagram of the shape connecting all five dots in box 4.

       PS1.A PS2.B P CE

©2019 **BIOZONE** International
ISBN:978-1-927309-71-1
Photocopying Prohibited

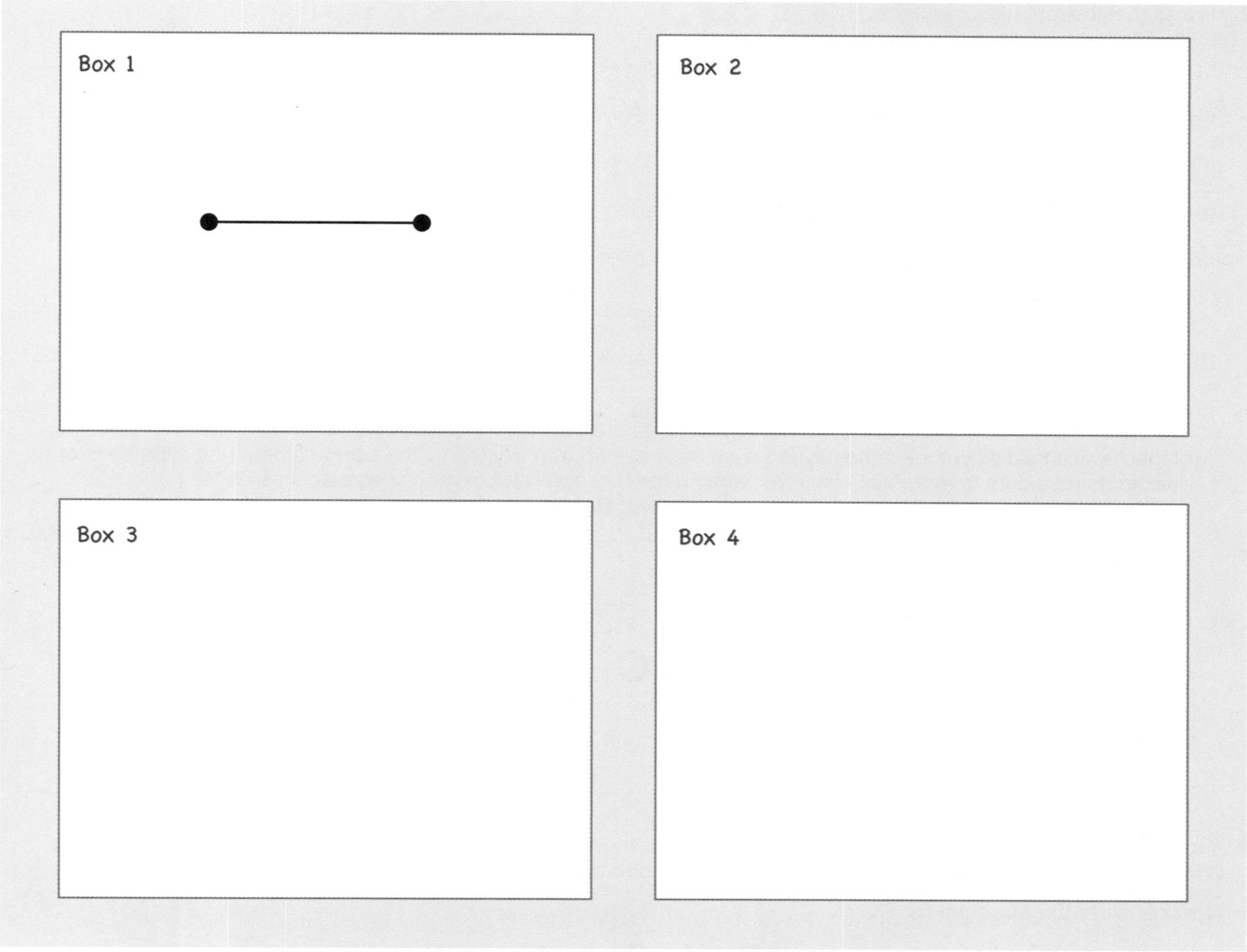

Box 1

Box 2

Box 3

Box 4

4. Why do the balloons orientate themselves in the shapes you drew above? _____

_____

_____

5. If each dot on the balloons represents an atom, what does the line you drew connecting the dots represent?

_____

6. (a) The molecule methane (CH_4) has carbon as its central atom with the hydrogen atoms surrounding it. Which box above contains the shape of a methane molecule?

_____

(b) Why would the molecule orientate to that shape? _____

_____

_____

EXPLAIN: Lewis structures

▶ Lewis structures (also called Lewis dot diagrams, Lewis dot formulas, or electron dot diagrams) are a useful diagrammatic tool in chemistry. They are used to show how the valence electrons of atoms combine during a reaction to fill the valence shells of each atom in the reaction.

▶ We have already seen a simple version of this in activity 20 "The Atom" when dealing with the formation of ions.

▶ You will recall that any neutral atom may lose, gain, or share electrons in order to fill the valence shell and become stable. If electrons are gained or lost, the atom becomes an ion. If the electrons are shared, a covalent bond forms.

▶ In all cases, the valence shell is full. In Lewis structures this is represented by four pairs of electrons around each atom in the diagram. Hydrogen does not follow this **octet rule** as it can only have up to two electrons.

©2019 **BIOZONE** International
ISBN: 978-1-927309-71-1
Photocopying Prohibited

7. Recall that the formula for water is H_2O.

(a) How many valence electrons does a neutral hydrogen atom have? _____

(b) How many electrons does a neutral hydrogen atom need to fill its valence shell? _____

(c) How many valence electrons does a neutral oxygen atom have? _____

(d) How many electrons does a neutral oxygen atom need to fill its valence shell? _____

(e) What is the total number of electrons in the valence shells of two hydrogen atoms and one oxygen atom?

_____

(f) What is the total number of pairs of electrons in the valence shells of two hydrogen atoms and one oxygen atom?

_____

(g) In the space below hydrogen and oxygen have been placed with oxygen as the central atom. Place the pairs of electrons (use dots to represent electrons) around the hydrogen and oxygen according these rules:
Only eight electrons around oxygen. Only two electrons around each hydrogen. The electrons must be in pairs:

H   O   H

▶ You should see from the structure you have drawn that there are two pairs of electrons around oxygen that are non-bonding, and one pair of electrons for each hydrogen atom.

▶ Now consider the structure for CO_2.

C ::
O :::
O :::

O : C : O
↓
:O : C : O:

Carbon has an atomic number of 6, so it also has six electrons. Two of those fill the inner electron shell, leaving four in the valence shell. The two oxygen atoms have 6 electrons in their valence shells. This gives a total of 4 + 6 + 6 = 16 electrons or 8 pairs to place around the atoms.

The central atom in this structure is C as this has the lowest electronegativity. Placing the electrons around the atoms is more tricky this time but it is worth starting by adding one pair of electrons to each bond (between the C and the Os), leaving 6 pairs. If we distribute three pairs to each oxygen atom, then both Os have full valence shells but C does not.

But atoms can share more than one pair of electrons. If we move one of the three pairs from each O to the bonding area between C and O then we find that all three atoms now have four pairs of electrons surrounding them. In this case C and O are bonded by double **covalent** bonds, whereas H_2O had two single covalent bonds.

8. Try drawing Lewis structures for these molecules:

(a) O_2

(b) CH_4

(c) NH_3

©2019 **BIOZONE** International
ISBN:978-1-927309-71-1
Photocopying Prohibited

(d) C_2H_6	(e) C_2H_4	(f) NH_4^+

EXPLAIN: Bonding and shape

▸ The bonding pairs between atoms in the Lewis structure can be represented as lines, similar to what you drew in your balloon investigation, so that NH_3 can be drawn as :

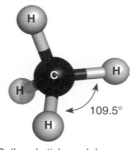

▸ It is important to realize at this point that the Lewis structures drawn so far are two dimensional and therefore do not represent a "real world" view of the molecule. Each atom is essentially a sphere around which the electron pairs are distributed.

▸ Recall your investigation 4.1 with the balloons. Box 4 represented a molecule with four atoms around a central atom, e.g. CH_4 (methane). The balloons projected from the central point as a tetrahedron, in three dimensions (right).

▸ We can also represent the three dimensional shape of CH_4 in other ways:

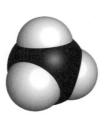

Space filling model

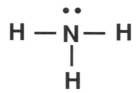

Ball and stick model

▸ But what exactly causes this shape? Recall the balloons spontaneously assumed this shape. The same occurs with the electron pairs around an atom.

▸ The two magnets shown right have reached an equilibrium between the repulsive force of the magnets and the attractive force of gravity. At this point the total potential energy of the system is at its lowest. Work is needed to move the top magnet (A) either up or down.

▸ Just as similar poles of the magnets repel each other, so the like charges of the electron pairs repel each other. Around a sphere, the four pairs of electrons orientate to positions that are 109.5° apart.

▸ Knowing that electron pairs repel each other this way (called Valence Shell Electron Pair Repulsion (VSEPR) theory) we can predict the shape of other molecules.

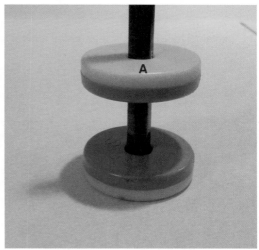

©2019 **BIOZONE** International
ISBN: 978-1-927309-71-1
Photocopying Prohibited

9. Draw a diagram in the box right predicting the three dimensional shape of NH_3:

▶ Recall the balloon investigation when only three balloons were attached to the central atom (Box 3). This formed a shape called a trigonal planar. Is this the shape that NH_3 would form? No. The balloon model is missing something that NH_3 has.

▶ Look at the structure for NH_3 on the previous page. Notice that it has one pair of non-bonded electrons. These act the same way as the other electron pairs and repel the other three bonded pairs.

▶ NH_3 is trigonal pyramidal (the non-bonded pairs are held slightly closer to the N and force the three legs of the pyramid down a little more than in CH_4). Again this is the most stable structure with the least potential energy.

10. Draw diagrams to predict the shape of the following molecules. Use the following terms to label your diagrams: linear, bent, tetrahedral.

NEED HELP?
See activity 62

(a) O_2

(b) CO_2

(c) CCl_4

(d) H_2O

11. Explain why CH_4 has a tetrahedral shape, while H_2S is bent: _____

_____

_____

_____

_____

_____

_____

28 Properties of Matter

ENGAGE: Matter as you know it

▶ Everything around us is made up of a particular combination of atoms or ions. That combination gives a particular substance certain properties, such as a liquid's viscosity or the hardness of the solid.

1. In groups, choose three everyday substances, e.g. glass or steel, and describe their properties (the ones you know or can think of). Try to explain how their use is related to the properties you have described:

_____

_____

_____

_____

_____

_____

_____

_____

EXPLORE: Properties of matter

▶ Exploring the properties of various substances can tell us a lot about the atoms or ions in the substances and how they are held together. This helps us to categorize materials. We can then use the properties of the materials in those categories to predict the properties of other substances and how they might be used.

▶ Testing conductivity can help us determine if there are free charges in the substance (e.g. ions or electrons).

INVESTIGATION 4.2: Investigating properties of matter   See appendix for equipment list.

 Magnesium (right) is a flammable metal. It burns with a bright, extremely hot flame, which can cause severe burns. Do not look directly at the flame. Sulfur is flammable. Igniting it produces sulfur dioxide gas, which is dangerous to inhale. Cyclohexane is volatile and flammable. Wear protective eyewear.

1. You will investigate various properties of the following substances: sodium chloride (NaCl), magnesium (Mg), magnesium sulfate ($MgSO_4$), sulfur (S), iron (Fe), copper, (Cu) copper sulfate ($CuSO_4$), distilled water (H_2O), ice (H_2O), cyclohexane (C_6H_{12}), quartz or glass (SiO_2).

2. Place a small sample (1 gram or 1-2 mL) of each substance on a watch glass or in a beaker.

3. Using a conductivity meter (or a simple circuit) test the conductivity of each of the substances. Record your observations in the table provided on the next page.

4. Test the solubility of the substances by placing 1 gram of each substance into 50 mL of distilled water and stirring with a stirring rod. Cyclohexane should be used in a fume hood. Add 1 mL to 10 mL of distilled water in a test tube. Record in the table whether or not each substance dissolves in water.

5. At the same time test the conductivity of any solutions formed. Record the results in the table.

6. Sulfur and sodium chloride will melt when heated by a Bunsen flame. Place a small amount of sulfur in a deflagrating (def-la-grating) spoon. In a fume hood, heat the sulfur over a low Bunsen flame until the sulfur begins to melt. **DO NOT** let the sulfur ignite and burn (this will produce toxic sulfur dioxide gas). If the sulfur does ignite, remove the spoon from the heat and cover it with a heat resistant pad or glass plate to cut off the air supply or place it into a gas jar to trap the gas given off. Close the fume hood and wait for the gas to clear.

7. While the sulfur is still molten, carefully test its conductivity. Don't touch the spoon with the electrodes or you will get a false reading! Let the sulfur cool and harden before disposing of it.

8. Clean the deflagrating spoon and repeat the procedure with sodium chloride. Record the conductivity in the table.

9. Glass tubing will melt if held over a strong Bunsen flame. Your teacher may demonstrate the heating of glass and test its conductivity when molten.

CE   P   PS3.C   PS2.B   PS1.A

Substance	Solid conducts ✔ ✘	Liquid conducts ✔ ✘	Solution forms in water ✔ ✘	Solution conducts ✔ ✘
NaCl				
Mg		✔		
MgSO$_4$		✔		
S				
Fe		✔		
Cu		✔		
CuSO$_4$		NA		
H$_2$O			NA	
C$_6$H$_{12}$	NA			
SiO$_2$				

▶ Before you interpret your results, other properties for the substances you tested should be noted. Some you may already know from experience, others you may need to test, normally by simple observation of the macroscopic structure of the substance (i.e. what is looks like, how it feels etc).

2. Fill in the table below. You may need to do some research or testing of the substance. Note: malleable means workable:

Substance	Appearance (color, shine etc)	State at room temperature	Malleable ✔ ✘	Brittle ✔ ✘	Melting point / boiling point (°C)
NaCl					/
Mg					/
MgSO$_4$					/
S					/
Fe					/
Cu					/
CuSO$_4$					/
H$_2$O			NA	NA	/
C$_6$H$_{12}$			NA	NA	/
SiO$_2$					/

3. Now put the substances into groups based on the similarities and differences of the properties you have investigated:

©2019 **BIOZONE** International
ISBN:978-1-927309-71-1
Photocopying Prohibited

EXPLAIN: The bonding continuum

4. Consider some other substances that you have encountered: NaCl, Li_2O, MgO, Na_2O, CO_2, O_2, CH_4, Cl_2
   Use your periodic table to find the electronegativities of each of the atoms for each of the substances above and calculate the difference between the electronegativities:

   (a) Na: _____ Cl: _____ Difference: _____

   (b) Li: _____ O: _____ Difference: _____

   (c) Mg: _____ O: _____ Difference: _____

   (d) Na: _____ O: _____ Difference: _____

   (e) C: _____ O: _____ Difference: _____

   (f) O: _____ O: _____ Difference: _____

   (g) C: _____ H: _____ Difference: _____

   (h) Cl: _____ Cl: _____ Difference: _____

5. Can you group these substances based on the difference in electronegativities? _____

   _____

   _____

6. Now determine the difference in electronegativities of the atoms in the substances HCl and H_2O:

   (a) H: _____ Cl: _____ Difference: _____

   (b) H: _____ O: _____ Difference: _____

   (c) What do you notice about the difference in electronegativities of the atoms in these molecules?

   _____

7. In the molecule H_2O, around which atom are you most likely to find the electrons at any one moment in time? Explain why the electrons are more likely to be found in the location you have predicted:

   _____

   _____

   _____

8. What can be said about the nature of intramolecular bonding (bonds within molecules). Can we easily place all molecules into discrete categories?

   _____

   _____

   _____

ELABORATE: Polarity

▶ You have seen that the bonding of atoms influences the shape of a molecule. You have also seen that in a molecule, the electrons are more likely to be found near the atom with the highest electronegativity.

▶ If the difference in electronegativity is very high, then the electron(s) will be entirely transferred from the atom with the lowest electronegativity to the atom with the highest electronegativity and **ions** will form.

▶ If the electronegativity is equal the electrons will be shared relatively evenly to form a **covalent bond**. If there is a slight difference in electronegativity then the electrons will be unevenly shared and a **polar covalent bond** occurs.

▶ For example, HCl is a polar molecule. The polarity can be represented as a diagram:

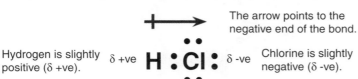

The arrow points to the negative end of the bond.

Hydrogen is slightly positive (δ +ve). δ +ve   δ -ve   Chlorine is slightly negative (δ -ve).

The uneven sharing of electrons produces a permanent **dipole**, with one end of the bond being negative and the other positive.

9. For each of the molecules below, draw a Lewis structure and draw on the polarity of the bonds:

(a) CO_2	(b) H_2O	(c) CH_4

(d) C_2H_6	(e) $CHCl_3$	(f) N_2

ELABORATE: Shape and polarity

▸ The shape of a molecule can be used to predict the polarity of the molecule. Some molecules have polar bonds but have a symmetrical shape and thus have no overall polarity.

INVESTIGATION 4.3: Observing the polarity of water and cyclohexane

See appendix for equipment list.

1. Fill a 50 mL burette with distilled water. Fill another burette with cyclohexane.

2. Rub a glass rod with a silk or polyester towel. This removes electrons from the glass.

3. Turn on the burette containing water so that it flows into a beaker.

4. Hold the rod close to the burette and observe the effect.

5. Repeat with the burette of cyclohexane and observe the result.

10. What was the effect of holding the rod close to the stream of water? _____

_____

_____

11. What was the effect of holding the rod close to the stream of cyclohexane? _____

_____

_____

▸ Now look at the structure of water and the structure of cyclohexane:

Water

Cyclohexane

©2019 **BIOZONE** International
ISBN:978-1-927309-71-1
Photocopying Prohibited

12. Explain why water bends towards the charged glass rod and cyclohexane does not. Draw a diagram in the box below to help your explanation:

_____

_____

_____

_____

_____

_____

_____

_____

13. It was stated that electrons are removed from the glass rod when rubbing it with silk. What would the effect of adding electrons to the glass be on the stream of water in the investigation above?

_____

_____

_____

EXPLAIN: Coulomb's law

▶ In chapter 3 you saw that electronegativity (the tendency of an atom to attract electrons) increases left to right along a period and up a group. Importantly, **electronegativity increases as the charge in the nucleus increases** and **decreases as the distance between the electrons and the protons increases** (shells are added).

▶ You have just seen that the polarity of a bond within a molecule is influenced by electronegativity. The greater the difference in electronegativity the greater the polarity of the bond (until an ionic bond is formed).

▶ These observations are described by **Coulomb's law**, below:

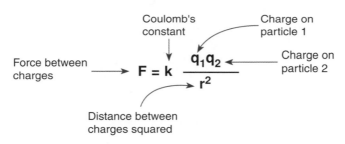

$$F = k \frac{q_1 q_2}{r^2}$$

Force between charges → F = k

Coulomb's constant

Charge on particle 1

Charge on particle 2

Distance between charges squared

▶ Put simply, the force acting between two charged particles increases as the magnitude (size) of the charges increases and decreases as the distance between them increases.

▶ We can verify this using simplified quantities placed into the equation and making hydrogen our reference. We can give the proton a charge of 1 and the electron a charge of -1. k is constant so can be ignored for simplicity:

▶ For a hydrogen atom, the force acting between the proton and the electron will be:

$$F = \frac{1 \times -1}{1^2} = -1$$

A negative force indicates an attraction between particles.

H

▶ For a lithium atom, the charge in the nucleus increases to 3 and the distance to the valence electron is roughly 3 times the distance between the hydrogen proton and its electron:

$$F = \frac{3 \times -1}{3^2} = -0.33$$

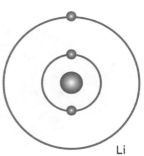

Li

▶ Thus we can see although the charge in an atom's nucleus may increase as protons are added, the distance between the protons and the electrons can make a big difference in the force acting between the particles.

▶ Shielding by inner electron shells also influences the attraction.

©2019 **BIOZONE** International
ISBN: 978-1-927309-71-1
Photocopying Prohibited

14. Use the equation for Coulomb's law to explain why the bonds in a water molecule are polar. (Note: the distance between the oxygen nucleus and the valence electrons is about 1.3 relative to the hydrogen nucleus and its electron).

_____

_____

_____

_____

15. Similarly Coulomb's law can be used to explain differences in the strength of ionic bonds. Consider the two ionic substances MgO and NaCl. You will have found earlier that the melting point of MgO is 2852°C whereas the melting point of NaCl is 801°C.

(a) The distance between a Na^+ ion and a Cl^- ion in NaCl is about 1.3 times greater than the distance between a Mg^{2+} ion and an O^{2-} ion in MgO. Use this information to determine the relative difference in the attractive force between a Na^+ ion and a Cl^- ion and an Mg^{2+} ion and an O^{2-} ion:

_____

_____

(b) Explain why there is such a large difference between the melting points of NaCl and MgO: _____

_____

_____

_____

EXPLORE: Giant networks

▸ Substances such as oxygen gas are discrete molecules. They contain a fixed number of atoms. For oxygen gas, this is two atoms joined together covalently.

▸ Ionic substances form ionic lattices made up of very large numbers of ions. The number of ions changes depending on the size of the crystal. A small grain of salt may contain 10 million Na^+ and Cl^- ions, a larger grain may contain 10 billion Na^+ and Cl^- ions. However the ratio of ions is always the same e.g. 1:1.

▸ Sometimes covalently bonding atoms can form a giant covalent network which extends throughout the material. Examples include carbon in the form of diamond or graphite.

▸ Metals also form giant networks, but the atoms are held together by the attractive forces of the metal nucleus to the valence electrons that move freely through the network. These metallic bonds can be very strong, explaining the high melting points of most metals.

16. Label the following substances as _discrete molecular_, _ionic lattice_, _giant covalent network_, or _metal_:

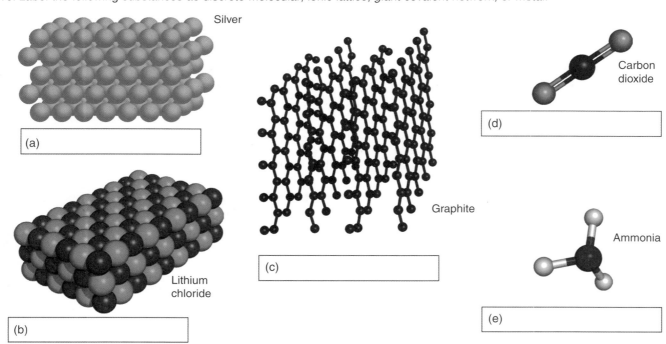

Silver

(a)

Lithium chloride

(b)

Graphite

(c)

Carbon dioxide

(d)

Ammonia

(e)

©2019 **BIOZONE** International
ISBN:978-1-927309-71-1
Photocopying Prohibited

EXPLAIN: Properties of hydrocarbons

▸ Hydrocarbons are molecular substances containing only hydrogen and carbon. The simplest hydrocarbons are a group called the alkanes. These have the formula C_nH_{2n+2} where n equals any whole number. The simplest alkane is methane (CH_4).

▸ Hydrocarbons are useful in studying the forces that hold the molecules together because the total number of atoms in simple single chain alkanes increases regularly as the number of carbon atoms increases. Examples of simple alkanes include ethane, propane, and butane (shown below).

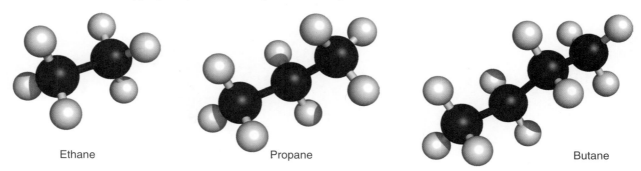

Ethane   Propane   Butane

▸ Methane and the first four alkanes (up to C_4H_{10}) are gases at room temperature and atmospheric pressure. The alkanes are then liquids up to $C_{17}H_{36}$. From $C_{18}H_{38}$ the alkanes are solid.

▸ The alkanes are useful in studying properties including melting point, boiling point, and vapor pressure. Consider the table below:

Alkane	Formula	Melting point (°C)	Boiling point (°C)	Vapor pressure (kPa) (at 20 °C)	Log_{10} vapor pressure (Log_{10} kPa)
Methane	CH_4	-182	-162	-	
Ethane	C_2H_6	-183	-89	-	
Propane	C_3H_8	-188	-42	-	
Butane	C_4H_{10}	-138	0	-	
Pentane	C_5H_{12}	-130	36	59.9	
Hexane	C_6H_{14}	-95	69	17.6	
Heptane	C_7H_{16}	-91	98	5.33	
Octane	C_8H_{18}	-57	126	1.47	
Nonane	C_9H_{20}	-54	151	0.59	
Decane	$C_{10}H_{22}$	-30	174	0.195	
Undecane	$C_{11}H_{24}$	-26	196	0.055	
Dodecane	$C_{12}H_{26}$	-10	216	0.018	
Tridecane	$C_{13}H_{28}$	-5	235	4.9×10^{-3}	
Tetradecane	$C_{14}H_{30}$	6	254	2.0×10^{-3}	
Pentadecane	$C_{15}H_{32}$	10	270	6.5×10^{-4}	

▸ Vapor pressure is the pressure resulting from the evaporation of a liquid (or solid) in a closed system. The more easily a substance evaporates, the greater its vapor pressure. Pressure is measured in kilopascals (kPa) (1 Pa = 1 newton per square meter).

▸ The vapor pressure of a substance changes with temperature, so the temperature must be stated for any given vapor pressure.

▸ In a closed system, a liquid (or solid) and its vapor form a dynamic equilibrium. As particles leave the liquid to form a vapor, the same number of particles leave the vapor and become liquid (right).

At equilibrium the number of particles leaving the liquid phase is equal to the number of particles entering the liquid phase.

17. Complete the table above by calculating the log_{10} value of the vapor pressure:

18. Plot the melting and boiling points of the first 15 alkanes on the grid below. On your x axis, define your alkanes by the number of carbons present:

NEED HELP?
See activity 60

19. Plot the $\log_{10}$ values for the vapor pressures of the alkanes pentane to pentadecane on the grid below:

20. Describe the shape of the graphs of melting and boiling points in alkanes: _____

_____

_____

21. Describe the shape of the $\log_{10}$ graph of vapor pressure: _____

_____

22. Consider the forces that hold the alkane molecules together as a gas or liquid. What can be said about the total strength of these forces as more carbon atoms are added to the alkane molecule?

_____

_____

▶ The electronegativities of carbon and hydrogen are very similar. This means that in any bond, the electrons are shared evenly. However at times an **instantaneous dipole** may occur. This happens when by chance the movement of the electrons in their orbits causes more of them to be closer to one atom than the other:

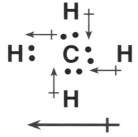

For an instant, the electrons around carbon atom may look like this, producing a slightly polar molecule.

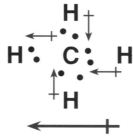

The instantaneous dipole of one molecule may induce an instantaneous dipole in a nearby molecule, causing them to be attracted to each other.

These instantaneous dipole interactions are called **van der Waals forces** and are the weakest of the intermolecular forces. They are important in the behavior of non-polar molecules and when multiplied on a large scale can be relatively strong, enough to allow a gecko's feet to stick to smooth surfaces.

23. Explain why the vapor pressure of water (2.34 kPa at 20°C) is far less than the vapor pressure of pentane (59.9 kPa at 20°C) which is a much bigger molecule.

_____

_____

_____

_____

_____

24. Consider the structures of pentane and pentan-1-ol (the simplest alcohol of pentane) below. Explain why the vapor pressure of pentane is much greater than the vapor pressure of pentan-1-ol (0.2 kPa at 20°C):

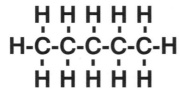

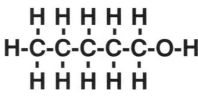

_____

_____

_____

_____

_____

©2019 **BIOZONE** International
ISBN: 978-1-927309-71-1
Photocopying Prohibited

EVALUATE: Properties of matter

25. You have investigated the properties of various substances and should now be able to explain the difference between different types of substances. Explain the differences between the following substances:

(a) Explain why water (H_2O) is liquid at room temperature but hydrogen sulfide (H_2S) is a gas: _____

_____

_____

_____

_____

_____

(b) Surface tension is an effect where the surface of a liquid is strong. It is caused by cohesive forces between the liquid's molecules. Explain why the surface tension of water (H_2O) is much greater than that of cyclohexane (C_6H_{12}):

_____

_____

_____

_____

(c) Why is solid NaCl ($NaCl_{(s)}$) unable to conduct electricity but liquid NaCl ($NaCl_{(l)}$) and NaCl in solution ($NaCl_{(aq)}$) can?

_____

_____

_____

(d) Explain why solid metal (e.g. copper) can conduct electricity but a solid ionic substance (e.g. NaCl) cannot:

_____

_____

_____

26. Fill in the table below with the particles, forces, examples, melting points (very high to very low) and characteristics of the substances listed:

Substance		Particles	Attractive forces involved	Examples	Melting point	Characteristics
Ionic lattice						
Network						
Metal						
Molecular	Polar					
	Non-polar					

29 Energy and Changes of State

ENGAGE: Cooling things down

▸ Ice is used to cool things down, be it water in a glass or food in an ice chest. But why? What is actually happening to make the substance being cooled reduce in temperature?

▸ In chapter one, you used temperature changes in water to investigate energy changes in burning corn chips, and you investigated latent heat of fusion and vaporization in substances.

▸ In chapter two, you investigated energy transfer (heat) and the specific heat of substances. These phenomena can be used to help explain the use of ice to cool things down.

1. What will happen to the temperature of the bottled water in the ice chest shown right as the ice melts?

_____

2. (a) What will happen to the temperature of the meltwater in the ice chest as the ice transitions from the solid phase (ice) to the liquid phase (water)?

_____

   (b) Where does the energy for the phase change of ice to water come from, assuming the ice chest is insulated and the lid is closed (i.e. close to an isolated system)?

_____

_____

▸ When it is very pure and placed in a clean, smooth container, water can be supercooled below its freezing point (0°C). A sudden impact on the bottle containing this supercooled water will cause the water to suddenly change phase from liquid to solid.

3. When a liquid changes to a solid is energy released or absorbed by the liquid?

_____

4. Would you expect the temperature of the supercooled water to increase or decrease when it changes from a liquid to a solid?

_____

EXPLORE: Changes of state

▸ In chapter one you explored some aspects of changes of state including the energy required to change state (e.g. heat of fusion).

▸ You have seen that solids melt to form liquids, and liquids boil to form gases. However, it is possible for solids to move directly to the gaseous state. This is called **sublimation**. The reverse of sublimation is **deposition**.

▸ Turning a solid to a liquid or a liquid to a gas is an **endothermic** process. Energy must be added to the system.

▸ Turning a gas into a liquid or a liquid to a solid in an **exothermic** process. Energy is released from the system as the substance changes state.

Iodine sublimes if heated gently

5. Label the following processes as endothermic or exothermic:

   (a) Ice melting: _____

   (b) Water boiling: _____

   (c) Carbon dioxide subliming: _____

   (d) Liquid mercury freezing: _____

   (e) Nitrogen gas condensing: _____

6. Label the diagram below with the name of each phase change and whether it is endothermic or exothermic:

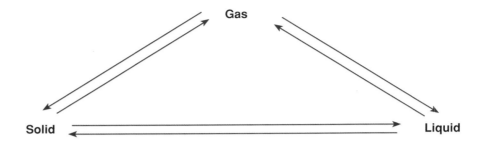

EXPLAIN: Energy and intermolecular forces:

▸ A change of state does not chemically change the components. Rather, the appearance of those components changes. Changes of state involve molecules either overcoming intermolecular forces or being attracted by them.

7. Are intermolecular forces being overcome or attracting molecules when:

(a) Water freezes to ice: _____

(b) Wax melts in the sun: _____

(c) Water vapor condenses in a cloud before rain: _____

(d) Ethanol evaporates from an open bottle: _____

8. For each of (a)-(d) above decide whether energy needs to be added (endothermic) or released (exothermic):

(a) _____

(b) _____

(c) _____

(d) _____

9. Why does sweating cool the body down? _____

_____

_____

EXPLAIN: Hydrogen bonds and water:

▸ You will recall that water molecules have strong intermolecular bonds between them due to the polar covalent bonds. These bonds between water molecules are a special type of intermolecular force called hydrogen bonds.

▸ Hydrogen bonds form when hydrogen forms a polar covalent bond with oxygen or another highly electronegative atom including nitrogen and fluorine.

▸ Hydrogen bonds are one of the strongest intermolecular bonds.

10. Explain the difference seen in the boiling points of the dihydrogen molecules:

_____

_____

_____

_____

_____

_____

_____

_____

_____

_____

30 Energy and Chemical Reactions

ENGAGE: Heating things up

▶ You may have heard of or even seen a thermite reaction (shown right). A thermite reaction occurs between a metal powder and a metal oxide. The reaction often produces an enormous amount of heat and must be done with extreme care.

▶ The reaction can be written simply as: $M_A + M_BO \rightarrow M_AO + M_B$.

1. A number of reactions that produce heat have been mentioned in this book so far. Write down those that you can remember and at least two others that produce heat:

_____

_____

_____

2. When a reaction releases energy, would the temperature of the surrounding environment increase or decrease?

_____

Nikthestunned CC 3.0

3. When a reaction uses energy would the temperature of the surrounding environment increase or decrease?

_____

4. (a) In the thermite reaction shown above, where is the heat coming from? _____

_____

(b) Why do you think you cannot smother a thermite reaction to put it out?_____

_____

EXPLORE: Which is the best fuel?

▶ Fuels are chemicals that release energy during a reaction. This energy can be used to do work (e.g. boiling water). The most useful fuels have a high energy density (lots of energy per gram) and are easy to store and transport.

▶ Alcohols meet these conditions reasonably well as they have a high energy density and are liquids.

INVESTIGATION 4.4: Determining the energy content of alcohols   See appendix for equipment list.

 Alcohols are highly flammable. Keep them away from an ignition source when not using them. Vapor is also flammable. Keep the lids of the bottles on when not in use. Wear eyewear .

1. Your teacher will assign you an alcohol to investigate. This could be methanol (CH_3OH), ethanol (CH_3CH_2OH), or propan-1-ol ($CH_3CH_2CH_2OH$).

2. Weigh the empty, dry soda can and record the mass in the table on the next page.

3. Fill the soda can with distilled water to about 2-3 cm from the top. Reweigh the soda can and record the mass on the table.

4. Fill the alcohol burner with one of the alcohols and weigh it. Record the mass in the table.

5. Place the soda can on the wire gauze or on the ring clamp and secure with the second clamp. Adjust the height of the soda can on the clamp stand so that the flame from the alcohol burner will be just touching the bottom of the soda can.

6. Place a thermometer in the water in the soda can, stir gently for a few seconds and record the temperature when the thermometer shows a stable temperature.

7. Light the alcohol burner and immediately start the stop watch. Time 7 minutes.

8. After 7 minutes remove the alcohol burner (and put it out) and immediately record the temperature of the water in the soda can.

9. Record the mass of the alcohol burner and calculate the mass of alcohol used.

SC   EM   PS1.B

Name of alcohol:	
Mass of dry, empty soda can (g)	
Mass of soda can with water (g)	
Mass of water in soda can (g)	
Mass of alcohol burner before burning (g)	
Temperature of water before heating (°C)	
Temperature of water after heating (°C)	
Temperature change of water (°C)	
Mass of alcohol burner after burning (g)	
Mass of alcohol used (g)	

▶ The specific heat of water = 4.2 J/g/°C. $\Delta Q = m \times \Delta T \times c$.
M(H) = 1.0 g/mol, M(C) = 12.0 g/mol, M(O) = 16.0 g/mol.

NEED HELP?
See activity 3

▶ **Enthalpy** (H) is a term used to describe the heat energy in a system. If there is a change of heat energy then there is a change in enthalpy (ΔH). ΔH is measured kJ.

5. Calculate the heat absorbed (Q) by the water for the alcohol you investigated: _____

_____

6. How much energy did the alcohol release? _____

7. Determine the molar mass of the alcohol you investigated: _____

8. Determine the number of moles of alcohol used (n=m/M): _____

_____

9. Calculate the energy per mole (in kJ/mol) released during combustion (enthalpy of combustion) of your alcohol:

_____

_____

10. The values for enthalpy of combustion ($\Delta_c H$) for the above alcohols are:
methanol = −726 kJ/mol, ethanol = −1368 kJ/mol, and propan-1-ol = −2020 kJ/mol.
Calculate your percentage error based on the heat of combustion value for your alcohol:

_____

_____

11. Explain any difference between your calculated enthalpy of combustion and the actual enthalpy of combustion:

_____

_____

_____

12. Convert your calculated enthalpy of combustion from kJ/mol into kJ/g: _____

_____

_____

©2019 **BIOZONE** International
ISBN:978-1-927309-71-1
Photocopying Prohibited

13. Methanol, ethanol, and propan-1-ol, all have essentially the same density (0.8 g/mL to 1 d.p.). The energy of fuels is often compared by the amount of energy released per gram. Why is this a more useful comparison than energy per mole?

_____

_____

_____

_____

14. Pool the class data and fill in the table below:

Alcohol	Enthalpy of combustion (kJ/g)	Average enthalpy of combustion (kJ/g)
Methanol		
Methanol		
Methanol		
Methanol		
Ethanol		
Ethanol		
Ethanol		
Ethanol		
Propan-1-ol		
Propan-1-ol		
Propan-1-ol		
Propan-1-ol		

15. Using the class data of the enthalpy of combustion for the three different alcohols, if each one could be purchased for the same price, which one would offer you the best value? Explain your choice:

_____

_____

_____

_____

_____

16. Balance the combustion equation for each of the alcohols below:

(a) Methanol: __CH_3OH + __O_2 → __CO_2 + __H_2O

(b) Ethanol: __CH_3CH_2OH + __O_2 → __CO_2 + __H_2O

(c) Propan-1-ol: __$CH_3CH_2CH_2OH$ + __O_2 → __CO_2 + __H_2O

17. Can you explain why there is a difference in the amount of energy released during the combustion of each type of alcohol per gram:

_____

_____

_____

EXPLORE: Energy changes in reactions

▶ You have already seen some exothermic reactions. These are often associated with the release of light and a flame, but not always. The following investigation demonstrates exothermic and endothermic reactions:

INVESTIGATION 4.5: Exothermic and endothermic reactions See appendix for equipment list.

⚠️ The chemicals you will be using are all irritants. Wear eyewear and gloves.

1. For each of the following reactions measure the initial and final temperature and record them in the table below:

2. To a 25 mL beaker add 1 gram of solid sodium hydroxide with 20 mL of water and mix.

3. To a 25 mL beaker add 1 gram of solid ammonium chloride to 10 mL of water and mix.

4. To a 25 mL beaker add 5 mL of 1 mol/L hydrochloric acid to 5 mL 1 mol/L sodium hydroxide.

5. In a beaker mix 1 gram of solid ammonium thiocyanate with 1 gram of solid barium hydroxide.

	Initial temperature (°C)	Final temperature (°C)	Temperature change (°C)	Endothermic or exothermic
$NaOH_{(s)} \rightarrow NaOH_{(aq)}$				
$NH_4Cl_{(s)} \rightarrow NH_4Cl_{(aq)}$				
$HCl_{(aq)} + NaOH_{(aq)} \rightarrow NaCl_{(aq)} + H_2O(l)$				
$2NH_4SCN_{(s)} + Ba(OH)_2.8H_2O_{(s)} \rightarrow$ $Ba(SCN)_{2(s)} + 2NH_{3(g)} + 10H_2O_{(l)}$				

18. Consider the first reaction of solid NaOH forming aqueous NaOH (i.e. dissolving NaOH). Note that NaOH is an ionic substance. When it dissolves, the ionic bonds are broken.

(a) Does breaking an ionic bond require energy? _____

(b) Hydrogen bonds between water molecules are also broken when the NaOH dissolves. Does breaking these bonds require energy?

_____

(c) The final step in the dissolving of NaOH is the formation of bonds between the Na$^+$ and OH$^-$ ions and the polar water molecules. The diagram below left shows how the water molecules orientate around the Na$^+$ ion. In the space below right draw a similar diagram to show how the water molecules orientate around the OH$^-$ ion.

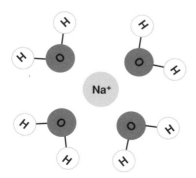

(d) Does forming the bonds between the water molecules and the Na$^+$ and OH$^-$ ions require energy or release energy?

_____

©2019 **BIOZONE** International
ISBN:978-1-927309-71-1
Photocopying Prohibited

(e) The overall process of NaOH dissolving in water is exothermic, it releases energy. What does this tell us about the amount of energy required to break the initial bonds and form new ones in this reaction?

_____

_____

(f) If a reaction releases energy what does this tell us about the energy in the reactants compared to the products?

_____

_____

19. Consider the second reaction of ammonium chloride dissolving in water. A similar process of bond breaking and forming occurs as with the NaOH. However the reaction is endothermic.

(a) What does this tell us about the energy required to break the initial ionic bonds compared to the energy released from the formation of bonds between the water and the NH_4^+ and Cl^- ions?

_____

_____

(b) Why does the water temperature decrease in this reaction? _____

_____

_____

EXPLORE: Enthalpy

▶ During a reaction, the change in enthalpy is equal to the enthalpy of the products – the enthalpy of the reactants (i.e. the final enthalpy – the initial enthalpy) or

$$\Delta H = H(\text{products}) - H(\text{reactants})$$

20. (a) If the products have less energy in them than the reactants, will ΔH be positive or negative? _____

(b) If energy is released (an exothermic reaction) will ΔH be positive of negative? _____

▶ It is not possible to measure the internal heat or enthalpy of a system, but it is simple to measure the change in the enthalpy of a system. If energy is lost from the system, then the temperature of the surroundings will increase. If the system gains energy then the temperature of the surroundings will decrease.

21. A student places a small piece of metal into dilute acid and measures an increase in the solution's temperature.

(a) Was the reaction exothermic or endothermic? _____

(b) Will the products contain more or less energy than the reactants? _____

(c) Will ΔH be positive or negative? _____

22. Consider the following reactions: 1: $CO_{2(g)} + H_{2(g)} \rightarrow CO_{(g)} + H_2O_{(g)}$ $\Delta H = +42$ kJ

$$2: S_{(s)} + O_{2(g)} \rightarrow SO_{2(g)} \Delta H = -296 \text{ kJ}$$

(a) Is reaction 1 endothermic or exothermic? _____

(b) Is reaction 2 endothermic or exothermic? _____

(c) On the axis below sketch a column graph to show enthalpy of the reactants and products and ΔH for each reaction.

EXPLORE: Finding ΔH

▶ The ΔH of a reaction can be estimated using the same technique used earlier, i.e. by measuring the temperature change in a known volume or mass of water.

▶ ΔH is often given a subscript to describe what the enthalpy change is related to. For example the enthalpy of combustion is shown as $\Delta_c H$. The enthalpy of formation of one mole of product from its elements is the enthalpy of formation, $\Delta_f H$. The enthalpy of a reaction is shown as $\Delta_r H$.

INVESTIGATION 4.6: Measuring enthalpy change in copper sulfate
See appendix for equipment list.

⚠ Copper sulfate is an irritant and toxic if ingested. Wear gloves and eyewear.

1. Obtain a clean and dry styrofoam cup.

2. Measure 100 mL of 0.1 mol/L copper sulfate solution in a 100 mL measuring cylinder and add to the cup.

3. Record the initial temperature of the solution. _____

4. Add about 1 gram of zinc powder and stir rapidly. Record the highest temperature the solution reaches.

_____

23. (a) What is the reason for carrying out the reaction in a styrofoam cup? _____

_____

(b) What is the exact volume of copper sulfate solution used? _____

_____

(c) Calculate the number of moles of copper sulfate in the solution ($c = n/V$): _____

_____

(d) Calculate the mass of copper sulfate in the solution ($n=m/M$) $M(CuSO_4) = 159.6$ g/mol:

_____

_____

(e) Calculate the temperature change for the reaction: _____

(f) Calculate heat produced by the reaction ($Q = m \times \Delta T \times 4.2$ J): _____

_____

(g) Calculate the amount of heat released per mole of copper sulfate that reacts: _____

_____

(h) Write a balanced equation for the reaction of copper sulfate and zinc including the value of ΔH:

_____

24. A student ignites 10 grams of magnesium metal. It burns in air completely. The equation for the reaction is:

$$2Mg_{(s)} + O_{2(g)} \rightarrow 2MgO_{(s)} \quad \Delta H = -1204 \text{ kJ}$$

(a) How much energy is released if 1 mole of magnesium is burned completely? _____

(b) How much energy was released when the student burned the magnesium metal? $M(Mg) = 24.3$ g/mol _____

_____

(c) Explain why MgO is less reactive the Mg and O_2: _____

_____

_____

©2019 **BIOZONE** International
ISBN:978-1-927309-71-1
Photocopying Prohibited

EXPLAIN: Modeling energy in chemical reactions

▶ Magnesium, paper, or many other substances often need an ignition source before they will burn. The paper in this book is unlikely to burst into flames on its own. Even a particularly flammable and volatile substance such as gasoline will not ignite and burn unless brought near an ignition source.

▶ Once they are started, these combustion reactions release a lot of energy. However, they cannot start the burning process by themselves. They need an input of energy, called the **activation energy**.

▶ The axes below show a graph of the energy changes in the exothermic reaction of substances A and B forming AB.

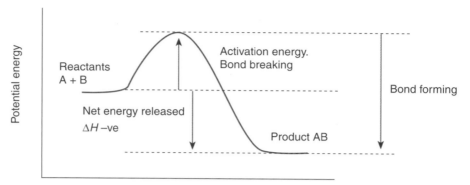

▶ Photosynthesis in green plants uses the Sun's energy to combine CO_2 and H_2O into $C_6H_{12}O_6$ (glucose) and O_2. CO_2 and H_2O contain relatively little chemical potential energy whereas glucose contains a large amount of chemical potential energy. For this reason, it is the main source of energy for aerobic respiration in living things.

25. Sketch a graph of the overall reaction of photosynthesis showing the energy changes between the reactants and the products:

▶ If you have studied biology in The Living Earth you will know that photosynthesis is not in fact a single reaction. The first stage (the **light dependent reactions**) uses light energy from the Sun to split water, producing hydrogen ions and oxygen gas. The simplified equation for the first stage is: $2H_2O + light \rightarrow 4H^+ + O_2$.

▶ The second stage (the **Calvin cycle**) uses the energy carrying molecule ATP to combine the hydrogen ions and carbon dioxide to form the molecule triose phosphate. Triose phosphate is later converted to glucose. The simplified overall equation for the second stage is: $3CO_2 + 6H^+ \rightarrow C_3H_6O_3$ (used to form glucose).

26. Sketch a graph of the two reaction steps of photosynthesis showing the energy changes between the reactants and the products:

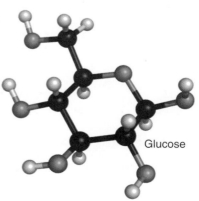

Glucose

27. What provides the activation energy for the light dependent reactions of photosynthesis?

_____

▶ If you have studied The Living Earth you will also know that respiration in plants and animals uses glucose (produced by photosynthesis in green plants) and through a series of reactions converts it back to CO_2 and H_2O and extracts the energy that was stored in it.

28. Sketch a graph of the overall reaction of respiration showing the energy changes between the reactants and products:

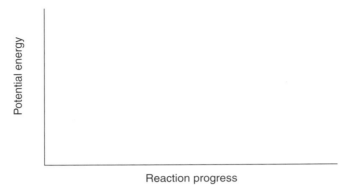

Potential energy

Reaction progress

▶ As with photosynthesis, respiration is a series of chemical reactions. It can be broken down into four major steps (right). The equations show the important components of each reaction and do not necessarily balance. At each step, energy is lost from the glucose molecule. In glycolysis, the Krebs cycle, and the electron transport chain this energy is used to produce **ATP**, the cell's energy carrying molecule.

1. **Glycolysis**: Glucose $\rightarrow$ 2 Pyruvate

2. **Link reaction**: Pyruvate + CoA $\rightarrow$ AcetylCoA + CO_2

3. **Krebs cycle**: Acetyl-CoA $\rightarrow$ CoA + $2CO_2$

4. **Electron transport chain**: $4H^+ + 4e^- + 2O \rightarrow 2H_2O$

29. Sketch a graph of the four respiration steps showing the energy changes between the reactants and the products:

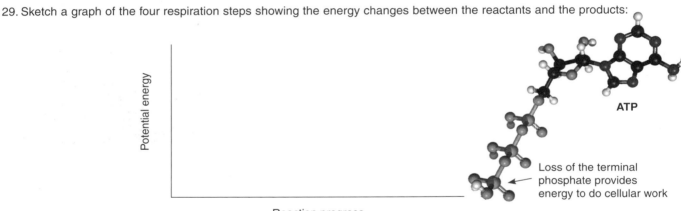

Potential energy

Reaction progress

ATP

Loss of the terminal phosphate provides energy to do cellular work

▶ Carry out your own research and you will find that photosynthesis and respiration are each a series of individual reactions. Some of these reactions are exothermic and others are endothermic. Overall, photosynthesis is endothermic because it stores energy in the energy-rich molecule glucose. Respiration is exothermic because it releases energy from the glucose molecule.

30. Photosynthesis starts with H_2O and CO_2 and ends with $C_6H_{12}O_6$. Respiration starts with $C_6H_{12}O_6$ and ends with CO_2 and H_2O. What can you say about the energy used and released in the reactions of photosynthesis and respiration?

_____

_____

_____

31. One mole of glucose contains 2870 kJ. During respiration one mole of glucose produces 32 moles of ATP. One mole of ATP produces 30.7 kJ of energy during metabolic reactions.
Calculate the percentage of energy stored in glucose that is transformed into useful energy via ATP:

_____

_____

©2019 **BIOZONE** International
ISBN:978-1-927309-71-1
Photocopying Prohibited

ELABORATE: Bond energies

▸ It takes energy to break a chemical bond. Energy is released when a bond is formed. The difference between the amount of energy used to break a bond and the energy released when new bonds form will determine if the reaction is endothermic or exothermic,

▸ **Average bond enthalpy** is the energy required to break one mole of a specified bond type in a gaseous state. By knowing the bond enthalpies of the reactants and products in a reaction we can calculate the overall enthalpy of the reaction without having to carry out any experiments.

▸ Consider the following reaction:

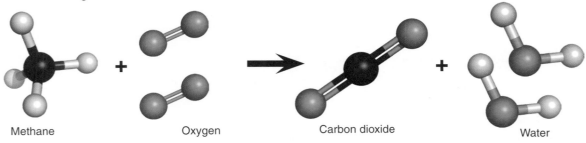

| Methane | Oxygen | Carbon dioxide | Water |

Bond	Average bond enthalpy
C – H	413 kJ/mol
O = O	498 kJ/mol
C = O	805 kJ/mol
O – H	464 kJ/mol

For any reaction
ΔH_r = the sum of the bond enthalpies in reactants – the sum of the bond enthalpies in products

▸ For the reaction above there are (4 x C–H bonds + 2 x O=O bonds) – (2 x C=O bonds + 4 x O–H bonds).

▸ Thus: (4 x 413 + 2 x 498) – (2 x 805 + 4 x 464) = 2648 – 3466 = –818 kJ/mol for the combustion of CH_4.

▸ The measured enthalpy of combustion for methane is –882 kJ/mol. If we take account for the fact that water returns to the liquid state and add in the enthalpy of vaporization for water (41 kJ/mol) then we get a more accurate answer: 2648 – (3466 +(2 x 41)) = –900 kJ/mol.

▸ The final discrepancy is due to the use of average bond enthalpies (for example the enthalpies of C–H vary from 439 kJ/mol to 411 kJ/mol depending on the molecule and its state).

32. At the start of this activity, you compared and calculated the enthalpy of combustion of three alcohols. You were also given the measured enthalpies of combustion for each alcohol. Now you can calculate the enthalpy of combustion using bond energies and compare this to the measured combustion enthalpy and your original answer.

   The bond enthalpies you will need are C–C 347 kJ/mol, C–H 413 kJ/mol, C–O 358 kJ/mol, O=O 498 kJ/mol, C=O 805 kJ/mol, O–H 464 kJ/mol.

   The enthalpy of vaporization for methanol is 35.2 kJ/mol, ethanol is 38.6 kJ/mol and propan-1-ol is 47.5 kJ/mol.

   To make it simpler, we will assume that there is complete combustion of each alcohol, with the only products formed being H_2O and CO_2.

   (a) Review your balanced equation for methanol on page 139. Write out the number of each type of bond in the reactants and products for the combustion of methanol (bonds are C–H, C–O, O–H, C=O) (it may help to draw the structures of each molecule involved).

   _____

   _____

   (b) Use the bond enthalpies to calculate the enthalpy of combustion for one mole of methanol: _____

   _____

   _____

   _____

©2019 **BIOZONE** International
ISBN: 978-1-9▪▪▪▪ 71-1
Photocopying ▪▪▪▪ d

(c) Calculate the enthalpy of combustion for ethanol: _____

_____

_____

(d) Calculate the enthalpy of combustion for propan-1-ol: _____

_____

_____

_____

(e) Compare your answers to your experimental value and to the stated value on page 138. Explain any differences:

_____

_____

_____

33. The models below show the alcohols butan-1-ol and butan-2-ol, both with the formula C_4H_9OH. Note the position of the OH group. The enthalpy of combustion (Δ_cH) for butan-1-ol = −2675.6 kJ/mol and for butan-2-ol = −2661.1 kJ/mol.

OH group

Butan-1-ol

OH group

Butan-2-ol

(a) Write a balanced equation for the complete combustion of butan-1-ol and butan-2-ol:

_____

(b) Both butan-1-ol and butan-2-ol burn completely with oxygen to form CO_2 and H_2O. Use the following average bond enthalpies to calculate the enthalpy of combustion for 1 mole of butan-1-ol and butan-2-ol.

C–C 347 kJ/mol, C–H 413 kJ/mol, C-O 358 kJ/mol, O=O 498 kJ/mol, C=O 805 kJ/mol, O–H 464 kJ/mol. The enthalpy of vaporization of butan-1-ol is 52.5 kJ/mol. The enthalpy of vaporization of butan-2-ol is 49.9 kJ/mol.

_____

_____

_____

_____

_____

(c) Does your calculated enthalpy of combustion match either of the stated enthalpies of combustion for butan-1-ol or butan-2-ol? Why is there a difference?

_____

_____

_____

(d) Can you explain why butan-1-ol and butan-2-ol have different values for the enthalpy of combustion?

_____

_____

_____

©2019 BIOZONE International
ISBN:978-1-927309-71-1
Photocopying Prohibited

31 Reaction Rates

ENGAGE: The rates of reactions

▶ Chemical reactions happen at a variety of rates. Some reactions are very fast, while others are extremely slow. In everyday life we come across a vast range of chemical reactions, many of which we don't realize are occurring.

1. Think about the chemical reactions that you might come across every day.

   (a) List some reactions you see every day that occur rapidly (i.e. they start immediately and finish within minutes):

   salt + water
   food baking

   (b) List some reactions you see every day that occur very slowly (i.e. they start slowly and take a long time to finish):

   plants growing

   (c) List some reactions you see or carry out every day that are deliberately sped up or slowed down to make them more useful to you:

   boiling water for pasta

EXPLORE: The effect of concentration

▶ The rate of a reaction can be changed simply by changing the concentration of one of the reactants.

2. Before beginning the experiment, predict what will happen to the rate of a reaction when the concentration of one of the reactants is increased:

   I think that the more bleach
   the faster it'll get clear

 INVESTIGATION 4.7: Concentration and reaction rate   See appendix for equipment list.

⚠ Bleach is corrosive and can harm skin and eyes. Wear gloves and eyewear.

CORROSIVE

1. Measure 10 mL of bleach (sodium hypochlorite, NaClO) into a test tube. This is a 100% bleach solution.

2. Make a 75% bleach solution by adding 5 mL water to 15 mL bleach in a measuring cylinder. Transfer 10 mL of this to a test tube.

3. Make a 50% bleach solution by adding 5 mL bleach 5 mL water to a test tube.

4. Make a 25% bleach solution by adding 15 mL water and 5 mL bleach in a measuring cylinder. Transfer 10 mL to a test tube.

5. Add a drop of blue food coloring into each test tube and mix with a clean spatula.

6. Label all 4 test tubes with their bleach concentration and place all the test tubes into a beaker of water or water bath at a constant 40-50°C.

7. Start a timer and record the time taken for the test tubes to go clear (see table next page).

8. This experiment could be carried out with the aid of a colorimeter or other light meter (often available as apps on smart phones) to accurately measure the color change.

SC EM P PS1.B

3. Graph the time for the color to change (reaction rate) vs the percentage concentration of the bleach on the grid below:

Bleach concentration	Time for color change
100%	1:25
75%	1:46
50%	2:45
25%	3:25

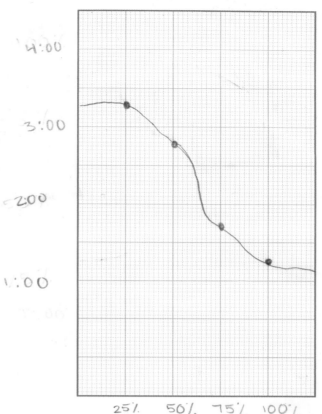

NEED HELP?
See activity 60

4:00

3:00

2:00

1:00

25%   50%   75%   100%

4. How has changing the concentration of the bleach affected the rate of the color change?

The more bleach there is the faster it gets clear

5. Do the results match your prediction? __Yes__

6. Suggest a reason why the rate of color change changes as concentration changes: _____

The bleach is what makes it clear so it makes sense the more bleach makes it go faste

EXPLORE: The effect of temperature

▶ How does changing the temperature of a reaction solution affect the rate of the reaction?

7. (a) Before beginning the experiment predict what will happen to the rate of a reaction when the temperature of the reaction solution is increased:

it will react faster

(b) Explain your prediction: _Cause the heat is rising the particles move faster + collide more_

©2019 **BIOZONE** International
ISBN:978-1-927309-71-1
Photocopying Prohibited

INVESTIGATION 4.8: Temperature and reaction rate

See appendix for equipment list.

 Oxalic acid and sulfuric acid are corrosive and can harm skin and eyes. Potassium permanganate is a strong oxidizer. Contact with the skin leaves lasting stains. Wear gloves and eyewear.

1. Add 15 mL of 0.1 mol/L potassium permanganate into each of three boiling tubes. Place one boiling tube into an ice bath, leave one at room temperature (measured), and place one in a water bath at 50°C.

2. Add together 15 mL of 0.5 mol/L oxalic acid, 30 mL of 4 mol/L sulfuric acid, and 60 mL of distilled water into each of three 250 mL beakers.

3. Place one beaker into an ice bath, keep one at room temperature (measured), and place one into a water bath at 50°C.

4. Record the temperature of the solution in each beaker.

5. Start the stopwatch and quickly add the potassium permanganate solution in the ice bath to the beaker in the ice bath. Record the time it takes for the solution to become colorless in the table below.

6. Start the stopwatch and quickly add the potassium permanganate solution at room temperature to the room temperature beaker. Again, record the time it takes for the solution to become colorless.

7. Start the stopwatch and quickly add the potassium permanganate solution in the 50°C water bath to the beaker in the 50°C water bath. Again, record the time it takes for the solution to become colorless.

8. Graph the time for the color to change (reaction rate) vs the temperature of the solution on the grid right:

Temperature (°C)	Time for color change
2	31:26
18	5:30
50	1:27

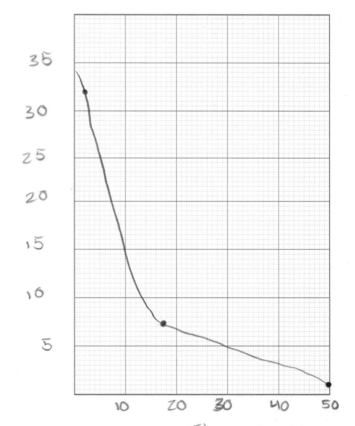

9. How has changing the temperature of the solution affected the rate of the color change? The hotter it is the faster the color changes

10. Do the results match your prediction? yes

11. Suggest a reason why the rate of color change changes as temperature changes: The heat breaks apart the molecules faster

EXPLAIN: Collision theory

▶ Collision theory describes the mechanism by which chemical reactions occur.

▶ In order for an atom or molecule to react with another atom or molecule they must collide with each other.

▶ The collision must be strong enough to break the bond holding the reactants together so that the reaction can occur and new products be formed.

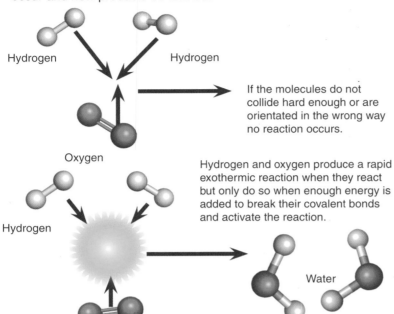

If the molecules do not collide hard enough or are orientated in the wrong way no reaction occurs.

Hydrogen and oxygen produce a rapid exothermic reaction when they react but only do so when enough energy is added to break their covalent bonds and activate the reaction.

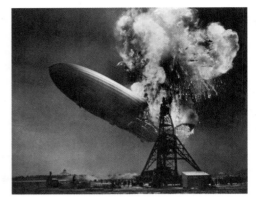

The Hindenburg disaster, 1937. The huge fireball seen in the photo was caused by burning hydrogen gas (used for buoyancy). The reason for the hydrogen's ignition is still not known, but may have been a spark from static electricity or possibly even lightning.

▶ The rate of a chemical reaction can be increased by several mechanisms:
   • increasing the temperature of the reactants,
   • increasing the concentration of reactants (or pressure for gaseous reactants),
   • increasing the surface area of solid reactants,
   • adding a catalyst.

12. Consider the graph below. How does increasing the temperature of the reactants increase the reaction rate?

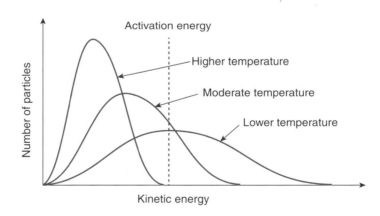

_____

_____

_____

13. In terms of collisions between particles, explain why increasing the concentration of reactants in solution would increase the rate of a reaction:

_____

_____

_____

_____

©2019 **BIOZONE** International
ISBN:978-1-927309-71-1
Photocopying Prohibited

ELABORATE: Catalysts

▶ Catalysts are important in many everyday and industrial reactions. Catalysts are chemicals that increase the rate of a reaction by lowering the activation energy required for the reaction to proceed.

▶ They do this by offering an alternative reaction pathway or orientating the reactants into the best positions for a reaction.

▶ Catalysts are not used up in the reaction.

▶ One of the most common everyday reactions involving a catalyst occurs in **catalytic converters**. These are found in the exhaust systems of gasoline and diesel fueled cars.

▶ The incomplete combustion of fuel and the reaction of nitrogen at high temperature with oxygen produces harmful gases (e.g. CO, NO). Catalytic converters convert these into less harmful gases (e.g. CO_2).

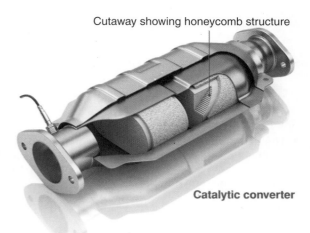

Cutaway showing honeycomb structure

Catalytic converter

14. Study the image of the catalytic converter shown above right. The catalytic compounds coat the honeycomb like inner structure of the converter. Why do you think the converter has this honeycomb like structure?

_____

_____

15. The catalytic converter operates at about 400°C, using the heat of the exhaust to maintain the temperature. Below this temperature the catalytic reactions are less successful. Why does the catalyst need to operate at a higher temperature?

_____

_____

_____

16. The graph below shows the reaction of two reactants A and B without a catalyst. Sketch onto the graph a line showing the reaction in the presence of a catalyst:

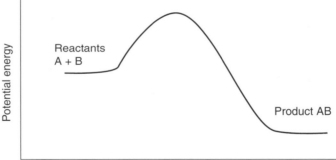

Reactants
A + B

Potential energy

Product AB

Reaction progress

▶ Living organisms are essentially a massive collection of chemical reactions. Every action we carry out, such as bending a finger, breathing, or digesting food involves hundreds of millions of chemical reactions.

▶ Most reactions in living organisms involve **enzymes**. Enzymes are biological catalysts, which vastly increase the rate of reactions.

▶ Recall that aerobic respiration begins with the process of glycolysis. There are nine different reaction "steps" in glycolysis. Each step has its own enzyme to catalyze the reaction.

▶ Enzymes have very specific three dimensional shapes that are able to attract and orientate the reactants so that a reaction occurs.

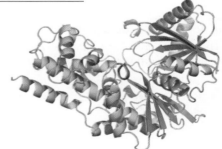

Hexokinase (above) catalyzes the first step in glycolysis.

17. It is estimated that there are 75,000 kinds of enzymes in the human body. Explain why so many enzymes are needed:

_____

_____

_____

©2019 **BIOZONE** International
ISBN: 978-1-927309-71-1
Photocopying Prohibited

32 Hot! Too Hot! Revisited

▶ At the beginning of this chapter you were shown products that produce heat (heat packs) or become very cold (cold packs) "instantly".

▶ You should now be able to explain the chemistry of these products and why they feel hot or cold.

The reusable heat pack

▶ The first product you were shown was the reusable heat pack. Recall that the contents were liquid before use (a solution of sodium ethanoate). After use, the contents were solid (crystallized sodium ethanoate). The heat pack could be reused by heating it in boiling water to return the contents to a liquid state.

1. (a) Why does the heat pack get warm when the liquid sodium ethanoate solidifies?

    _____

    _____

    _____

    _____

    (b) Explain what is happening in terms of energy when the heat pack is used and renewed:

    _____

    _____

    _____

The nonreusable heat pack

▶ The nonreusable heat pack contained iron powder that reacted with oxygen in the air to produce heat.

2. (a) Is this an exothermic or endothermic reaction? _____

    (b) Draw a graph showing the energy change for the reaction:

The nonreusable cold pack

▶ The instant cold pack contained solid ammonium nitrate and water in separate capsules. Mixing them together caused the ammonium nitrate to dissolve and make the pack get cold.

3. Describe what is happening in terms of bonds breaking and forming in the cold pack reactions and explain why this results in the pack feeling cold:

    _____

    _____

    _____

    _____

    _____

©2019 **BIOZONE** International
ISBN:978-1-927309-71-1
Photocopying Prohibited

33 Summative Assessment

1. Sulfur hexafluoride (SF6) is a molecule with a central sulfur surrounded by six covalently bonded fluorine atoms (single covalent bonds). The octahedral structure of the molecule is shown below:

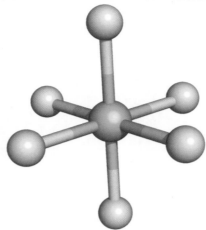

Why is the molecule this shape? _____

_____

_____

_____

_____

2. Define the term exothermic and give an example of an exothermic reaction: _____

_____

_____

_____

3. (a) Define the term endothermic: _____

_____

(b) Sketch a graph showing the enthalpy change for an endothermic reaction:

4. The reaction of carbon with oxygen is $C_{(s)} + O_{2(g)} \rightarrow CO_{2(g)}$ $\Delta_r H$ −393.5 kJ/mol

(a) Explain what the notation for the reaction means: _____

_____

_____

(b) How much energy is released is 2.6 moles of carbon is reacted completely? _____

_____

_____

©2019 **BIOZONE** International
ISBN: 978-1-927309-71-1
Photocopying Prohibited

EM | P | PS2.B | PS1.B | PS1.A

5. Draw Lewis structures for the following molecules:

(a) C_2H_2

(b) F_2

6. Complete the Lewis structure for:

(a) HCN

(b) O_3

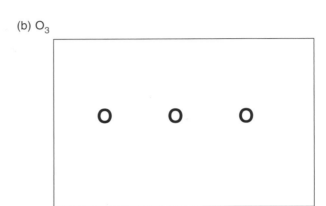

7. In the water stream below draw the orientation of water molecules as they pass by the charged glass rod:

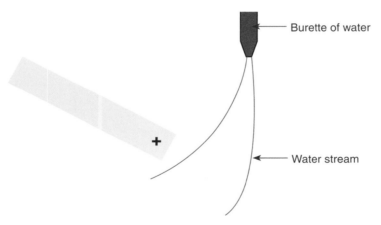

Burette of water

+

Water stream

8. Study the table below:

	Solid conducts	Liquid conducts	Melting point	Dissolves in water	Solution conducts
A	✗	✔	High/very high	✔	✔
B	Variable	Variable	Very high	✗	✗
C	✔	✔	Very high	✗	NA
D	✗	✗	Low	✗	NA

Use the letters A, B, C, D to identify the :

(a) Metal: _____

(b) Ionic substance: _____

(c) Discrete molecular substance: _____

(d) Giant covalent network: _____

©2019 **BIOZONE** International
ISBN:978-1-927309-71-1
Photocopying Prohibited

9. Use Coulomb's law to explain trend in melting points of the lithium salts below:

NEED HELP?
See activity 62

$$F = k \frac{q_1 q_2}{r^2}$$

Melting point lithium salts (°C)

LiF	LiCl	LiBr	LiI
845	605	550	449

_____

_____

_____

_____

_____

10. Explain why the vapor pressure of H_2O is less than the vapor pressure of H_2S: _____

_____

_____

_____

_____

_____

11. (a) Sketch a graph showing the enthalpy change for the reaction $H_2O_{(l)} \rightarrow H_2O_{(g)}$:

(b) Explain your diagram: _____

_____

_____

_____

12. Sketch a graph showing the enthalpy change for the reaction $Mg + \frac{1}{2}O_2 \rightarrow MgO$ $\Delta_f H -601.6$ kJ/mol:

13. What is the role of an enzyme in terms of the energy involved in a reaction. Sketch a graph to explain your answer:

_____

_____

_____

_____

14. Two investigations were set up testing the effect of surface area on reaction rate as shown below. The mass of the calcium carbonate chips was kept the same for the two investigations:

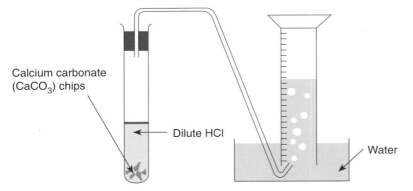

Calcium carbonate (CaCO₃) chips

Dilute HCl

Water

	Size of CaCO₃ chips
Investigation 1	Large
Investigation 2	Small

The graph below shows the production of gas for investigation 1 and investigation 2:

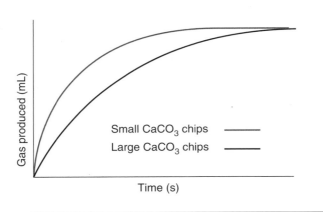

Gas produced (mL)

Small CaCO₃ chips ———

Large CaCO₃ chips ——

Time (s)

(a) What was the effect of reducing the size of the CaCO₃ chips?

_____

_____

_____

(b) Explain your answer in terms of collision theory:

_____

_____

_____

_____

_____

(c) The students decided to increase the concentration of the HCl and run the investigation again using a new set of small CaCO₃ chips. How will this affect the rate of the reaction?

_____

_____

_____

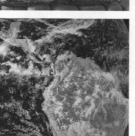

NASA

Instructional Segment 5

Chemistry of Climate Change

Activity number

Anchoring Phenomenon

It's heating up: Evidence shows the planet is warming.

34 41

What regulates weather and climate?

☐ 1 Describe the current composition of the Earth's atmosphere. Analyze and interpret graphs about the change in the composition of the Earth's atmosphere throughout its history. Are changes in atmospheric composition (e.g. levels of carbon dioxide, oxygen, and methane) correlated with changes in the Earth's climate, e.g. warm periods, glaciation events. Analyze data for levels of atmospheric CO_2 and CH_4 to compare current levels to levels 30-50 years ago. What is the relationship between human developments in energy use and agriculture and changes in atmospheric composition over this period?

37

☐ 2 Develop or use a model based on data to describe how carbon cycles through the biosphere (the living components of the Earth), the geosphere (the rocks and soil), and the atmosphere (the air) . Refine your model to quantify these exchanges. What can such models tell us about what is happening to carbon in the atmosphere?

37 42

☐ 3 The vast majority of the Earth's energy input comes from the Sun. Most of this sunlight is absorbed and transformed into thermal energy. Complete a quantitative model of the energy flows into, within and out of the Earth system. Do the energy flows balance? These energy flows are the basis for the Earth's climate systems. Analyze data to understand how these energy flows have changed over the course of Earth's history.

38

☐ 4 Use your understanding of the Earth's atmosphere and molecular structures to explain the greenhouse effect. How does the greenhouse effect make the Earth a habitable planet? What are the important greenhouse gases and predict what would happen in your quantitative model if the volume of greenhouses gases in the atmosphere increased? Recognize that the relationship between greenhouse gases in the atmosphere and the Earth's "thermal blanket" is made more complex by feedbacks within components of the Earth system. Use and develop models to show how feedback loops in the Earth system affect climate, e.g. through altering ice cover and cloudiness.

38

What effects are humans having on the climate?

☐ 5 In earlier chapters, you used combustion to investigate the energy content of food (fuel) and explored energy flows in both small and large systems. In your food calorimetry experiment, mass that was apparently 'lost' was released as CO_2 and H_2O gas. The combustion of hydrocarbon fuels is no different. In this chapter you will look at the effects of fossil fuel combustion on the Earth system.

35

☐ 6 Use bond energies to calculate the enthalpy of complete combustion of some common fuels. Most hydrocarbons and similar fuels are used to provide heat. Why are different types of fuels used for different purposes? How is the structure of the fuel molecule related to its use?

35

☐ 7 Use graphs and analyze data about fuel use, and describe the relationship between the consumption of fuels (particularly fossil fuels) and human population growth. Explain the relationship between available fuels, available energy, and the development of technology. How has this changed in the last 2000 years? For most of the industrial era, coal has been the fuel of choice. Evaluate the costs and benefits of extracting and using coal (or any other fossil fuel). Include reference to its ability to provide usable energy as well as the effect of its combustion on the environment.

36 42

☐ 8 Analyze geoscience data and climate models to make connections between human combustion of fossil fuels, levels of greenhouse gases in the atmosphere, and predicted future climate change. Use your feedback models in #4 to identify linkages between components of the Earth system and predict the impacts of continued increases in the Earth's average surface temperature.

38 42

☐ 9 Evaluate competing solutions to the problems associated with the use of limited natural resources. You should consider economic, social, and environmental costs, risks, and benefits. Consider how different solutions might reduce the effect on the environment (e.g. of greenhouse gas emissions) while still providing for the needs of the growing human population.

39 40 42

34 It's Heating Up

ANCHORING PHENOMENON: Evidence shows the planet is warming

Statements that the Earth is warming are often accompanied by dramatic images such as the one shown on the right. Although these images may be overly dramatic, data from observatories around the world do show the Earth's surface temperature is increasing as is the surface temperature of the oceans.

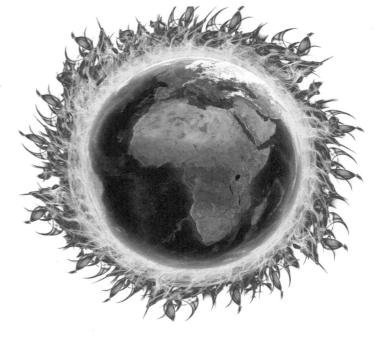

Average surface temperature since 1880

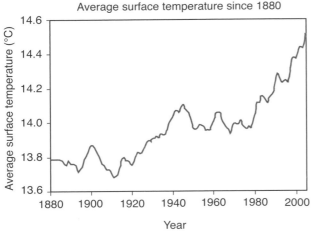

Average sea temperature since 1890

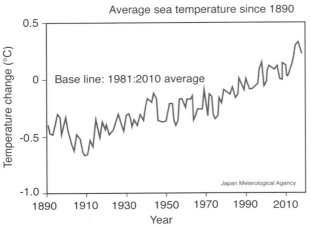

Base line: 1981:2010 average

Japan Meterological Agency

Average Arctic sea ice extent (area of ocean with at least 15% sea ice) for spring 1980-2014

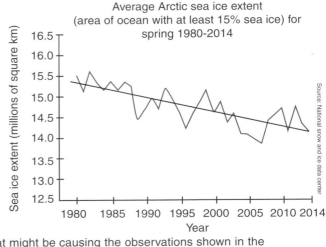

Source: National snow and ice data center

1. In groups, discuss why the globe appears to be warming. What might be causing the observations shown in the graphs above? Summarize your ideas below:

_____

_____

_____

_____

_____

2. Climate change is a controversial topic, with some people contesting the scientific evidence, or providing contradictory arguments. In groups, discuss climate change and the various arguments around it. Summarize your discussion below:

_____

_____

_____

_____

_____

©2019 **BIOZONE** International
ISBN:978-1-927309-71-1
Photocopying Prohibited

35 | Combustion and Hydrocarbons

ENGAGE: Clean vs sooty

▶ Turn on and light a Bunsen burner. You will know that a Bunsen has a yellow and a blue flame.

1. How do you switch from one to the other? _____

_____

2. What causes the flame to become yellow? _____

_____

3. Which flame is cooler, the yellow or blue flame? Can you explain why?

_____

_____

4. Which flame produces the cleanest flame? Can you give a reason for this?

_____

_____

EXPLORE: Combustion and energy

▶ Bunsen burners burn the hydrocarbon propane (C_3H_8).

5. Write a balanced equation for the burning of propane gas with oxygen (O_2) to form carbon dioxide and water:

_____

▶ So far you have only written combustion equations for the complete combustion of a hydrocarbon (above). The only products formed are carbon dioxide and water. However, when you switched the Bunsen burner to a yellow flame above, you may have noticed that the yellow flame appeared smoky. Clearly, something other than just carbon dioxide and water is being produced.

▶ The smoke is particles of unburned carbon (C). When it accumulates on a surface we call it soot. Sometimes the carbon burns but incompletely forming carbon monoxide (CO).

▶ We can write these as equations:

In **limited** oxygen: propane + oxygen → carbon monoxide + water

In **restricted** oxygen: propane + oxygen → carbon + water

▶ **Incomplete combustion** usually results in a combination of carbon products (e.g. CO_2 + CO).

Smoky flames indicate incomplete combustion

6. (a) Write a balanced equation for propane and oxygen forming carbon monoxide and water:

_____

(b) Write an equation for propane and oxygen forming carbon and water:

_____

(c) What do you notice about the moles of oxygen used in each equation: _____

_____

(d) Where might conditions of limited or restricted oxygen occur? _____

_____

_____

_____

©2019 **BIOZONE** International
ISBN: 978-1-927309-71-1
Photocopying Prohibited

SF | EM | SSM | CE | PS3.D | PS1.B

7. (a) Recall the bond energies from chapter 4. Use bond energies to calculate the enthalpy of the complete combustion of propane. C–C 347 kJ/mol, C–H 413 kJ/mol, O=O 498 kJ/mol, C=O 805 kJ/mol, O–H 464 kJ/mol:

_____

_____

_____

(b) Would you expect the incomplete combustion of propane to produce more or less heat?

_____

(c) Explain why: _____

_____

_____

(d) How would this affect the amount of fuel used to produce a certain amount of heat? _____

_____

_____

▶ Alkanes such as propane are not the only type of fuel. The alkynes, e.g. acetylene (ethyne, C_2H_2), are also sometimes used. Other fuels include alcohols (usually ethanol, C_2H_5OH)). Solid fuels include carbohydrate polymers such as cellulose (mostly as wood), and coal (mostly pure carbon).

8. Complete the following complete combustion equations:

(a) __C_2H_5OH + __O_2 → __CO_2 + __H_2O

(b) __C_2H_2 + __O_2 → __CO_2 + __H_2O

(c) __$C_{12}H_{22}O_{11}$ + __O_2 → __ CO_2 + __H_2O

(d) __C_8H_{18} + __O_2 → __CO_2 + __H_2O

(e) __C_4H_{10} + __O_2 → __CO_2 + __H_2O

The oxyacetylene torch produces one of the hottest flames of all common fuels at over 3000 °C.

EXPLORE: Alkenes and alkynes

▶ In the previous chapter you were introduced to the simplest hydrocarbons, the alkanes. It is worthwhile exploring the related groups of the alkenes and alkynes.

▶ **Alkanes** have all single covalent bonds between the carbon atoms.
Alkenes are distinguished by having at least one double covalent bond between two carbon atoms.
Alkynes have at least one triple covalent bond between two carbon atoms.

▶ The images below show the structures of propane, propene, and propyne.

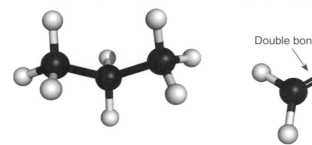

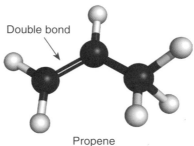

Double bond

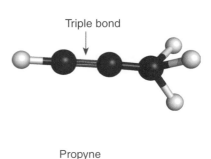

Triple bond

Propane   Propene   Propyne

▶ The general formula for an alkane is C_nH_{2n+2}. For an alkene it is C_nH_{2n}, and for an alkyne it is C_nH_{2n-2}.

▶ Alkenes, especially ethene (C_2H_4), and sometime alkynes, are used as starter molecules for making plastics.

9. Complete the following equations:

(a) __C_3H_6 + __O_2 → __CO_2 + __H_2O

(b) __C_3H_4 + __O_2 → __CO_2 + __H_2O

©2019 **BIOZONE** International
ISBN:978-1-927309-71-1
Photocopying Prohibited

ELABORATE: Fuel use and energy density

▶ Most hydrocarbons and similar fuels are used to provide heat. Sometimes the heat is simply for cooking or home heating (e.g. in gas stoves, heaters, or wood fires). At other times, the heat is used to produce steam that drives turbines in thermal power stations. In the transport industry, hydrocarbons and their derivatives (and sometimes alcohols) are use to provide energy to produce mechanical work.

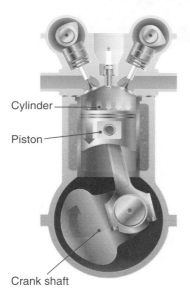

Cylinder

Piston

Crank shaft

- In an internal combustion engine, fuel is injected into the cylinder and ignited (left). The explosion forces the piston down. This helps turn the crank shaft and so produces a rotating shaft. In this case, heat is a waste product.

- Gasoline is a mixture of short chain hydrocarbons. The shape of the molecules is important. Regular single chain hydrocarbons, such as the alkanes, tend to explode too early in an internal combustion engine. To stop this from happening, single chain alkanes are reformed at the refinery to produce branch chained alkanes, such as isooctane (2,2,4-trimethylpentane (top right)).

- A jet engine (bottom right) ignites fuel to produce exhaust. The exhaust turns a turbine connected to a fan that provides air for the combustion of the fuel. The high pressure gases produced by the burning fuel provides the thrust to push the aircraft forward.

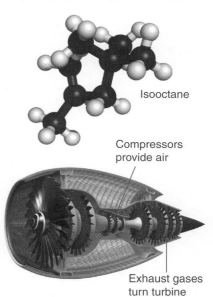

Isooctane

Compressors provide air

Exhaust gases turn turbine

▶ Fuels must also be able to deliver energy at the rate needed. Gasoline delivers a high energy output relatively quickly. But for a Top Fuel dragster (right) the rate of combustion of gasoline is far too slow. Nitromethane is used instead. This has less energy per gram than gasoline but combusts nearly eight times faster. It delivers energy to the engine more quickly, allowing top fuel dragsters to reach 500 kmph in just over 3 seconds.

 10. From groups of five. Each person in the group should research one of the vehicle types below and the fuel it uses. Identify why it uses that fuel. Each person should report back to the group with a summary of their findings. Record a summary of each person's findings below:

Vehicle types: *Jet plane (e.g. passenger jet), small domestic car, heavy transport truck, cargo ship, IndyCar (race car).*

_____

_____

_____

_____

_____

_____

_____

©2019 **BIOZONE** International
ISBN: 978-1-927309-71-1
Photocopying Prohibited

36 Fuels and People

ENGAGE: What fuels do you use?

▶ Fuel is what allows our industrial world to work. Without it, the factories stop, food production of farms would plummet, and what little food was produced could not be cooked or processed. The amount of fuel you use every day is enormous, but most of this use is indirect. You don't personally use the fuel, but manufacturers or producers of things you use or need use the fuel on your behalf.

▶ A simple example might be the shirt you are wearing. If it is made from cotton then diesel fuel was used to run the machinery that planted, irrigated, sprayed, and harvested the cotton. Diesel was used in the trucks that took the cotton to the mill where it was spun into thread. The factory used electricity, but that may have been generated by coal, or gas, or solid uranium pellets fueling a nuclear power station. Diesel fueled trucks would have transported the materials to factories were the shirt was made and then again to the shop were you bought it. Don't forget the processes that made the dyes that color the shirt. Or made the tractor, or any of the dozens of other implements used to make the shirt. All these stages in manufacture were powered by fuels. A large proportion of these fuels would be fossil fuels consisting of short chain alkane derivatives.

The harvester and tractor run on diesel fuel.

1. Think of two things that you do or use every day and make a list of how fuels (of any kind) are used in the process of getting them to you. Compare your ideas and list with others in your class:

(a) _____

_____

_____

(b) _____

_____

_____

EXPLORE: Fuels and energy density

▶ The amount of energy in a fuel can be measured in two important ways: its **specific energy** and its **energy density**.

▶ **Specific energy** is the amount of energy per unit of mass of the fuel.

▶ **Energy density** is the amount of energy per unit of volume of the fuel. The graph below shows the specific energy and energy density of a selection of fuels:

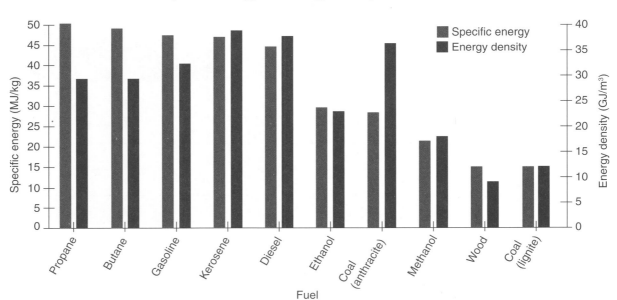

Specific energy and energy density of fuels

©2019 **BIOZONE** International
ISBN:978-1-927309-71-1
Photocopying Prohibited

PS1.B PS3.D ESS3.A CE EM

2. (a) Which fuel has the greatest specific energy? _____

   (b) Which fuel has the greatest energy density? _____

EXPLORE: Fuels and industry

▶ Fuel is anything that can be used to power machinery or provide heat. Before the steam engine or electricity, wind and water were the fuel that (directly) powered mills and pumps (e.g. windmills or water wheels).

▶ We tend to think of fuel in terms of fossil fuels such as oil or coal. In industry, much of the fuel used is fossil fuel, but much of the electricity used by industry is generated from other energy sources such as nuclear or hydropower.

▶ The graph below shows the primary energy consumption by source and sector in the United States for 2017.

US Primary energy consumption by source and sector 2017

37% of US primary energy consumption comes from petroleum. Of this, 72% is used by the transportation industry.

29% of US primary energy consumption is used by the transportation sector. Of this, 90% comes from petroleum.

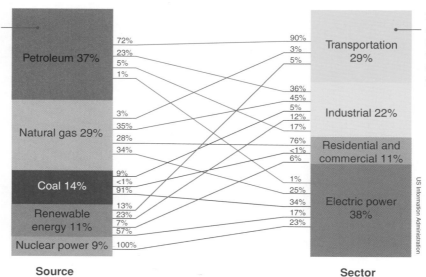

Source   **Sector**

3. (a) Which fuel type is used the most? _____

   (b) Which sector uses the most fuel? _____

   (c) What is the total percentage of fossil fuels used to provide usable energy? _____

   (d) What are the products of burning fossil fuels? _____

   (e) Explain why coal, renewals, and nuclear are not used by the transport industry: _____

   _____

   _____

   (f) Which fuel makes up the greatest percentage of the electricity production sector: _____

EXPLORE: How much fuel is used?

▶ Fuel use has increased every year since our human ancestors began to burn wood to cook food. Human population growth and fuel consumption are closely linked.

▶ As the human population has increased, so has the consumption of coal, gas, and other energy resources. Some of this comes from use of technology with high energy demands, but that technology has itself helped increase food supplies, living standards, life expectancy, and the human population itself.

▶ Now, even as we develop more fuel efficient technologies the rapid increase in the human population drives an every higher demand for energy and its associated fuels.

▶ Most of the coal and natural gas used goes to produce electricity, whereas oil is used mostly in the transportation industry. Some oil is used in industry to make plastics.

©2019 **BIOZONE** International
ISBN: 978-1-927309-71-1
Photocopying Prohibited

4. (a) Use the data in the two tables right to produce a graph to show the growth of the human population and the consumption of coal, oil, and natural gas since 1840.

You will need a left and right Y axis on your graph. The left Y axis will have a scale for population and the right Y axis will have a scale for fuel consumption.

Use different colors to help you distinguish your lines.

Year	Population (billions)
1850	1.26
1900	1.65
1910	1.75
1920	1.86
1930	2.07
1940	2.30
1950	2.52
1960	3.01
1970	3.68
1980	4.44
1990	5.31
2000	6.12
2010	6.93
2016	7.41

Year	Coal consumption terrawatt-hours	Crude oil consumption terrawatt-hours	Natural gas consumption terrawatt-hours
1840	356	0	0
1860	1061	0	0
1880	2542	33	0
1900	5728	181	64
1920	9833	889	233
1940	11586	2653	875
1960	15442	11097	4472
1980	21082	34728	15020
2000	27734	41747	25373
2016	43403	51384	37264

Data from Our world in Data

NEED HELP?
See activity 60

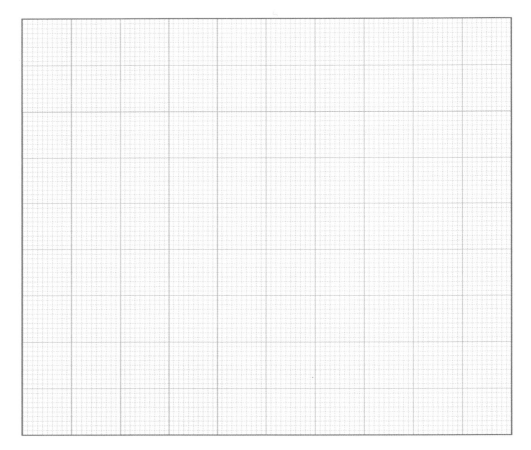

(b) Describe the relationship between fossil fuel use and human population: _____

_____

_____

(c) Which fuel has had the most rapid rise in consumption? _____

(d) In which year did oil consumption overtake coal consumption? _____

©2019 BIOZONE International
ISBN:978-1-927309-71-1

EXPLAIN: Fuel, energy and technology

▶ There is an argument that the history of human social, technological, and cultural development is linked directly to our ability to harness and transform energy.

▶ One of the earliest uses of energy was the invention of ways to provide reliable fire. Energy could then be used to cook food, hunt animals, produce weapons, and provide light.

▶ Domesticating animals and using them to provide mechanical power (horsepower) increased the work that could be done by one person. Using coal and charcoal to provide heat enabled the smelting of iron and metal alloys, expanding the range of tools that could be used.

▶ The development of the steam and internal combustion engines provided ways for the energy in fuels to be transformed into reliable and powerful mechanical work. These new powerful machines needed fuels that were equal to the task. Coal was the key mineral and fuel for the Industrial Revolution, being energy dense and easy to transport and use. It was more effective at powering the new machinery being developed than wood or charcoal.

▶ Harnessing other types of mechanical work (e.g. water) to drive electrical turbines (e.g. water turbines) produced reliable electrical energy.

▶ At each of these steps, the ability of one person to do work increased. At each step, the resources that became available to a person increased. But the resources required also increased. Iron production requires coal and charcoal to provide heat and act as reducers. Iron machinery allows the components of engines to be manufactured (again from iron). Engines need fuel - coal and oil. And so there is a continuing increase in resources required and produced.

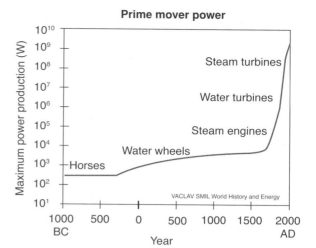

Prime mover power

Maximum power production (W)

VACLAV SMIL World History and Energy

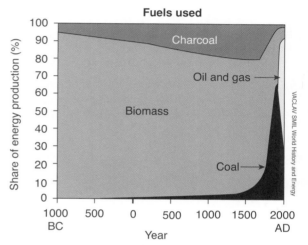

Fuels used

Share of energy production (%)

Charcoal

Oil and gas →

Biomass

Coal →

VACLAV SMIL World History and Energy

Domesticating horses and cattle allowed one person to plow an entire field, drive a mill, or carry a greater load. This allowed the utilization of more resources and their more efficient use.

More efficient ways of using energy resources increased the power available. A tractor can do the work of many horses. Now many fields can be plowed and planted by one person, allowing more food to be produced.

Transforming energy into electricity makes usable energy available to the masses. 100,000 years ago the average person used about 20,000 kJ of energy a day. Today it is close to a million kJ a day, from using cars, computers, and appliances.

5. In the last 3000 years, which two technological developments signalled sudden increases in the energy available to humans to do work:

_____

6. Explain how energy and resources have shaped human social and technological development: _____

_____

_____

_____

7. Describe how the fuels used changed over time and explain why: _____

_____

_____

ELABORATE: Coal and oil

Coal

▶ Coal is fossil plant material. It was formed from the remains of land-based plants buried in shallow swamps during the Carboniferous period (359 to 299 mya) and then compacted under sediments to form a hard black rock.

▶ Burning coal produces about a third of the world's energy needs. Nearly eight billion tonnes of coal are produced globally each year. Burning coal produces vast quantities of greenhouse gases and pollutants, contributing to smog and global warming.

Using coal	
Benefits	**Costs**
Huge supplies (billions of tonnes)	High CO_2 production when burned.
High net energy yields.	High particle pollution from soot.
Can be used to produce syngas and converted to other fuels.	Low grade coals produce high pollution and contribute to acid rain.
Relatively easy to extract when close to the surface.	High land disturbance through mining, including subsidence.
Important in industry as coke (reducer).	Noise and dust pollution during mining.

Best practice for coal extraction

▶ When plans are put in place to open a coal mine, best practice dictates that economic, environmental, social, and even political costs and benefits are considered.

▶ By considering these aspects, the net benefit (or cost) of the mine can be identified. Some costs and benefits of coal production are indicated above right, but there are many more, including economic benefits such as the creation of jobs and building of industry, or social costs, such as the loss of land use and effects on health.

▶ It is preferable (and appropriate) that a mine's operators allocate some of the mine's revenue to pay for some of the environmental and social costs, including repairing environmental damage and restoring the original environment (if possible) when the mine closes. Large mines can cost tens of millions of dollars to close and rehabilitate.

Preparing the mine

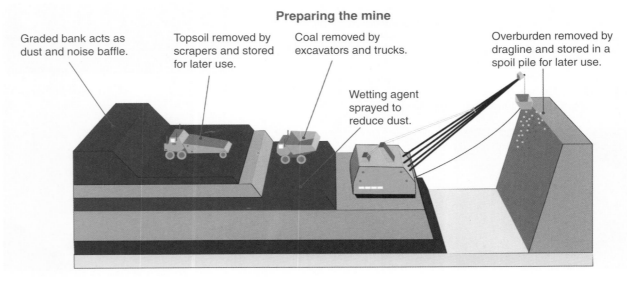

Graded bank acts as dust and noise baffle.

Topsoil removed by scrapers and stored for later use.

Coal removed by excavators and trucks.

Wetting agent sprayed to reduce dust.

Overburden removed by dragline and stored in a spoil pile for later use.

Remediating the mine

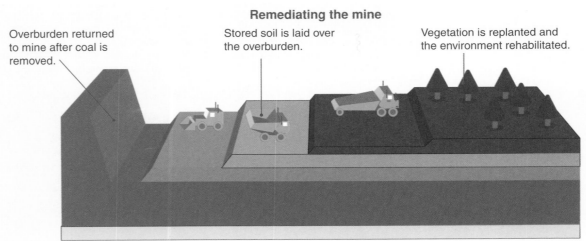

Overburden returned to mine after coal is removed.

Stored soil is laid over the overburden.

Vegetation is replanted and the environment rehabilitated.

8. For each of the following, list two benefits of coal production:

(a) Economic benefits: _____

(b) Social benefits: _____

©2019 **BIOZONE** International
ISBN:978-1-927309-71-1
Photocopying Prohibited

9. For each of the following, list two costs of coal production:

(a) Environmental costs: _____

(b) Economic costs: _____

(c) Social costs: _____

Oil and natural gas

▶ Oil is formed from the remains of plant and animal plankton, which settled to the bottom of shallow seas and lakes about the same time as the coal-forming swamps. These remains were buried and compressed under layers of nonporous sediment. The process occurs so slowly that oil (like coal) is essentially non-renewable.

▶ Oil and natural gas are both composed of a mixture of hydrocarbons and are generally found in the same underground reservoirs. Natural gas is generally defined as a mixture of hydrocarbons with four or fewer carbon atoms in the chain (as these are gaseous at standard temperatures and pressures). Oil is defined as the mixture of hydrocarbons with five or more carbon atoms in the chain.

▶ Crude oil can be refined and used for an extensive array of applications including fuel, road tar, plastics, and cosmetics.

Natural gas is often found in the same reservoirs as oil. Drilling rigs require specialized facilities to store the gas. Because of this, much natural gas is either vented, or reinjected to maintain pressure in the reservoir.

Transport of natural gas requires specialized equipment. Liquid natural gas (LNG) tankers are able to cool the gas to -162 °C and transport it as a liquid (saving space). Gas can also be piped to shore if facilities are nearby.

Oil may be found in materials that make extraction using conventional drilling impossible. These **non conventional oils** (e.g. oil shale) are often mined in the same way as coal and the oil washed from them.

Crude and heavy oils require refining before use. Crude oil is separated into different sized fractions by a distillation tower. Heavy oils may be heated under pressure to break them into smaller more usable molecules.

Peak oil

▶ The future of the production of any mineral can be estimated from its current and historical production rates. Called a **Hubbert Curve** after its discoverer, it shows that the extraction rate of any non-renewable resource will fit into a bell shape curve (right). Plotting the amount of mineral extracted on a graph gives the shape of part of the curve, from which the rest can be estimated. Using these curves, peak production and the time until the resource runs out can be estimated.

▶ Hubbert curves are constantly applied to estimate peak oil. Peak oil is difficult to predict accurately and depends on what type of oil is included in the prediction (e.g. crude, oil shales) and how much new oil is being discovered (e.g. the Lula field off the coast of Brazil discovered in 2006).Global oil production decreased dramatically in the mid 1970s and it was thought peak oil may have been reached, but production has since continued to increase.

10. (a) What is the significance of peak oil: _____

_____

_____

_____

(b) What factors affect our estimate of peak oil? _____

_____

_____

EVALUATE: Are coal and oil worth it?

CA EP&Cs V: The spectrum of what is considered in making decisions about resources and natural systems and how those factors influence decisions (V a)

Is it worth it?

▸ The effort in and return from exploiting a resource must be considered. Put simply, "Is it worth it?"

▸ This question must consider not only the energy return but the economical, social, and environmental aspects of that return.

▸ Is it worth removing 100 hectares of forest for 10,000 barrels of oil or 10,000 tonnes of coal? Does the type of forest matter? What value do we place on the services provided by the forest, including recreation and aesthetics, shelter, air and water purification, climate moderation, and protection from erosion.

11. The diagram below shows a simplified map of a region where two possible areas could be surface-mined for coal. Use the information below and in this activity to evaluate the costs and benefits of mining at each proposed site. Produce a reasoned argument for which mine site is best when costs and benefits are considered.

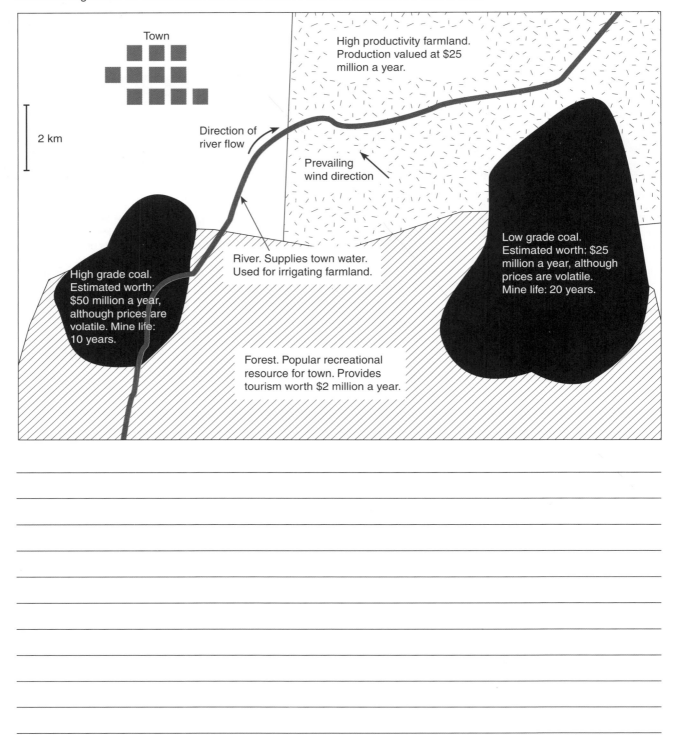

_____
_____
_____
_____
_____
_____
_____
_____
_____
_____
_____

©2019 **BIOZONE** International
ISBN:978-1-927309-71-1
Photocopying Prohibited

EVALUATE: The cost of oil

Oil and oil spills

▶ Oil is arguably one of the most important chemicals in human economics. It provides energy for transport and electricity and the raw materials for many consumer products, including plastics. Billions of dollars a year are spent on removing it from the ground and billions more in revenue made from its sale.

▶ However, crude oil is a very toxic substance and removing it from reservoirs is difficult and dangerous. Some of the greatest man-made environmental disasters have occurred because of the search for and transport of oil.

▶ For example, the **Deepwater Horizon disaster** in 2010 produced an oil slick that, at its peak, covered 6500 km^2 of ocean.

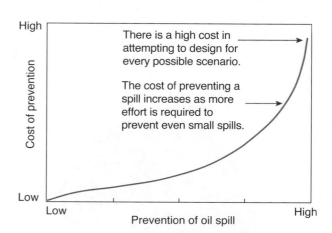

Cost of preventing oil spills

▶ Preventing oil spills is important as oil is extremely damaging to the environment. However the cost of prevention is high. It is more costly to build a double hulled tanker than a single hulled tanker. These extra costs are eventually passed on to the consumer.

▶ At some point, the extra cost of prevention measures become too high for the oil company and the consumer. At this point the cost of prevention measures outweighs the benefit of preventing spills (the reduction of damage to the environment).

▶ A cost-benefit analysis done soon after the **Exxon Valdez** grounding in 1989 found the benefit to the environment of requiring the oil industry to use double hulled oil tankers was less than half the cost to the oil industry of upgrading oil tankers, even in the most favorable scenarios. In other words, it was less costly to clean up the mess than prevent the spill. Of course this doesn't take into account that any oil spill is detrimental to the environment.

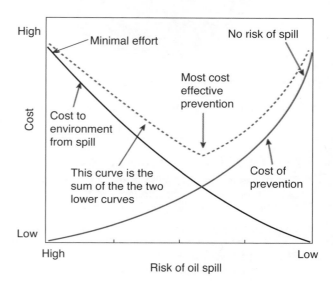

12. Why is oil an important resource? _____

_____

_____

_____

13. Why does the cost of preventing an oil spill increase rapidly close to 100% prevention? _____

_____

_____

_____

_____

14. How does a cost-benefit analysis help us decide what level of risk is acceptable when dealing with oil and oil spills?

_____

_____

_____

_____

_____

_____

©2019 **BIOZONE** International
ISBN: 978-1-927309-71-1
Photocopying Prohibited

37 Atmospheric Chemistry

ENGAGE: The atmosphere is mixture of gases

▶ How many gases is the atmosphere made of? You are probably aware that nitrogen and oxygen are the major components of the atmosphere, making up 99% of the air by volume. But there are many other gases, all in very small percentages.

▶ The pie chart below shows the percentages of gases in the atmosphere:

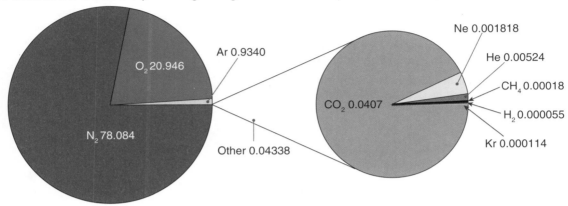

1. (a) Where do you think the oxygen in the atmosphere come from? _____

   (b) Why do you think there is a very low percentage of carbon dioxide? _____

   _____

EXPLORE: Changes in the atmosphere

▶ The gases in the atmosphere are not constant. Over the eons of Earth's history, the percentages of the different gases that make up the atmosphere has changed. The Earth's early atmosphere contained virtually no oxygen, but a lot of carbon dioxide and ammonia.

▶ Oxygen did not become a prominent gas in the atmosphere until the evolution of oxygenic (oxygen-producing) photosynthesis. The evolution of life on Earth has had a great influence on the composition of the atmosphere. The graph below shows the changes in atmospheric carbon dioxide, oxygen, and methane along with significant evolutionary milestones of life on Earth.

Changes in atmospheric gases

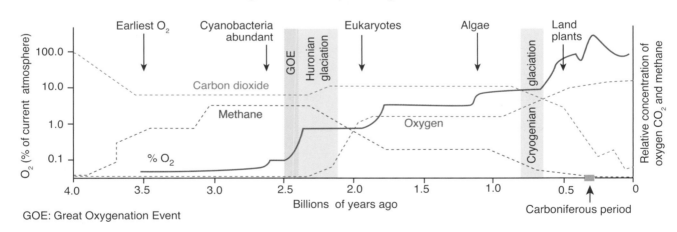

GOE: Great Oxygenation Event

2. Describe the relationship between the concentration of oxygen in the atmosphere and the evolution of life:

   _____

   _____

3. What has happened to the relative concentration of carbon dioxide in the atmosphere over time?

   _____

   _____

©2019 **BIOZONE** International
ISBN:978-1-927309-71-1
Photocopying Prohibited

EXPLORE: Greenhouse gases in the atmosphere

▶ Atmospheric CO_2 is monitored in many locations around the globe. The Earth System Research Laboratory is a web site that shows the daily CO_2 level for Mauna Loa in Hawaii. Access it via **Biozone's Resource Hub** or directly by typing in https://www.esrl.noaa.gov/gmd/ccgg/trends/monthly.html

▶ If you explore the website you will find interactive graphs showing the atmospheric CO_2 concentrations for any month dating back to 1960.

▶ The data on the right shows the CO_2 concentration for the years 1970 to the end of 1972 and 2016 to the end of 2018 in parts per million (ppm).

4. Plot the data on the grids provided below.

Month (1970)	Atmospheric CO_2 (ppm)	Month (1971)	Atmospheric CO_2 (ppm)	Month (1972)	Atmospheric CO_2 (ppm)
January	325	January	326	January	327
February	326	February	327	February	328
March	327	March	327	March	328
April	328	April	328	April	330
May	328	May	329	May	330
June	327	June	329	June	329
July	326	July	327	July	328
August	324	August	325	August	326
September	323	September	323	September	325
October	323	October	324	October	325
November	324	November	326	November	326
December	325	December	326	December	327

Month (2016)	Atmospheric CO_2 (ppm)	Month (2017)	Atmospheric CO_2 (ppm)	Month (2018)	Atmospheric CO_2 (ppm)
January	402	January	406	January	408
February	404	February	406	February	408
March	405	March	407	March	409
April	407	April	409	April	410
May	408	May	410	May	411
June	407	June	409	June	411
July	404	July	407	July	409
August	402	August	405	August	407
September	401	September	403	September	405
October	402	October	404	October	406
November	403	November	405	November	408
December	404	December	407	December	409

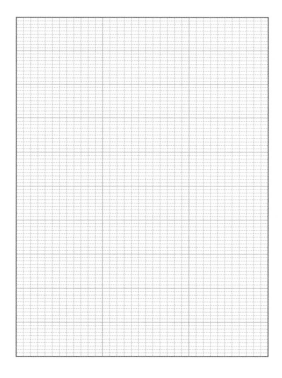

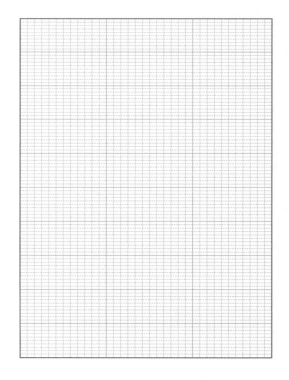

The data below shows the annual atmospheric methane (CH_4) concentration in parts per billion (ppb).

Year	Atmospheric CH$_4$ (ppb)	Year	Atmospheric CH$_4$ (ppb)	Year	Atmospheric CH$_4$ (ppb)
1986	1670.07	1998	1765.55	2010	1798.96
1988	1693.16	2000	1773.29	2012	1808.02
1990	1714.41	2002	1772.72	2014	1822.59
1992	1735.47	2004	1777.01	2016	1843.13
1994	1742.04	2006	1774.98		
1996	1751.47	2008	1787.00		

5. Plot the data on the graph below:

NEED HELP?
See activity 60

6. (a) For the plot of CO_2 concentration, can you see a trend in the data? Has it changed between the two plots?

_____

_____

_____

(b) Describe any trend you identify in the data for the concentration of atmospheric CH_4:

_____

_____

▶ Both CO_2 and CH_4 are known as greenhouse gases. They radiate heat (from sunlight) reflected from the Earth back to the Earth rather than letting the heat escape into space. In this way they help retain heat in the atmosphere and are important in maintaining the planet's habitable surface temperature.

7. What would be the effect on atmospheric temperature of the trends seen in the CO_2 and CH_4 data?

_____

_____

EXPLAIN: Carbon cycling

▶ Carbon cycles through the atmosphere (as carbon dioxide) and biosphere by the processes of respiration and photosynthesis. The respective rates of these processes are important in determining the concentration of carbon dioxide in the atmosphere. Other process such as volcanic eruptions can add carbon dioxide to the atmosphere from geosphere, while the dissolving of carbon dioxide into the oceans add it to the hydrosphere.

Photosynthesis and carbon

▶ Photosynthesis removes carbon from the atmosphere by fixing the carbon in CO_2 into carbohydrate molecules. Plants use the carbohydrates (e.g. glucose) to build structures such as wood.

▶ Some carbon may be returned to the atmosphere during respiration (either from plants or from animals). If the amount or rate of carbon fixation is greater than that released during respiration then carbon will build up in the biosphere and be depleted in the atmosphere (diagram, right).

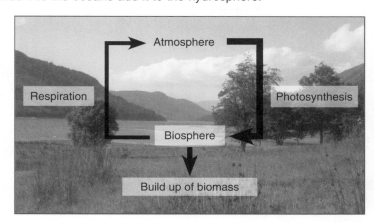

Respiration and carbon

▶ Cellular respiration releases carbon into the atmosphere as carbon dioxide as a result of the breakdown of glucose.

▶ If the rate of carbon release is greater than that fixed by photosynthesis then carbon may accumulate in the atmosphere over time (diagram bottom right). Before the Industrial Revolution, many thousands of gigatonnes (Gt) of carbon were contained in the biosphere of in the Earth's crust (e.g. coal).

▶ Deforestation and the burning of fossil fuels have increased the amount of carbon in the atmosphere.

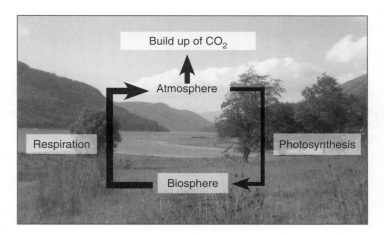

8. Explain how the concentration of atmospheric carbon dioxide is regulated by photosynthesis and respiration:

_____

_____

_____

_____

_____

ELABORATE: Modeling changes to the carbon cycle

▶ Scientists has been able to estimate the mass of carbon stored in the Earth's various reservoirs (e.g. rocks). They have also been able to estimate the rate at which carbon cycles from reservoir to reservoir.

▶ This data can be used to produce a crude but informative model of the carbon cycle. The table below shows the data for the reservoirs and rates of exchanges.

Reservoir	Amount in reservoir (gigatonnes (Gt))	Exchanges
Atmosphere	840	Movements included absorption and release by the ocean, and living organisms. Combustion of fossil fuels is adding carbon dioxide to the atmosphere.
Biomass	2610 (610 in plants and animals, ~ 2000 in soil)	Approximately 123 Gt per year is absorbed by photosynthesis, with 120 Gt per year being released by respiration.
Ocean	41,000	About 92 Gt per year is absorbed but 90 Gt per year is released.
Sedimentary rocks	60 million	Exchanges between rocks and other reservoirs and generally very small.
Fossil fuels	10,000	About 9 Gt per year into atmosphere from combustion of fossil fuels.

©2019 **BIOZONE** International
ISBN: 978-1-927309-71-1
Photocopying Prohibited

9. (a) Open a spreadsheet and type in headings for the rates of exchange and their values (below). Enter column headings for year and the mass of carbon and the effect of this on surface temperature. Enter headings for the other reservoirs in the cells below this (below):

	A	B	C	D	E	F
				Atmospheric carbon dioxide (Gt)	Cumulative gain in temperature (°C)	
1	Exchanges (Gt)		Year			
2				0		
3	Combustion of fossil fuels			1		
4		9		2		
5				3		
6	Absorbed by ocean			4		
7		92		5		
8				6		
9	Released by ocean			7		
10		90		8		
11				9		
12	Rate of photosynthesis			10		
13		123				
14						
15	Rate of respiration					
16		120				
17						
18		Reservoir (C in Gt)				
19	Year	Ocean	Living organisms	Fossil fuels		
20		0				
21		1				
22		2				
23		3				
24		4				
25		5				
26		6				
27		7				
28		8				
29		9				

(b) The change in atmospheric carbon is the sum of the exchanges between the reservoirs. This can be written as a simple spreadsheet formula. In cell D2 enter the value for atmospheric carbon (840). Now, in cell D3 enter the formula for the change in atmospheric carbon: **=D2+$A$4+$A$10+$A$16-$A$7-$A$13**. It is important that the cells and $ symbol are entered correctly so that cell references remain constant.

(c) Copy this formula into down to cell D12 using the fill down feature of the spreadsheet:

C	D	E
Year	Atmospheric carbon dioxide (Gt)	Cumulative gain in temperature (°C)
0	840	
1	=D2+$A$4+$A$10+$A$16-$A$7-$A$13	=(D3-D2)* 0.0017
2	=D3+$A$4+$A$10+$A$16-$A$7-$A$13	=E3+(D4-D3)* 0.0017
3	=D4+$A$4+$A$10+$A$16-$A$7-$A$13	=E4+(D5-D4)* 0.0017

(d) Formulae for the changes in the other reservoirs can be entered in the appropriate cells. First enter the initial value for the reservoir. Fill the cells down to the ten years shown:

18		Reservoir (C in Gt)		
19	Year	Ocean	Living organisms	Fossil fuels
20	0	41000	2610	10000
21	1	=B20+$A$7-$A$10	=C20+$A$13-$A$16	=D20-$A$4
22	2	=B21+$A$7-$A$10	=C21+$A$13-$A$16	=D21-$A$4
23	3	=B22+$A$7-$A$10	=C22+$A$13-$A$16	=D22-$A$4
24	4	=B23+$A$7-$A$10	=C23+$A$13-$A$16	=D23-$A$4

(e) Lastly a formula for the effect of atmospheric carbon on the temperature can be entered into cell E2. A 2016 study found that there is a global temperature increase of 1.7 °C per trillion tonnes of CO_2. We can therefore work out the temperature change per tonne of carbon dioxide and multiply that by the mass of extra carbon dioxide in the atmosphere (remembering that our values are in gigatonnes) to find the cumulative change in temperature over time. In cell E3 enter the formula **=(D4-D3)* 0.0017**. In cell E4 enter the formula **=E3+(D4-D3)* 0.0017**. Fill this down.

(f) Using your spreadsheet, what is the net gain per year of atmospheric carbon dioxide? _____

(g) Explain your answer to 9. (f): _____

_____

_____

_____

(h) You can vary the rate of exchange between the reservoirs. Try changing the rate of combustion. What the effect of increasing the rate of combustion on the amount of carbon dioxide in the atmosphere? What about decreasing it?

(i) Research the carbon cycle, especially the exchanges of carbon between reservoirs. How can the spreadsheet be improved to better model the changes in atmospheric carbon dioxide?

©2019 **BIOZONE** International
ISBN:978-1-927309-71-1
Photocopying Prohibited

10. Use the table on page 173 and your spreadsheet to develop a diagram that models the carbon cycle:

Carbon cycling
▶ The carbon cycle is a natural system in which the element carbon moves between reservoirs via biological and geological pathways.

▶ Humans can alter the carbon cycle by moving carbon from one reservoir (fossil fuels) and adding it to another (the atmosphere) without there being an equivalent return pathway.

EVALUATE: Comparing atmospheric carbon dioxide past and present

▶ The graphs below show the long term changes to atmospheric CO_2.

Changes in atmospheric CO_2

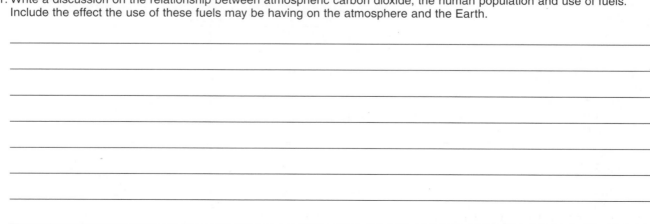

Changes in atmospheric CO_2 since 1000 AD

Expanded in detail on the next graph (note the different vertical scale)

280.0   282.9   383.9

Atmospheric CO_2 (ppm)

Year

Changes in atmospheric CO_2 since 1955

Sources: NASA Goddard Space Flight Center; NOAA / CMDL

Atmospheric CO_2 (ppm)

Year

11. Write a discussion on the relationship between atmospheric carbon dioxide, the human population and use of fuels. Include the effect the use of these fuels may be having on the atmosphere and the Earth.

_____

_____

_____

_____

_____

_____

_____

_____

38 Global Warming and Climate Change

ENGAGE: Venus and Earth

▶ Venus and Earth are sometimes referred to as sister planets due their similar mass and volume. But they are very different in terms of their climatic conditions.

▶ Earth has an atmosphere of mostly nitrogen and oxygen, with carbon dioxide making up less than one percent of the atmosphere. Most of Earth's carbon in its rocks, as carbonates or other minerals. Venus, however, carries most of it carbon in its atmosphere, as carbon dioxide.

▶ The Venusian atmosphere is 96% carbon dioxide and 3% nitrogen. This results in Venus having a catastrophic greenhouse effect, with its surface temperature reaching 464°C. It position closer to the Sun than Earth boiled off any surface water early in its history. Gaseous water is a potent greenhouse gas and helped cause a runaway greenhouse effect. Carbon dioxide in the atmosphere remained there, instead of being rained out as part of a water cycle. This accelerated the heating of the planet, resulting in the cloud blanketed planet we see today.

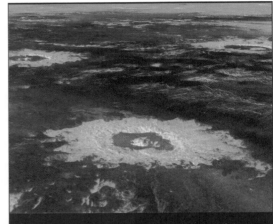

Impact craters on the surface of Venus (false-color image reconstructed from radar data)

1. Describe the differences between the atmospheres of Earth and Venus: _Earth is mostly nitrogen + oxygen whereas Venus is mostly carbon dioxide_

2. How might this explain their different climates? _Venus is much hotter with a much larger greenhouse effect_

EXPLORE: The greenhouse effect

▶ You have seen that the Earth's atmosphere is made up of a mix of gases including nitrogen, oxygen, and water vapor, with small quantities of CO_2, methane, as well as other trace gases (e.g. helium).

▶ Water vapor, CO_2, and methane are called **greenhouse gases** because they produce a warming (or greenhouse) effect, which makes the surface temperature of the Earth less extreme (more moderate).

▶ The **greenhouse effect** is the natural process by which heat is kept within the atmosphere by greenhouse gases, which trap the heat that would normally radiate back into space. About 75% of the natural greenhouse effect is due to water vapor. The next most significant agent is CO_2.

▶ Because of the greenhouse effect, the Earth has a mean surface temperature of about 15°C. This is 33°C warmer than it would have without an atmosphere.

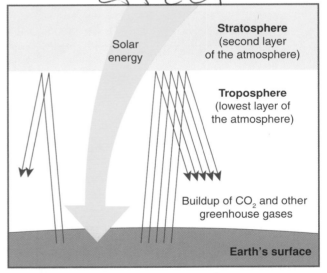

Stratosphere (second layer of the atmosphere)

Solar energy

Troposphere (lowest layer of the atmosphere)

Buildup of CO_2 and other greenhouse gases

Earth's surface

3. (a) What is the greenhouse effect? _the gasses make the surface temp moderate enough to live on_

   (b) What are the two most important gases in causing the greenhouse effect? _CO_2_

   (c) A common analogy for the greenhouse effect is a person wrapped up in a blanket. What part of this "model" represents the Earth and what part represents the atmosphere?
   Stratosphere + gasses bouncing off it

   (d) Adding another blanket to the person in the model would be the same as doing what to the Earth's atmosphere?
   containing it more

EXPLORE: Energy from the Sun

▶ The Sun provides the energy required to power all life on Earth. It produces almost unimaginable amounts of energy, 174 petawatts, or 174 quadrillion joules per second.

▶ The diagram below represents a model of the energy received and reflected by the Earth (known as Earth's **energy budget**). A large amount of incoming solar radiation is absorbed by the atmosphere or reflected off clouds or the Earth's surface.

▶ About 51% of the incoming solar radiation reaches the Earth's surface. Some (0.023%) of this is used by photosynthesis in plants to build organic molecules. The rest drives atmospheric winds and ocean circulation and is eventually radiated back into space.

4. (a) Use the information provided to complete the calculations:

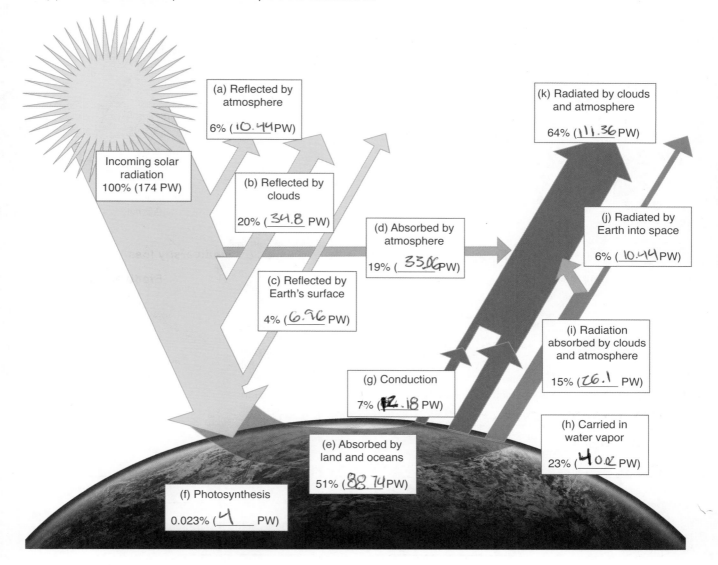

(a) Reflected by atmosphere
6% (10.44 PW)

Incoming solar radiation
100% (174 PW)

(b) Reflected by clouds
20% (34.8 PW)

(c) Reflected by Earth's surface
4% (6.96 PW)

(d) Absorbed by atmosphere
19% (33.06 PW)

(g) Conduction
7% (12.18 PW)

(e) Absorbed by land and oceans
51% (88.74 PW)

(f) Photosynthesis
0.023% (4 PW)

(k) Radiated by clouds and atmosphere
64% (111.36 PW)

(j) Radiated by Earth into space
6% (10.44 PW)

(i) Radiation absorbed by clouds and atmosphere
15% (26.1 PW)

(h) Carried in water vapor
23% (40.02 PW)

(b) What would be the effect of adding more clouds in the atmosphere to the radiation reaching the Earth's surface?

it would create a barrier to get past

(c) How might this affect Earth's surface temperature? it will make it colder blocking the suns heat

(d) The rate of energy radiated by the Earth is in equilibrium (balance) with the energy being received. What would be the effect of increasing the amount of greenhouse gases in the atmosphere on this equilibrium?

it would increase the energy being recieved to balance

EXPLAIN: Feedback loops and global warming

▶ Feedback occurs when the output of a system is used as input in that same system forming a circuit or loop. Any change continues to influence the activity of the system. There are many feedback loops on Earth, both counterbalancing and reinforcing, operating at the same time.

▶ **Counterbalancing** (or negative) **feedback** tends to stabilize a system around a mean (average or stable condition) whereas **reinforcing** (positive) **feedback** tends to increase departures from the mean. The terms negative and positive do not refer to the outcome but to the way the feedback acts in the loop.

▶ The diagram below shows a feedback loop involving components of climate change, desertification (change of fertile land to desert), and biodiversity.

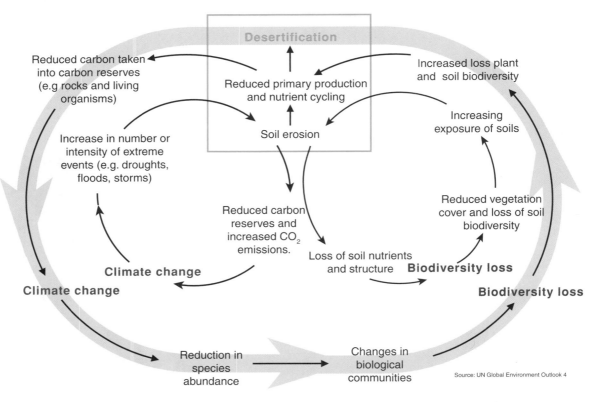

Source: UN Global Environment Outlook 4

5. Does the diagram show a reinforcing (positive) or counterbalancing (negative) feedback loop? Explain your answer:

counterbalancing cause its
stabalizing itself + creating
a balanced atmosphere

6. The diagram below shows a reinforcing (positive) feedback loop for methane in the environment:

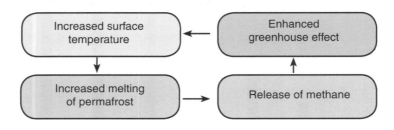

Explain how positive feedback loops like this can cause runaway global warming: there
are holes in the loop
which may create problems
+ release too much + also trap
too much in

©2019 **BIOZONE** International
ISBN:978-1-927309-71-1
Photocopying Prohibited

EXPLORE: Cyclical changes

▶ The energy the Earth receives from the Sun is not constant. The angle of the Earth relative to the Sun affects the energy received by the Northern and Southern Hemispheres resulting in the seasons. The orbit and rotation of the Earth can also play a big part in the amount of solar energy the planet receives.

▶ These changes in orbit, rotation, and tilt can combine to cause extreme changes in the Earth's climate, e.g. producing ice ages. The Earth experiences three main orbital and rotational cycles:

Axial tilt (obliquity)

Relative to its orbital axis, the Earth's rotational axis is at an angle of about 23.4°. This angle is responsible for seasonal changes. The angle is not constant and changes between 22.1° and 24.5° over a period of about 41,000 years. The greater the degree of tilting the greater the difference between the summer and winter seasons.

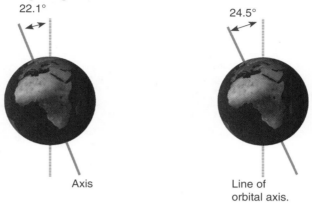

22.1°   24.5°

Axis   Line of orbital axis.

Precession

Like a spinning top, Earth wobbles about its axis. This causes the Earth's axis to describe a cone in space. An entire cycle takes about 26,000 years. Precession alters the direction the Earth's axis is pointing. For example, during June, the Northern Hemisphere is pointed towards the Sun. However 13,000 years ago the occurrence of the seasons would have been opposite to what they are today.

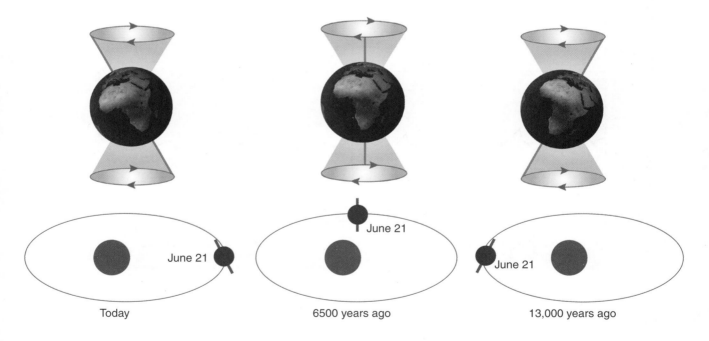

Today   6500 years ago   13,000 years ago

Orbital eccentricity

The Earth's elliptical orbit changes its eccentricity from very nearly circular (eccentricity of 0.000055) to slightly elliptical (eccentricity 0.0679). Circular orbits tend to make the differences between the seasons rather mild, while more elliptical obits make the differences greater. The changes in eccentricity have a cycle of about 100,000 years.

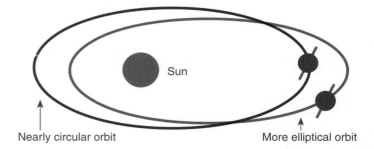

Sun

Nearly circular orbit   More elliptical orbit

©2019 **BIOZONE** International
ISBN: 978-1-927309-71-1

Effect of cycles

▶ The combination of obliquity, precession, and eccentricity change (called Milankovitch cycles) have major effects on the Earth's climate, especially if the extremes of each coincide.

▶ Obliquity, precession, and eccentricity change can all be calculated for hundreds of thousands of years in the past and future. Their effects can then be combined to produce a graph showing the maximum solar radiation received by Earth. Comparisons can then be made between already collected data to identify any correlations:

Milankovitch cycles and past climates data

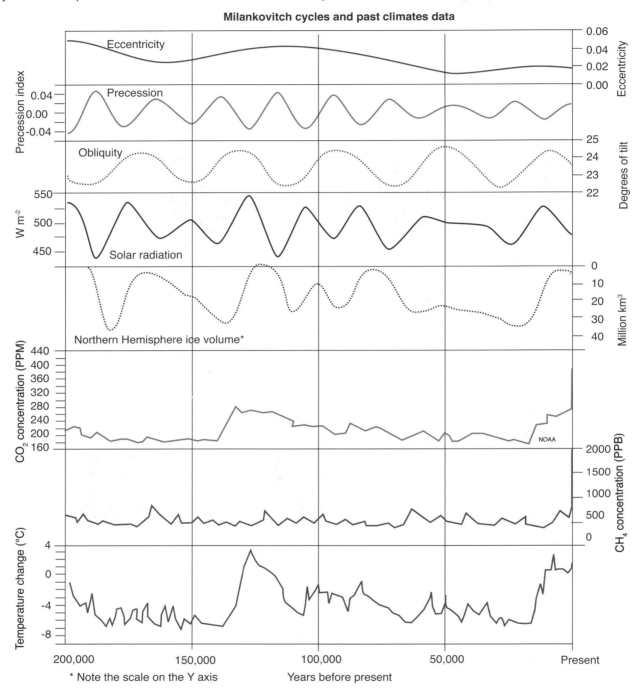

* Note the scale on the Y axis   Years before present

7. Is there any relationship between Milankovitch cycles and Earth's climate? _____

_____

_____

8. You may often hear the statement: "*Global warming is a natural occurrence. It has happened before, it's no different this time*". Using evidence from the graphs above write a response to this statement:

_____

_____

_____

©2019 **BIOZONE** International
ISBN:978-1-927309-71-1
Photocopying Prohibited

EXPLAIN: Ice sheet feedback loops

▶ The surface temperature of the Earth is partly regulated by the amount of ice on its surface, which reflects a large amount of heat into space. However, the area and thickness of the polar sea-ice is rapidly decreasing. From 1980 to 2008 the Arctic summer sea-ice minimum almost halved, decreasing by more than 3 million km². The 2012 summer saw the greatest reduction in sea-ice since the beginning of satellite recordings.

▶ This melting of sea-ice can trigger a cycle where less heat is reflected into space during summer, warming seawater and reducing the area and thickness of ice forming in the winter. At the current rate of reduction, it is estimated that there may be no summer sea-ice left in the Arctic by 2050.

A model where sea ice is retained

Arctic sea-ice summer minimum (white area) **1980**: 7.8 million km²

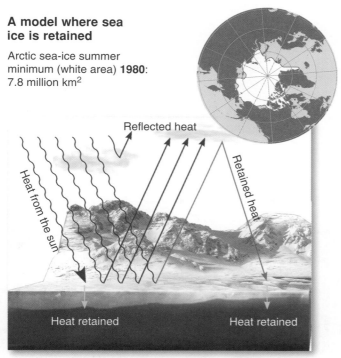

The high **albedo** (reflectivity) of sea-ice helps to maintain its presence. Thin sea-ice has a lower albedo than thick sea-ice. More heat is reflected when sea-ice is thick and covers a greater area. This helps to reduce the sea's temperature.

A model where sea ice is decreasing

Arctic sea-ice summer minimum (white area) **2012**: 3.41 million km²

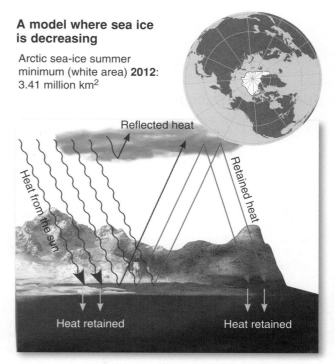

As sea-ice retreats, more non-reflective surface is exposed. Heat is absorbed instead of reflected, warming the air and water and causing sea-ice to form later in the fall than usual. Thinner and less reflective ice forms, perpetuating the cycle.

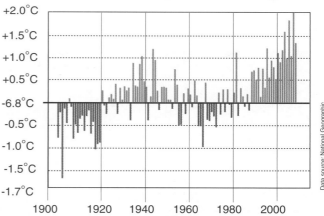

*Figure shows deviation from the average annual surface air temperature over land. Average calculated on the years 1961-2000.

9. (a) Describe what has happened to the extent of Arctic sea ice since 1980: _____

_____

_____

(b) Describe what has happened to Arctic air temperature since the early 1900s: _____

_____

_____

(c) How does low sea-ice albedo and volume affect the next year's sea-ice cover? _____

_____

_____

10. What type of feedback system is operating here? _____

ELABORATE: Building climate models

▸ Climate models are used to understand climate. They are mathematical representations and are very complex because the many different factors affecting the climate must be accounted for.

▸ Scientists use models to break the Earth's climate systems into components that can be more easily studied and understood. As the knowledge about a system grows, more components can be added so that it more closely represents the real system.

▸ The factors affecting the Earth's climate are interconnected. A change in one factor affects another. Scientists manipulate the various components of the model and see what the outcome is.

▸ Climate models are tested by comparing the results from the model to known climate data. A good model will closely match known data.

▸ Climate models have been in use since the 1950s, but these very early versions really only modeled the weather in a particular region.

▸ In 1988, the Intergovernmental Panel on Climate Change (IPCC) was established. Its role is to analyze published climate data and inform the international community about their findings.

▸ Climate models have become more sophisticated and accurate over time, as shown in the diagrams below. This is because our knowledge about factors contributing to climate has increased and also because developments in computing and mathematics have allowed us to predict more complicated scenarios more accurately.

Climate models are used to predict events such as the El Niño Southern Oscillation and future climate patterns.

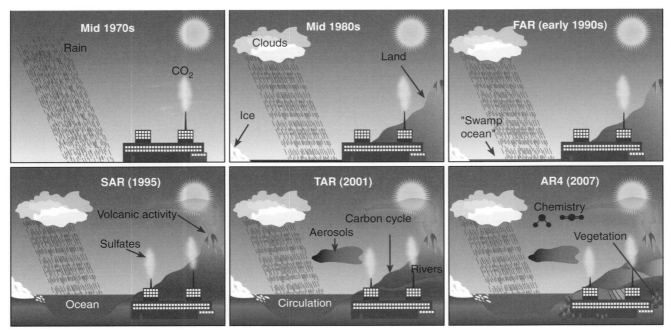

11. (a) How has the complexity of climate models changed over time? _____

_____

_____

_____

_____

(b) Do you think a complex model will provide more accurate forecasts than a simple model? Explain your answer:

_____

_____

_____

_____

_____

ELABORATE: Using geoscience data

▶ Climate change always seems to be mentioned in the same sentences as carbon dioxide, methane, or particles emissions.

▶ However evidence for past climates and climate change can come from a variety of seemingly unrelated areas. Oxygen isotopes in coral is an example.

▶ Oxygen comes in two common isotopes ^{16}O (light) and ^{18}O (heavy). In water, this causes water molecules with ^{18}O to be heavier than water containing ^{16}O. ^{18}O water evaporates less than ^{16}O water. Therefore there is less ^{18}O in the atmosphere and in rain than in seawater. Temperature affects the amount of ^{18}O in the atmosphere.

▶ The data below shows the difference in ^{18}O in rainwater compared to the ocean at different temperatures.

NEED HELP?
See activity 60

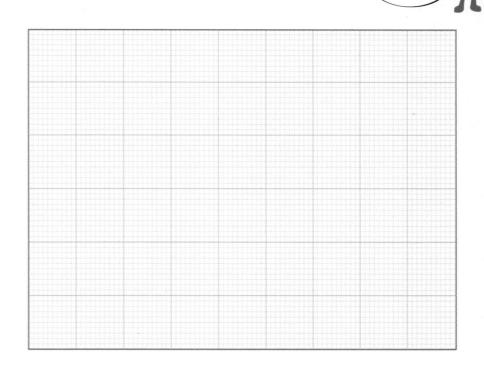

Difference in ^{18}O (%) in rainwater compared to seawater	Temp. °C
-5.5	-57
-5.2	-53
-4.7	-50
-5.0	-44
-4.2	-36
-3.8	-34
-2.8	-27
-3.5	-19
-2.7	-19
-1.6	-10
-1.5	0
-1.9	4
-1.2	1
-0.6	5
-1.0	8
-0.6	11
-0.5	21

12. (a) Draw a scatter graph of local temperature vs the difference in ^{18}O in rainwater compared to seawater.

(b) How is the amount of ^{18}O in rainwater affected by temperature? _____

_____

_____

▶ Coral shells formed in cold waters have a larger proportion of heavy oxygen than shells formed in warmer waters. Measuring oxygen isotopes in core samples taken from corals gives scientists another method of studying climate.

▶ The graph below shows the percentage of ^{18}O in coral samples from 1940 to 1990.

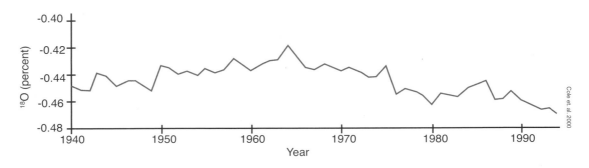

13. Is there any evidence of a warming climate from the graph? Explain your answer:

_____

_____

_____

_____

EVALUATE: Using climate models

▶ There are elements of uncertainty, even in well tested models. The major source is human activity and, in particular, how will consumption of fossil fuels change in the future? The level of greenhouse gases in the atmosphere will have a significant impact on future climate change.

▶ The IPCC often run a number of different scenarios to predict climate change. Between them, the results provide a best-case and worst-case scenario.

▶ The graphs right show possible Earth surface temperature's based on two scenarios. The solid line represents the predicted mean, with the uncertainty shown by the transparent region to either side.

▶ Two possible models are shown (there are others):

RCP2.6:greenhouse gas (GHG) emissions peak between 2010 and 2020

RCP8.5: GHG emissions peak continue to rise throughout the 21st century.

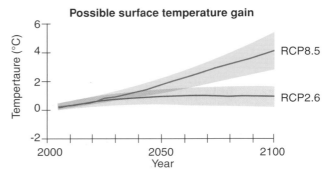

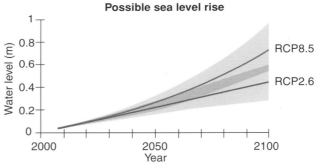

14. Use the graphs above (and any other data in this activity) to make an evidence-based forecast of the future rate of climate change, including an analysis of whether or not the rate will increase or decrease. You may use extra sources of information to further support your analysis. Use extra paper if you need it and attach it to this page:

_____

_____

_____

_____

_____

_____

_____

_____

39 Soil Chemistry and Its Role in Climate Change

ENGAGE: Humans and resources

▶ The image below is a composite showing the Earth at night. The bright areas are cities and population centers. In general, the brighter the area, the bigger the human population there.

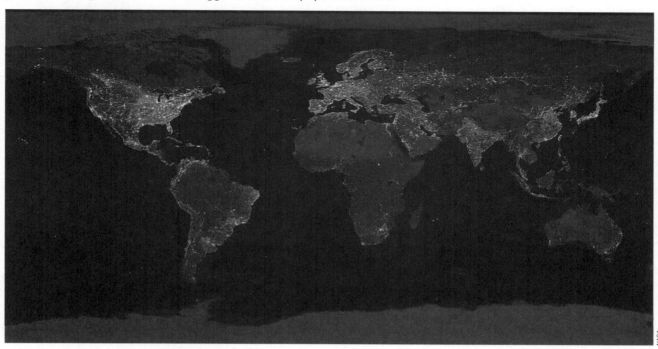

1. The dark areas above are regions with little human settlement. In groups discuss why you think there are no settlements in these places. Is there a common theme for these areas?

_____

_____

_____

_____

_____

_____

EXPLORE: Soils

▶ Soil is a valuable but fragile resource and can be easily damaged by inappropriate farming practices. For example, clearing rainforests for agricultural production has not proved sustainable, as tropical soils are thin and nutrient poor.

▶ Healthy soils are 'alive' with a diverse community of organisms, including bacteria, fungi, and invertebrates. These organisms improve soil structure and help to create **humus** (soil organic matter).

▶ Overgrazing and deforestation may cause **desertification**. When farmers cultivate soils, they must be careful not to compact the soil, which causes it to lose its structure. The continual use of heavy machinery can cause soil compaction.

▶ Soils known as loams consist of around 20% clay, 40% sand, and 40% silt. Loams are generally considered the most ideal soil, as they retain water and nutrients, but drain freely (right).

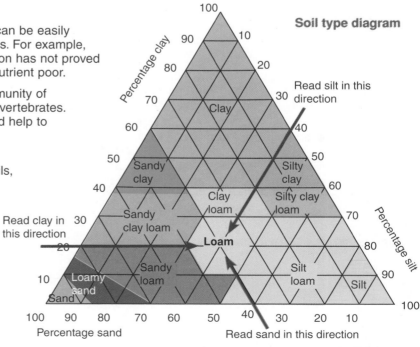

Soil type diagram

©2019 **BIOZONE** International
ISBN: 978-1-927309-71-1
Photocopying Prohibited

CE ETS1.C ESS3.A

2. Explain the term loam and how it applies to a soil's properties: _____

_____

3. Using the scale on soil samples 1 and 2 (right), calculate the percentage of sand, silt and clay in each sample and then use the soil triangle to identify the type of soil:

Soil sample 1: % sand: _____ % silt: _____ % clay: _____

Soil type: _____

Soil sample 2: % sand: _____ % silt: _____ % clay: _____

Soil type: _____

4. How does poor soil management lead to soil degradation? _____

_____

_____

_____

_____

EXPLORE: The chemistry of fertilizers

▶ Mineral fertilizers are used to increase the growth of plants by providing the optimal quantities of the elements they need to carry out life's processes. Plants are the world's food producers. The most important elements they need, which are provided by fertilizers are nitrogen, phosphorus, and potassium.

▶ Nitrogen-containing fertilizers include urea. These are formed using ammonia which is produced by the **Haber process**. This industrial process requires large amounts of energy and combines gaseous nitrogen (which is very stable) and hydrogen. The required energy may be produced from renewable resources (e.g. hydroelectric power) but the hydrogen comes from crude oil. The reaction for the formation of ammonia is $N_2 + 3H_2 \rightarrow 2NH_3$.

▶ The ammonia is converted directly to fertilizer or to ammonium salts that are then used to produce fertilizers.

▶ Phosphorus is almost as important in fertilizers as nitrogen. Like any mineral, it is a finite resource. Some recent estimates put peak phosphorus in 2030, but newer estimates of global reserves dispute this, calculating there is at least 100 years of phosphorus available.

▶ Phosphorus is mined as various ores. Rock phosphate is reacted with sulfuric acid to produce phosphoric acid (H_3PO_4). The phosphoric acid is then reacted with ammonia to produce monoammonium phosphate: $NH_3 + H_3PO_4 \rightarrow (NH_4)H_2PO_4$.

▶ Potassium fertilizer may come as KCl or K_2SO_4. KCl is the most common form and is obtained by mining. K_2SO_4 is produced by reacting KCl with H_2SO_4 at high temperature.

5. (a) Name the three important elements in fertilizers: _____

   (b) Why are these elements in fertilizers? _____

   _____

   _____

6. Briefly describe how the three fertilizers are produced: _____

_____

_____

_____

©2019 **BIOZONE** International
ISBN:978-1-927309-71-1
Photocopying Prohibited

EXPLAIN: Soil acidity

▶ The acidity of soil plays a major role in what can grow there and the growth form of the plant. A good example of this seen in hydrangea flowers.

▶ Hydrangeas have blue flowers when grown in acidic soil (pH <7.0) and pink flowers when grown in neutral to basic soils (≥ 7.0). The color change is a result of the mobility and availability of aluminum ions (Al^{3+}) at different pH.

▶ At low pH Al^{3+} is highly mobile. It binds with other ions and is taken up into the plant, reacting with the usually red/pink pigment in the flowers to form a blue color. In soil pH at or above 7.0, the aluminum ions combine with hydroxide ions to form insoluble and immobile aluminum hydroxide ($Al(OH)_3$). The plant doesn't take up the aluminum and remains red/pink. Other conditions (e.g. high phosphorus levels) can also affect aluminum mobility and availability.

Soil pH <7.0

Soil pH ≥ 7.0

▶ Soil pH is important in pasture land where acidic soil can severely reduce the growth of grass and thus lower farm production, especially on dairy farms. Acidic soils can also promote the growth of weed species, such as buttercup, which compete for space and further reduce grass growth.

▶ Peat soils can be especially acidic with pH vaues as low as 4.5. Farmers can raise the pH closer to neutral by adding lime (right), which is mostly calcium carbonate ($CaCO_3$).

7. Complete the table below to show what conditions cause color change in hydrangea flowers:

	Blue flower	Red/pink flower
pH		
Al^{3+} availability		

8. Litmus paper (right) is used to determine if a solution is acidic or basic. How is hydrangea flower color like litmus paper?

_____

_____

_____

_____

_____

©2019 **BIOZONE** International
ISBN: 978-1-927309-71-1

ELABORATE: Soil chemistry and climate change

▶ Nitrogen fertilizers are the single biggest type of fertilizer applied to crops. They help plants grow leaves and green material, and so are especially important in pasture land.

▶ However over-fertilizing can lead to nitrogen pollution and an increase in the soil bacteria that produce nitrous oxide (N_2O). Nitrous oxide is a greenhouse gas that has 300 times more heat trapping ability than carbon dioxide.

▶ Studies in the late 2000s found that soil bacteria can produce up 5 kg of N_2O for every 100 kilograms of nitrogen fertilizer applied. Considering the huge tonnage of nitrogen fertilizers added to crops each year, that is also a large volume of N_2O gas produced each year.

▶ Atmospheric concentration of nitrous oxide has increased from around 270 ppb in 1750 to 320 ppb today. The most dramatic increase occurred in the 1960s when inexpensive synthetic nitrogen fertilizers became readily available.

▶ The massive increase in fertilizer use sparked the "**green revolution**" when crop production rapidly increased. This in turn resulted in a rapid increase in the human population, from around 3 billion people in 1960 to 7.5 billion today.

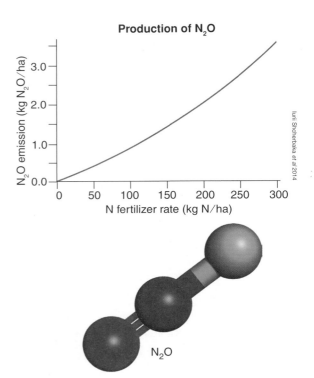

Production of N_2O

Finding the human fingerprint

Nitrogen occurs as two isotopes ^{15}N and ^{14}N. When nitrogen is plentiful, soil bacteria preferentially use ^{14}N. This can be used to trace N_2O gas to fertilized crops. By measuring the ^{15}N to ^{14}N ratio in N_2O gas sampled over time it is possible to see a change in the ratio towards more ^{14}N.

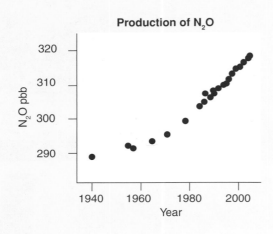

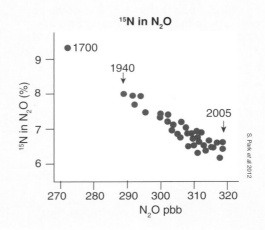

9. Work in groups to research the costs and benefits of fertilizer use. You should use a range of digital and print resources for your reference material. Try to come up with answers to the following points:

▶ What impact have synthetic fertilizers had on the environment and the human populations?

▶ Is there a compromise between the need to produce food for the human population and the effect on the environment? Use the space below to summarize your ideas, then as a group produce a short media presentation on your findings:

©2019 **BIOZONE** International
ISBN:978-1-927309-71-1
Photocopying Prohibited

EVALUATE: Soils, agriculture, and solutions to climate change

▶ You have seen how human populations rely on healthy productive soils in order to produce enough food and increased production has historically been driven by the application of fertilizers. Yet fertilizers and industrialized farming practices are costly in terms of energy.

▶ The challenge for farmers and researchers now and in the future is to manage the physical, chemical, and biological processes controlling soil carbon, nitrogen dynamics, and greenhouse gas emissions from soils.

▶ The table below outlines seven agricultural and land management practices that aim to provide for human needs into the future and reduce greenhouse emissions from agriculture. **Carbon sequestration** is important. This is the removal of carbon from the atmosphere to storage.

What does a sustainable future for farming look like

Farming practice	Definition	Effect on greenhouse gas emissions	Environmental benefits
1 Cover crops	Crops planted to protect and improve soil and nutrients rather than for harvest, especially when the land would otherwise have been barren.	Sequesters carbon in plants and soil. Adding a cover crop to a conservation tillage system can nearly double the rate of carbon sequestration.	Decrease in soil erosion, better retention of nutrients, increased soil organic matter, improved water quality.
2 Conservation tillage	Leaving 30% or more of the crop residue behind after planting. No-till avoids tilling completely (soil is undisturbed).	Soil is disturbed less, so carbon storage in the soil is increased. Reduces carbon dioxide emissions from farm equipment.	Reduces erosion and water pollution because runoff from the soil is reduced.
3 Organic agriculture	Crop rotation, compost, and biological pest control are used to maintain soil productivity and control pests without synthetic pesticides and fertilizers.	On average, organic agriculture involves 60% less direct energy input compared to intensive production. Soils under organic production can store more carbon.	Organic farming has been shown to lead to better retention of soil nutrients, reduced rates of soil erosion, and reduced runoff of water and nutrients.
4 Grazing land management	Modifying grazing practices to reduce greenhouse gas emissions (e.g. rotational grazing and reduced livestock densities).	Reduces soil compaction and maintains ground cover so increases carbon sequestration by the soil. Lower stocking rates reduce emissions of CH_4 and N_2O.	Reduces erosion and water pollution because ground cover is maintained and runoff is reduced.
5 Sustainable forest management	Managing plants to provide wildlife habitat, increase biodiversity, and capture carbon.	Increased plant growth increases carbon sequestration in plant biomass.	Improves water quality and ecosystem resilience (ability of the ecosystem to resist damage and recover from disturbance).
6 On-farm anaerobic digesters	Digesters extract methane from animal waste. The methane can be used as fuel to generate electricity.	Significantly reduces methane emissions. Potential to significantly reduce fossil fuel consumption.	Improved air quality and reduced odor.
7 Retaining or restoring native ecosystems	Returning land its natural state or preventing them from being destroyed through development.	Improved carbon sequestration in accumulated leaf litter, increased organic matter in soils, and increased plant root mass.	Reduced erosion and improved water quality. Improves ecosystem resilience overall.

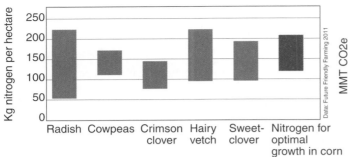

Figure 1: Cover crops can provide the nitrogen needed for optimal growth of corn.

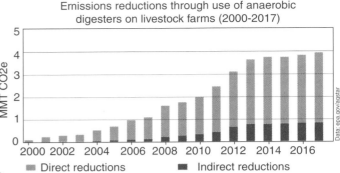

Figure 2: Since 2000, anaerobic digesters on livestock farms in the US have reduced direct and indirect emissions by 34.6 MMTCO2e (million metric tons CO_2 equivalent).

Treatment	Soil loss (tonne/ha)
Bare plot	73.8
Conventional tilling	17.3
Minimal tillage	2.1

Table 1: Soil loss for three tillage systems on a typical agricultural soil in Venezuela.

	Moisture retention in soil (%)			
	Maize	Pigeon peas	Soybeans	Cowpeas
Plowed	9.7	10.8	7.3	12.3
No tillage	13.3	12.1	10.6	15.4

Table 2: Effect of tillage regime on soil moisture retention at 0-10 cm depth under different crops two weeks after planting.

Site	Regime	Soil C (tonne C/ha)
Site 1	MiG_{21}	46.6*
	Ext_{50+}	40.4*
Site 2	MiG_{25}	36.2
	Ext_{50+}	32.2
Site 3	MiG_5	59.5*
	Ext_{50+}	45.1*
Site 4	MiG_3	50.9*
	Ext_{50+}	42.8*

Table 3: Total soil carbon for the top 50 cm of soil at four sites (VA, USA). **MiG** = Management-intensive grazing or short rotational grazing. **Ext** = extensive grazing (low stocking continuous). Subscript refers to number of years under that regime. Asterisks indicate a significant difference between management treatments.

Data from numerous field studies indicate short rotation grazing regimes (MiG) can increase productivity and lead to substantially higher soil carbon. In one study of grazing regimes in the southeastern US (Conant, 2003), total organic soil carbon average 22% greater under MiG. However, the benefits are dependent on available moisture and the findings may not apply to arid lands or during drought conditions.

10. (a) Divide your class into seven groups. Each group should choose one of the farming practices described on the previous page and evaluate its features and design in terms of its capacity for sustainable use of a resource (soil) and its ability to sequester carbon and reduce greenhouse gas emissions. Some additional data has been provided in the tables and figures above. You may use this information and any other research or case studies to support your evaluation (visit the **BIOZONE Resource Hub** for more information). Summarize the main points of your group's evaluation in a shared document, including any supporting evidence.

(b) Present your group's findings to the class. The class must then decide collectively what goal and targets are required to conserve the soil resource and best manage it to sequester carbon.

(c) It is not practical to implement all of these farming practices at the same time. In your original groups, **select two** farming practices that you think are compatible and would provide the greatest benefits in terms of use of the soil resource and reducing greenhouse gas emissions. Write your two practices below and briefly explain why you made this choice. Include a summary of the likely costs and benefits involved, including social, environmental, energetic, and economic considerations. Share your findings with the class.

40 Living With Limited Resources

ENGAGE: Recycling in your neighborhood

▶ Many cities, towns, and neighborhoods have recycling facilities. Some require a person to take the recycling to a specific center. Others have trucks than pick up the recycling from the curb.

▶ Some places only recycle certain materials while others recycle a wide range of materials.

1. (a) Does your neighborhood have recycling collection? _____

   (b) Do you have to sort the recycling into different containers or is there just the one container?

   _____

   _____

   (c) Does the recycling need to be cleaned before pick up?

   _____

2. When you are out and about (e.g. at the mall) are there recycling facilities? Are the garbage cans separated out into plastics and glass for example, or is there only one garbage can for all?

   _____

   _____

EXPLORE: Waste management

▶ Much of the waste produced by industrialized countries contains valuable resources, which could be used again if properly processed. As resources become limited and competition for them grows, individuals and companies are exploring ways to use resources as efficiently as possible. This includes reusing waste materials.

▶ Although most materials can theoretically be reused or recycled, there are always some situations where it is impractical. In those cases, waste may be burned to extract energy or taken directly to a landfill (garbage dump).

▶ The schematic below shows an integrated resource recycling scheme, which reduces waste as much as possible.

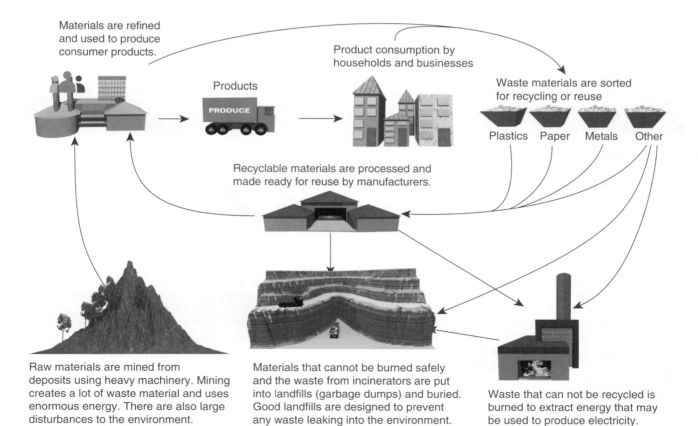

Materials are refined and used to produce consumer products.

Product consumption by households and businesses

Products

PRODUCE

Waste materials are sorted for recycling or reuse

Plastics Paper Metals Other

Recyclable materials are processed and made ready for reuse by manufacturers.

Raw materials are mined from deposits using heavy machinery. Mining creates a lot of waste material and uses enormous energy. There are also large disturbances to the environment.

Materials that cannot be burned safely and the waste from incinerators are put into landfills (garbage dumps) and buried. Good landfills are designed to prevent any waste leaking into the environment.

Waste that can not be recycled is burned to extract energy that may be used to produce electricity.

CE ETS1.C ESS3.A

3. List three reasons why waste should be recycled: _____

_____

_____

4. Why is putting waste in a landfill the least preferred option of a waste management scheme? _____

_____

_____

5. (a) In what way is incinerating (burning) waste a useful part of a management scheme? _____

_____

_____

   (b) Why is incineration one of the least preferred options in a management scheme? _____

_____

EXPLAIN: Recycling, reusing, energy, and cost

▶ Recycling, like any resource extraction method, requires energy. This may be in the form of collecting and sorting material, transport to manufacturers, and the energy used in melting or remelting a material. In order for recycling to be advantageous, it must cost less energy than producing a new item or material from the original resource.

▶ Some materials returned from recycling do not return the same quality of product as new material (e.g. wood) and are often made into inferior product (a process called down-cycling). In these cases, new material needs to be added, so recycling is not a closed loop or a total solution. However, it does significantly reduce the need for new materials, extending the life of the resource and reducing the energy spent on producing new material.

▶ In general, metals can be 100% recycled. They are relatively easy to melt down and recover from scrap. Aluminum requires 96% less energy to make from recycled cans than it does to process from bauxite (ore). What matters the most when producing materials is the cost of extracting and refining the raw materials versus the cost of collecting, sorting, and reprocessing used materials.

▶ New technology for recycling has helped to reduce the cost of collecting and sorting. For example, in San Francisco, no pre-separation of recyclable material is needed. Although some workers are still required, most of the separation work is carried out by the city's state-of-the-art recycling facility. Magnets remove steel, eddy currents separate aluminum, and vacuum tubes and separators remove plastics.

Glass recycling. Modern recycling plants can sort materials automatically using the physical properties of the materials.

Energy savings using recycled material

Recycled material	Energy saving (%)
Aluminum	95
Plastic	88
Copper	75
Steel	60
Paper	60
Glass	34

Reusing sometimes takes a while

▶ Reusable objects, such as reusable shopping bags or take away coffee cups, have recently become fashionable. However many people do not realize how long these things need to be reused before they become "environmentally friendly". For example a single use paper cup has a cost of production and a cost of dumping. These costs are fixed for every cup A reusable cup has a much higher cost of production and a cost of cleaning. In this case, the production cost reduces over time while the cleaning cost remains the same.

Energy cost of reusable vs disposable cups

Cup type	Cup mass (g)	Material specific energy (MJ/kg)	Energy per cup (MJ/kg)
Ceramic	292	48	14
Plastic	59	107	6.3
Glass	199	28	5.5
Paper	8.3	66	0.55
Foam	1.9	104	0.20

©2019 **BIOZONE** International
ISBN:978-1-927309-71-1
Photocopying Prohibited

▶ The data at the bottom of the opposite page and the graph (right) show how many uses it takes before recyclable items (glass, plastic, or ceramic) reach the same energy per cup value as single use items (paper and foam). It does not account for the cost of disposal.

Energy cost per cup per use

Ceramic ······ Paper ·······
Plastic —— Foam - - - - -
Glass - - - -

Energy per use (MJ) vs Number of uses

6. Explain why recycling saves energy compared to mining and refining new materials:

_____
_____
_____
_____

7. Estimate the energy per use after 100 uses of:

(a) A foam cup: _____

(b) A ceramic cup: _____

(c) A plastic cup: _____

EVALUATE: Costs and convenience

8. You are the mayor of a city. Counselors have come to you with two possible recycling programs for the city. Evaluate the programs from the information below and decide which would be most effective in increasing participation in recycling from the public, reduce the amount of waste being taken to the land fill, and be the most cost effective (considering social, environmental, and economic costs).

System one: Recycling is mixed (all recyclable items in one bin). A single hauler picks up curbside recycling, which is charged to users at a fixed fee (every household pays the same regardless of waste generated). Drop off facilities are available. High value recyclable waste, such as aluminum, is paid for at the recycling station on a per kilogram basis.

System two: Recycling must be presorted into glass, plastic and metals, and paper. Households can choose between two haulers which charge a pay-as-you-throw fee (the more waste generated the more they are charged. Charges also depend on the hauler). Households can bypass this fee by taking recyclables to a recycling facility for free. High value recyclable wastes such as aluminum cans are not paid for.

In both systems, a separate hauler takes rubbish to the landfill. This is charged at a fixed fee for all households.

Present you reasoned decision here. You can use more paper if you wish and attach it to this page: _____

41 It's Heating Up Revisited

In this chapter you have been shown several lines of evidence for global warming and climate change and some of its possible causes. You should now be able to better describe the complex phenomenon of climate change and the evidence that supports it. You should also be able to explain the possible causes of climate change.

1. Write a short essay on the evidence for climate change, the possible effects of climate change, and humanity's role in enhancing or reducing these effects. Publish your work in a shared forum so that others can comment or critique your work and you can develop or strengthen your writing as needed. Use the space below to create a mind map (network of connected ideas) to help you plan your essay:

©2019 **BIOZONE** International
ISBN:978-1-927309-71-1
Photocopying Prohibited

42 Summative Assessment

1. (a) Draw a diagram in the space below to show absorption and reflection of incoming solar radiation as it arrives from the Sun and passes through the Earth's atmosphere to the surface and is reflected back into space:

(b) Describe the greenhouse effect and explain why it is important to Earth's climate: _____

_____

_____

_____

(c) If the concentration of carbon dioxide in the atmosphere in the system you drew in 1(a) increased, how would this affect the balance of energy coming in and going out of the system?

_____

_____

_____

2. (a) Use the following labels to complete the diagram of the carbon cycle shown right: *atmosphere, geosphere, oceans, respiration (R), photosynthesis (PS)*.

(b) Add arrows to show deforestation (D) and combustion (C) of fossil fuels:

(c) Combustion and deforestation result in another 9 petagrams of carbon being added to the carbon cycle. Add this value to the diagram.

(d) About 3 petagrams is taken up by photosynthesis and 2 petagrams is taken up by the oceans. Add these values to the appropriate labels on the diagram.

(e) How much extra carbon is actually added to the atmosphere by deforestation and combustion?

_____

Exchanges

Land, plants, animals, soil

Burial   Weathering

Coal, oil, gas

3. Explain the difference between reinforcing (positive) and counterbalancing (negative) feedback loops and give one example of each that affects the Earths climate:

_____

_____

_____

_____

©2019 **BIOZONE** International
ISBN: 978-1-927309-71-1
Photocopying Prohibited

SC   CE   ETS1.C   ESS3.D   ESS3.A   ESS2.D

4. We've all heard of "fake news". It refers to "news" articles or reports that supposedly report facts but are more sensationalist than anything else. The internet is full of "fake news" posted on various websites. Sometimes it appears on reputable websites including news networks that have posted an article without realizing the errors in it or checking the legitimacy of the claims. At other times "fake news" is deliberately posted on websites that push a specific agenda (aim), which may be a climate-related, social, or political issue.

The two articles below are articles on climate change. One article contains factual information or published data deliberately misused to provide evidence for its argument. That other uses factual data presented without any bias.

Article 1: Sunspots and climate change 1

The Sun is the ultimate producer of climate on our planet. The energy the Earth receives from the Sun drives short term cycles, including weather systems. The energy output from the Sun changes over long term cycles and these changes directly affect the Earth's long term climate. Some of these long term changes are related to sunspots. Historical data clearly shows that the Sun's energy output is related to global temperature. Current data from modern observations also shows the current trend in global warming is directly related to sunspot cycles. It is often stated that global warming began around the 1850s with the advent of the Industrial Revolution when carbon dioxide started to be produced in large quantities. But temperature data shows a warming trend since the 1600s. If anything, the current warming is just part of a longer cycle and temperatures are just returning to near where they were around a thousand years ago.

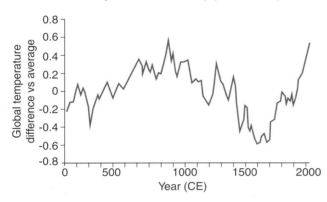

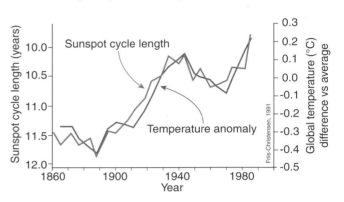

Article 2: Sunspots and climate change 2

The solar cycle has an average period of 11 years over which sunspots develop and fade on the surface of the Sun. During the solar cycle, the energy output of the Sun also changes. Along with this, the total length of the solar cycle indicates the energy output. A longer cycle length indicates a cooler Sun. Although these changes to the Sun's energy output have influenced the Earth climate in the past (and still do now) the major influence on the planet's current warming trend is the rapid rise in anthropogenic (man-made) CO_2. Changes in global surface temperature are strongly correlated with rises in CO_2, especially in the time period from 1980 to today. Although global temperature has risen since the end of the ice age (around 4 to 7 °C in 5000 years (NASA)) the global temperature has increased 0.8°C in the last century alone, roughly 10 times faster than the rate of ice age recovery (NASA).

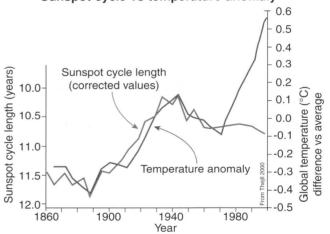

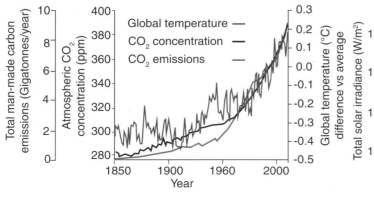

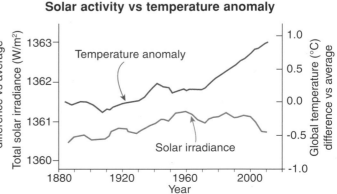

©2019 **BIOZONE** International
ISBN:978-1-927309-71-1
Photocopying Prohibited

Your task is to read the articles on the opposite page and determine which is legitimate and which is "fake news". Present a reasoned argument for your decision. You may need to do some extra research around some of the claims in each article. However if you look carefully there are clues in each article and its supporting material that will help you decide which is fake and which is not.

5. A mining company explores two potential surface mining areas using a drill to provide core samples. The costs and mineral content of each site is shown below:

	Area 1 (surface area approximately 20 km²)	Area 2 (surface area approximately 14 km²)
% gold (value per kilogram = $43,000)	0.00008%	0.00005%
% silver (value per kilogram = $650)	0.005%	0.007%
% copper (value per kilogram = $4.70)	0.08%	0.2%
% lead (value per kilogram = $1.80)	2%	3%
% zinc (value per kilogram = $2.15)	1.2%	2.1%
Average depth of ores (m)	100 m	50 m
Access to mine site	Moderate	Difficult
Start up cost	$40 million	$50 million
Extraction rate (total rock + ore per day)	5000 tonnes	4800 tonnes
Cost of running mine facility	$9 per tonne	$7.40 per tonne
Cost of restoring the environment per km²	$1,200,000	$2,100,000
Approximate mine lifetime	15 years	12 years

Use the data to decide which of these areas is the most suitable for mining, giving any reasons and calculations to support your decision:

_____

_____

_____

_____

_____

_____

_____

_____

_____

_____

_____

_____

_____

6. **Cars and fossil fuel use**
    Some students were discussing how to reduce the air pollution caused by cars. Each made a statement (below):

    Student 1: "Cars using gasoline have higher fuel consumption than cars using diesel. One liter of diesel takes you further than one liter of gasoline. Therefore all cars should run on diesel so that we use less fossil fuel, which produces less carbon dioxide and is better for the environment."

    Student 2: "Diesels produce more particulate matter from the exhaust and more NOx gases. This creates smog and more air pollution. Therefore diesels should be banned."

    Student 3: "We should use electric cars because they don't use fossil fuels or produce carbon dioxide."

    Student 4: "If everyone used electric cars there would no off-peak time for electricity generation. The power stations would have to use more fuel, which can produce carbon dioxide anyway. And we don't know the effect of used batteries on the environment."

    Student 5: "People should be encouraged to use public transport. That would reduce the number of cars on the road."

    Student 6: "People aren't going to want to give up their cars for something that's less convenient or more expensive."

    Research these arguments. Construct an argument on what the solution (to vehicular pollution) might be, given that people want more powerful cars, but also want to reduce air pollution. You argument may be presented in the form of a media presentation or poster.

©2019 **BIOZONE** International
ISBN:978-1-927309-71-1
Photocopying Prohibited

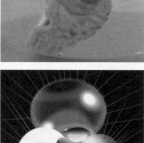

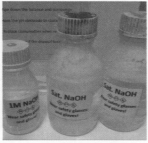

Instructional Segment 6

Reaction Dynamics and Ocean Acidification

Activity number

Anchoring Phenomenon

Seashells by the seashore: The chemistry of seashells.

43

How can you alter chemical equilibria and reaction rates?

☐ 1 Recall your investigation of reaction rates in chapter 4 and the effect of changes in temperature and concentration of reactants to the rate at which a reaction occurs. The reaction you investigated (bleaching of colored water) was not reversible. However many reactions in chemistry are reversible. Investigate this using HCl, NaOH and their effect on red and blue litmus paper.

44

☐ 2 Many chemical systems remain stable even though components within the system change. A dynamic equilibrium is an example of stability where reactions in one direction are equal and opposite to those in the reverse direction. Investigate the concept of dynamic equilibrium using a beaker containing water and covered with cling wrap. Use a model system to demonstrate how changes to reactants, products, or reaction rate affect the equilibrium that is established. Use the example of the equilibrium reaction between Fe^{3+} and SCN^- to explain how changing the conditions in a chemical system can alter equilibrium in favor of the reactants or products. Explain the results in terms of Le Châtlier's principle and then use this to explain the common ion effect.

44 48

☐ 3 Investigate the pH of common laboratory acids and bases as well as a range of common household substances. What does the pH scale represent? To understand the pH scale better, calculate the pH of solutions with known H^+ concentration and the (conversely) the H^+ concentration of solutions of known pH. Use your understanding of chemical equilibria to explain why some acids and bases are weak (do not fully dissociate when in water).

46

☐ 4 Recall from your earlier model of the carbon cycle that the oceans act as a large reservoir for CO_2 from the atmosphere. Analyze data showing trends in CO_2 concentrations in the ocean and atmosphere as evidence of counterbalancing feedback between these two Earth systems. How would this feedback affect the rate of Earth's warming? Explain the effect of CO_2 on the pH of water in terms of carbon dioxide chemistry. Investigate how this equilibrium reaction is affected by temperature and salinity. Use the results of your investigations to predict the effect of a warmer Earth on the ability of the oceans to act as a carbon sink.

46

☐ 5 Describe the relationship between chemistry of carbon dioxide in the oceans and the availability of carbonate to shell-building marine organisms. Examine the evidence for the effect of higher CO_2 on aragonite saturation and the health and survival of shell-building marine creatures such as corals. What does the evidence indicate? Now you can use your understanding of chemical equilibria to explain these observations. Do the biological effects of lower ocean pH extend beyond the effects on shell-builders? How might fish be affected and is there any evidence for lower pH causing changes in physiology or behavior? How might changes to marine creatures affect ocean diversity in general?

46 47

How can you predict the relative quantities of products in a chemical reaction?

☐ 6 Apply your understanding of Le Châtlier's principle to processes in industrial chemistry to explain how you would increase the amount of a desired product in a chemical reaction. Think about how changes in pressure and temperature shift the equilibrium forward or backwards and describe how the system could be designed to achieve your specific goal. Suitable industrial systems include the production of ammonia in the Haber process, the production of sulfuric acid, and the production of methanol.

44 45 48

43 Seashells by the Seashore

ANCHORING PHENOMENON: The chemistry of seashells

What's in a seashell?

▶ The photos below show calcium carbonate and a seashell reacting in hydrochloric acid. Notice that a gas is being produced during the reaction. In both cases, when the gas was tested, it proved to be carbon dioxide.

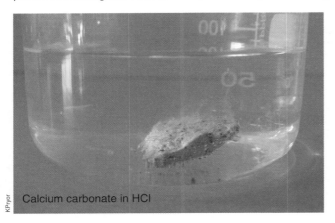
Calcium carbonate in HCl

Seashell in HCl

▶ Carbon dioxide gas is produced when carbonates react with acids. For the reaction of calcium carbonate with hydrochloric acid, the equation is $2HCl + CaCO_3 \rightarrow CaCl_2 + CO_2 + H_2O$.

▶ The reaction solutions were tested to identify any ions present. Calcium can be identified by adding sodium hydroxide. A white precipitate (solid) of calcium hydroxide forms. It remains even if excess sodium hydroxide is added. Both solutions produced positive results for calcium ions.

Thin seashells

▶ Studies of the shells of many marine organisms with calcium carbonate shells have shown their shells appear to have become thinner over time. The graph below compares shell weight in the planktonic foraminifera *Globerigina bulloides* (below) over time. Bars indicate ±1 standard deviation of the mean.

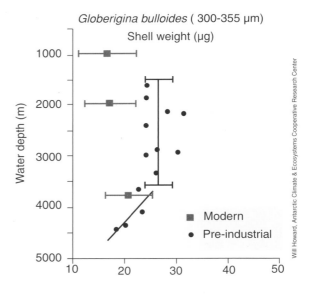

Globerigina bulloides (300-355 µm)

1. What are seashells mostly composed of? _____

2. Discuss in groups what might be causing sea shells to thin. Summarize your ideas: _____

_____

_____

_____

_____

44 Reversible Reactions

ENGAGE: Reversible reactions

▶ Many of the chemical reactions you have studied so far have been ones that go to completion. This means all the reactants combine to form products, with none left over when the reaction finishes. Sometimes reactions are reversible, the products can reform back into reactants.

1. Decide if the "reaction" is reversible:

   (a) A cake baking: _____

   (b) Scrambling eggs: _____

   (c) Water evaporating when being heated in a closed container:

   _____

   (d) Paint drying on a wooden board: _____

   (e) Blue copper sulfate crystals being heated to produce white copper sulfate crystals:

   _____

How easily can you "unmake" this cake?

2. Explain why the following are not reversible reactions under normal conditions:

   (a) Laundry drying on a line: _____

   _____

   _____

   (b) Adding magnesium ribbon to dilute HCl: _____

   _____

   _____

   (c) Paper burning: _____

   _____

   _____

EXPLORE: A reversible reaction

INVESTIGATION 6.1: Reversible reactions with red and blue litmus.   See appendix for equipment list.

 Caution is required when handling HCl and NaOH as they are corrosive. Wear protective eyewear, gloves and clothing.   CORROSIVE

1. Add 5 mL of dilute HCl to a test tube. Into a separate test tube add 5 mL of dilute NaOH solution.

2. Hold a piece of red litmus paper so 1 cm of the end is in the NaOH solution. Record the color change:

   _____

3. Now place the same 1 cm end of the litmus paper into the HCl. Record the color change:

   _____

4. Place the end the litmus paper back into the NaOH. Record the color change:

   _____

5. Place the end of the litmus paper in the HCl one more time. Record the color change:

   _____

©2019 **BIOZONE** International
ISBN: 978-1-927309-71-1
Photocopying Prohibited

SC SSM CE PS1.B

6. Now hold blue litmus paper so that 1 cm of the end is in the HCl. Record the color change:

_____

7. Now place the same 1 cm end of the litmus paper into the NaOH. Record the color change:

_____

8. Place the end the litmus paper back into the HCl. Record the color change:

_____

9. Place the end of the litmus paper in the NaOH one more time. Record the color change:

_____

▸ The chemical used in both the red and blue litmus paper is litmus. Litmus in the red form can be written as HLt and litmus in the blue form can be written as Lt^-.

▸ The equation for placing red litmus into NaOH is:

$HLt_{(aq)}$ (red) + $NaOH_{(aq)}$ → $H_2O_{(l)}$ + $Na^+_{(aq)}$ + $Lt^-_{(aq)}$ (blue)

▸ And placing blue litmus into HCl can be written as:

$Lt^-_{(aq)}$ (blue) + $HCl_{(aq)}$ → $HLt_{(aq)}$ (red) + $Cl^-_{(aq)}$

▸ In the equations above the compounds and ions involved in the color change are HLt, H^+, and Lt^-.

Litmus powder

3. (a) Write an equation for the color change of red litmus to blue litmus:

_____

(b) Write an equation for the color change of blue litmus to red litmus:

_____

4. (a) Under what conditions does HLt form? _____

(b) Under what conditions does Lt^- form? _____

EXPLORE: Forwards and backwards

▸ Some reactions do not go to completion. As the product is made, some of those products break up back into reactants so that there is always some reactant left, even when the reaction appears to have finished.

▸ This can be represented by the general equation $aA + bB \rightleftharpoons cC + dD$.

▸ The symbol $\rightleftharpoons$ means the reaction goes in both directions. The forward direction is left to right. The reverse direction is right to left.

5. Imagine a beaker half full of water (below right). The beaker is sealed with cling wrap. Some of the water will evaporate to form gaseous H_2O. At some point the rate of gas forming will equal the rate of condensation.

(a) What might happen to the rate of gas forming if the beaker is warmed by placing it in the sun, or on a heat pad?

_____

(b) How might this affect the amount gas in the system compared to the liquid water?

_____

(c) The beaker is placed in a fridge. What would happen to the rate of gas formation now?

_____

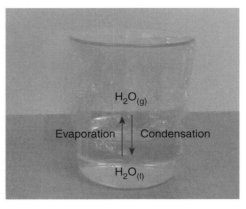

$H_2O_{(g)}$

Evaporation | Condensation

$H_2O_{(l)}$

©2019 **BIOZONE** International
ISBN:978-1-927309-71-1
Photocopying Prohibited

(d) How would this affect the amount of gaseous water compared to liquid water in the system?

_____

▶ The equation for the system is: $H_2O_{(l)} \rightleftharpoons H_2O_{(g)}$

6. (a) In which direction does adding heat drive the system? _____

   (b) In which direction does removing heat drive the system? _____

INVESTIGATION 6.2: Modeling equilibrium reactions.
See appendix for equipment list.

1. **Reaction A**: Fill a large beaker or basin (e.g. 1 L) to three quarters full with water. This is the "reactants". Add a few drops of food coloring (optional) to help see the water more clearly. Beside the full beaker, place an equal sized empty beaker or basin. This is the "products".

2. Place a small (e.g. 100 mL) beaker into the full reactants basin so that it fills (do not force fill it). Transfer the contents to the products basin.

3. Now place the 100 mL beaker into the products basin, let it fill, and transfer the contents back to the reactants basin.

4. Continue this back and forth process until the volumes of reactants and products remains steady.

5. At this point you have reached an **equilibrium**.

6. **Reaction B**: Now add some more reactant to the "reaction" by filling the reactant basin until it is three quarters full again. Continue the back and forth process as in steps 2 and 3 until the equilibrium is re-established.

7. **Reaction C**: Now remove some product by emptying the products basin to waste until it is one quarter full. Continue the back and forth process as in steps 2 and 3 until the equilibrium is re-established.

8. **Reaction D**: Now empty the products basin and reset the reactants basin to three quarters full. You will now alter the rate of the forward and reverse reactions. Use the 100 mL beaker for the forward reaction, transferring reactants to products. Use a 50 mL beaker to transfer products to the reactants.

9. Continue this until an equilibrium is reached.

10. **Reaction E**: Reset the reactants and products again. You will now change the rate of the backwards reaction. Use the 50 mL beaker for the forwards reaction (from reactants to products) and the 100 mL beaker for the backwards reaction. Continue this until an equilibrium is reached.

7. (a) Describe the rate of the forward reaction compared to the backward reaction at the start of reaction A:

_____

_____

   (b) Describe the rate of the forward reaction compared to the backward reaction as reaction A neared and then reached equilibrium:

_____

_____

   (c) What happened in reaction B when more reactant was added to the reaction? _____

_____

_____

(d) What happened in reaction C when some product was removed from the reaction? _____

_____

_____

_____

(e) Describe the reaction that occurred in reaction D in terms of reactants, products, and the equilibrium that was established:

_____

_____

_____

(f) Describe the reaction that occurred in reaction E in terms of reactants, products, and the equilibrium that was established:

_____

_____

_____

EXPLAIN: Dynamic equilibrium

▶ How can a system be dynamic and yet remain the same? The previous investigations showed that an equilibrium is established when the rate of the forwards reaction equaled the rate of the backwards reaction. Thus the reactions continue but at equal rates, producing no noticeable change. This can be shown on a graph, as shown below left:

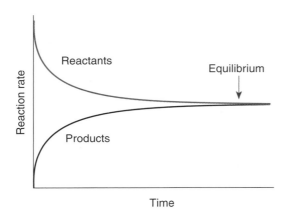

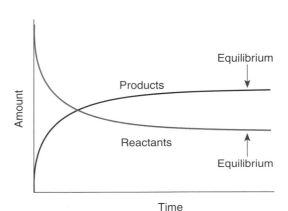

▶ The amount of products and reactants do not need to be equal at equilibrium, in fact in most cases they are not (above right). But as the amount of product increases the amount of products returning to reactants also increases. So if the rates of the forward and backwards reactions are not equal at the start, they will become equal as reactants turn into more products.

▶ The images below shows six test tubes containing the complex ion, iron thiocyanate $FeSCN^{2+}_{(aq)}$.

- Iron thiocyanate is a complex ion that forms when potassium thiocyanate (KSCN) solution is added to iron nitrate $(Fe(NO_3)_3$ solution.

- The reaction between Fe^{3+} and SCN^- can be written as:

$Fe^{3+} + SCN^- \rightleftharpoons FeSCN^{2+}$

The enthalpy for the forward reaction is negative (it is exothermic).

- - The iron thiocyanate ion produces a blood red solution.
  - Fe^{3+} has a pale yellow-brown color.
  - SCN^- is colorless.

- By changing the conditions of the equilibrium, the solution can be made lighter or darker.

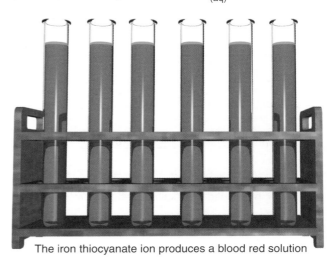

The iron thiocyanate ion produces a blood red solution

©2019 **BIOZONE** International
ISBN:978-1-927309-71-1
Photocopying Prohibited

8. (a) Predict what would happen to the color of the solution in the test tubes if the Fe^{3+} ion was removed from the left-hand side of the equation:

_____

_____

(b) Predict what would happen to the color of the solution in the test tubes if the more Fe^{3+} was added to the left-hand side of the equation:

_____

_____

9. The image below shows the results of changing the conditions in the test tubes. The changes are detailed below:

- Test tube 1: $Fe(NO_3)_3$ added (adds Fe^{3+}).
- Test tube 2: KSCN added (adds SCN^-).
- Test tube 3: NH_4Cl added (decreases Fe^{3+} ion by forming a complex with Cl^-).
- Test tube 4: $AgNO_3$ added (decreases SCN^- by forming a precipitate of AgSCN).
- Test tube 5: Cooled in ice water.
- Test tube 6: Heated in hot water bath.

(a) Explain why adding more Fe^{3+} to test tube 1 produces a deeper red color: _____

_____

_____

(b) Explain why adding more SCN^- to test tube 2 produces a deeper red color: _____

_____

_____

(c) Why would removing Fe^{3+} ions (test tube 3) make the solution lighter? _____

_____

_____

(d) In test tube 4, which direction did the reaction shift (forwards or backwards). Explain why it shifted in this direction:

_____

_____

(e) The solution in the ice bath (test tube 5) became darker. This means the reaction moved in the forwards direction. Why did it move in this direction?

_____

_____

(f) Test tube 6 was heated and became lighter. This means the backwards endothermic reaction occurred. Can you explain why?

_____

_____

EXPLAIN: Le Châtelier's principle

▶ The previous investigations have demonstrated how equilibria behave when conditions change. For example, for the reaction $Fe^{3+} + SCN^- \rightleftharpoons FeSCN^{2+}$, the equilibrium shifts to the right (the forward reaction) if more Fe^{3+} is added (e.g. the concentration of Fe^{3+} is increased). This removes some of the Fe^{3+} from the solution. If the temperature is increased then the equilibrium shifts to the left (the backwards endothermic reaction) to remove some of that heat (i.e. the energy is used to drive the endothermic reaction).

▶ These observations about equilibria were summarized by Henry Louis Le Châtelier, a French chemist who published many papers on equilibria in the late 19th and early 20th centuries.

▶ **Le Châtelier's principle** states: When a system at equilibrium is subjected to change (e.g. in temperature, pressure, concentration, or volume) the system changes to a new equilibrium and this change partially counteracts the change applied to the system.

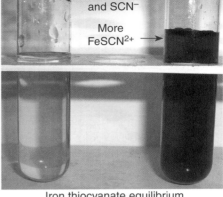

Iron thiocyanate equilibrium

▶ In other words an external stress can change the system and the system reacts in a way that reduces or opposes the change as much as possible.

▶ For example consider the system $A_{2(g)} + B_{2(g)} \rightleftharpoons A_2B_{2(g)}$ (right).

The system on the left has more gas molecules than on the right. If the pressure is increased, the equilibrium will shift to the right to decrease the pressure. It does this by reducing the number of gas molecules, increasing the number of A_2B_2 molecules and reducing the number of A_2 and B_2 molecules to produce a lower total number of gas molecules.

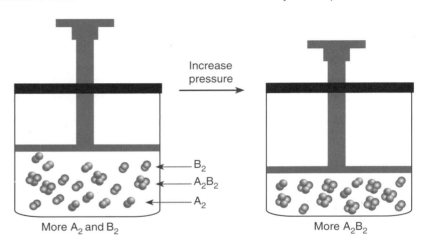

10. Imagine the pressure in the system above left was decreased. Draw a diagram similar the one above right to show how the system and molecules would react:

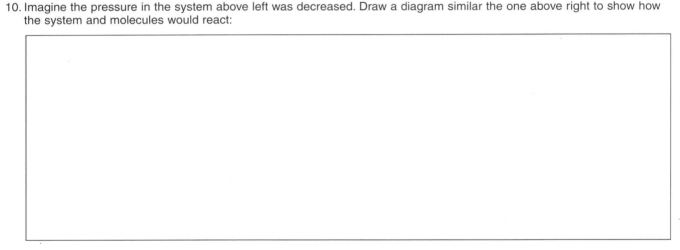

11. The equilibrium between hydrogen and iodine can be written as $H_{2(g)} + I_{2(g)} \rightleftharpoons 2HI_{(g)}$.

(a) In which direction would the equilibrium shift if the system's pressure was increased? Explain your answer:

_____

_____

_____

(b) A chemist wanted to produce more HI from the system. How would he be able to do this?

_____

_____

©2019 **BIOZONE** International
ISBN:978-1-927309-71-1
Photocopying Prohibited

ELABORATE: The common ion effect

▶ Consider two ionic compounds: Sodium fluoride (NaF) and potassium fluoride (KF). When they dissolve in solution they form the ions: $Na^+_{(aq)} + F^-_{(aq)}$ and $K^+_{(aq)} + F^-_{(aq)}$. The ion common to both solutions is F^-.

▶ If these solutions were mixed together then the ions in solution would be $Na^+_{(aq)}$, $K^+_{(aq)}$, and $F^-_{(aq)}$.

▶ When a solution of an ionic substance is made, the ions dissociate (separate) according to how soluble they are. Some ionic substances are very soluble (e.g. KCl) and other are not (e.g. $BaSO_4$).

▶ Sodium fluoride (a salt) is soluble in water. At 20°C, a saturated solution of NaF can be produced by dissolving 4.06 g of the salt in 100 mL of water. At this point, the equation for the dissociation of NaF can be written as:

$$NaF_{(s)} \rightleftharpoons Na^+_{(aq)} + F^-_{(aq)}$$

▶ A saturated solution is one where no more substance can be added to the solution without it precipitating out to form a solid.

Sodium fluoride is a salt

In chemistry, an ionic compound formed by the neutralization reaction of an acid and a base is called a **salt**.

▶ Now imagine that a small amount of KF is added to the saturated NaF solution. How would this affect the equilibrium and what would be the result? We can apply Le Châtelier's principle to find out.

12. (a) Adding F^- to the solution (in the form of KF) would shift the equilibrium in which direction?

_____

(b) Explain your answer above: _____

_____

_____

(c) What would be the effect on the saturated solution? _____

13. Using your answers above, describe the common ion effect: _____

_____

EVALUATE: Using the common ion effect

▶ A student set up several saturated solutions of sodium chloride (NaCl). She aimed to manipulate the solutions to produce solid NaCl without directly adding more NaCl.

14. (a) Why is a saturated solution used in this experiment: _____

_____

_____

(b) Write an equilibrium equation for NaCl in a saturated solution: _____

▶ The student has several solutions and solids available: concentrated HCl, KCl solid, concentrated NaOH, saturated Na_2SO_4 solution, and solid $CaCl_2$.

15. Describe the effect of each of the substances on the saturated solution of NaCl and use Le Châtelier's principle to explain the effect.

_____

_____

_____

_____

_____

_____

_____

_____

_____

_____

45 Industrial Chemistry

ENGAGE: Your stuff is the work of chemists

▶ An understanding of chemistry has allowed humans to produce substances that are entirely new to this universe. What's more, we are able to produce these substances on immense scales. Every year we produce more than 300 million tonnes of plastic, a substance that does not exist naturally.

▶ Almost everything you have or use has in some way made use of or been made by industrial chemistry. From the stainless steel spoon you used to eat your breakfast to the shampoo you used to wash your hair to the artificial leather on your shoes.

▶ Industrial chemistry takes the principles and ideas of chemists and scales them up to produce the vast quantities of substances needed to keep society as we know it working. Without the huge factories producing ammonia or sulfuric acid many common fertilizers would be in short supply, limiting the amount of food we could grow. Without the massive iron smelters we wouldn't have the steel needed to produce virtually anything requiring strong structural support, e.g. cars, bridges, chairs, or buildings.

▶ Many of the most important industrial processes are based on simple chemical equilibria.

EXPLAIN: Producing ammonia

▶ The main industrial procedure for producing ammonia world wide is the Haber process. This process manipulates the equilibrium between nitrogen, hydrogen, and ammonia. It was first demonstrated by Fritz Haber in 1909 and industrial scale production began in 1913.

▶ Ammonia is an important precursor chemical in the production of nitrates. The Haber process was first developed to replace the need to mine nitrates for use in fertilizer production and other industrial processes. However, most of the nitrates initially produced ended up being used for munitions in both the First and Second World Wars.

▶ The reaction for the formation of ammonia from nitrogen and hydrogen is:

$$N_{2(g)} + 3H_{2(g)} \rightleftharpoons 2NH_{3(g)} \quad \Delta H = \text{-92 kJ}$$

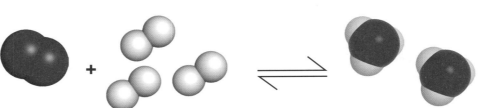

1. (a) Is the forward reaction endothermic or exothermic? _____

    (b) To produce the greatest amount of NH_3 in which direction should the equilibrium shift? _____

    (c) Can this be achieved by raising or lowering the temperature of the reaction? _____

    (d) What would the effect of this be on the rate of the reaction? _____

    _____

▶ The rate of the ammonia reaction is very slow (almost zero at room temperature). A catalyst is used to counter this.

2. (a) What is the effect of a catalyst on the rate of the reaction? _____

    (b) What would be the effect of using a catalyst on the position of the equilibrium? _____

▶ The catalyst works most efficiently at around 400°C. This shifts the equilibrium to the left. To counteract this, the pressure of the system is increased, although this comes at an energetic (therefore economic) cost.

3. (a) What is the effect of increasing the pressure on the system? _____

    _____

    (b) Explain this effect: _____

    _____

    _____

©2019 **BIOZONE** International
ISBN:978-1-927309-71-1
Photocopying Prohibited

  PS1.B ETS1.C SC

▶ The graph below shows the effect of temperature and pressure on the percentage of ammonia formed during the reaction of N_2 and H_2.

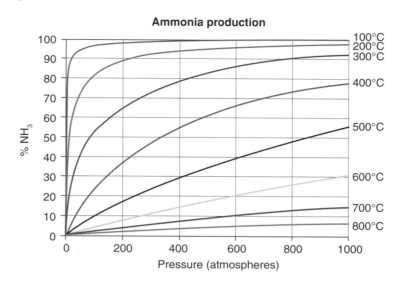

Ammonia production

4. (a) What is the effect of increasing the temperature of the reaction? _____

_____

(b) What is the effect of increasing the pressure of the reaction? _____

_____

▶ Because the reaction is so slow, the amount of product produced at 200°C is very low even if the percentage of product produced from reactants is high. The Haber process reacts nitrogen and hydrogen over a catalyst at 200 atmospheres and 400°C to produce ammonia. The yield is about 15% but at a much faster rate than at lower temperatures. This is a compromise between speed and cost.

5. Why is a compromise of 200 atmospheres and 400°C used in the production of ammonia?

_____

_____

_____

_____

_____

Getting the hydrogen

▶ Hydrogen gas is not readily available and must be produced industrially by steam reforming of methane. The production of hydrogen is worth over $100 billion a year.

▶ The reaction is carried out in two stages: The first stage is: $CH_{4(g)} + H_2O_{(g)} \rightleftharpoons CO_{(g)} + 3H_{2(g)}$ ΔH 206 kJ

6. (a) Under what conditions would the first reaction be carried out in order to produce the greatest amount of hydrogen?

_____

_____

_____

_____

(b) To increase the hydrogen produced, the hydrogen is constantly removed from the system. How would this help produce more hydrogen?

_____

_____

_____

▶ In the second stage (the water-gas shift reaction) carbon monoxide can then be reused to produce more hydrogen:
$CO_{(g)} + H_2O_{(g)} \rightleftharpoons CO_{2(g)} + H_{2(g)}$ ΔH −45 kJ.

▶ The reaction involves two phases, the first at high temperature and the second at low temperature. Different catalysts are used at each phase.

7. (a) What is the effect of running the system at a high temperature? _____

_____

(b) What is the effect of then lowering the temperature? _____

_____

Getting the nitrogen

▶ Some of the hydrogen produced by steam reforming is used to produce pure nitrogen for use in the production of ammonia. Air is fed into a reactor along with the hydrogen: $4N_{2(g)} + O_{2(g)} + 2H_2 \rightleftharpoons 2H_2O_{(g)} + 4N_{2(g)}$

8. The equilibrium lies far to the right. What does this mean in terms of the ease of producing the products?

_____

_____

_____

EXPLAIN: Producing sulfuric acid

▶ Sulfuric acid is used in the manufacture of fertilizers, dyes, fabrics, detergents and many other everyday materials. It is important in its use as an electrolyte such as in lead-acid batteries used to start car engines. Over 230 million tonnes of sulfuric acid are produced each year.

▶ The process is carried out in several steps.

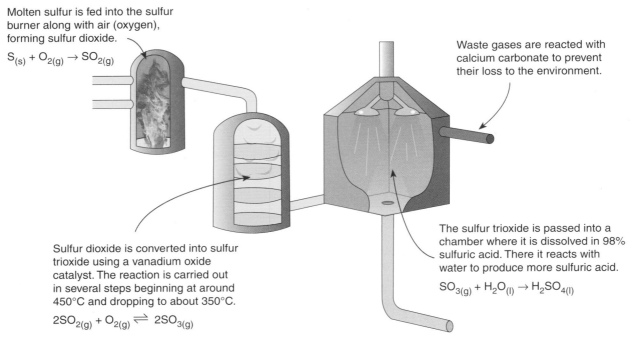

Molten sulfur is fed into the sulfur burner along with air (oxygen), forming sulfur dioxide.

$S_{(s)} + O_{2(g)} \rightarrow SO_{2(g)}$

Waste gases are reacted with calcium carbonate to prevent their loss to the environment.

Sulfur dioxide is converted into sulfur trioxide using a vanadium oxide catalyst. The reaction is carried out in several steps beginning at around 450°C and dropping to about 350°C.

$2SO_{2(g)} + O_{2(g)} \rightleftharpoons 2SO_{3(g)}$

The sulfur trioxide is passed into a chamber where it is dissolved in 98% sulfuric acid. There it reacts with water to produce more sulfuric acid.

$SO_{3(g)} + H_2O_{(l)} \rightarrow H_2SO_{4(l)}$

9. The equilibrium reaction between sulfur dioxide and oxygen is: $2SO_{2(g)} + O_{2(g)} \rightleftharpoons 2SO_{3(g)}$ ΔH −196 kJ.

(a) Would this reaction be carried out under high or low pressure? _____

(b) Explain why constantly removing the SO_3 favors the forward reaction: _____

_____

_____

(c) Why is the reaction carried out at a high temperature when the equilibrium suggests this would not be favorable?

_____

_____

EXPLAIN: Producing methanol

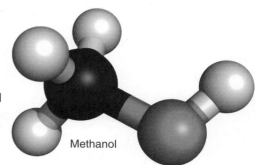

Methanol

▶ Methanol is an important precursor molecule for many industrial processes including the manufacture of polymers such as Perspex (poly(methyl 2-methylpropenoate)), terylene (a polyester), as a fuel or component of fuel, or even in herbicides (weed killers) and insecticides.

▶ Methanol can be made using part of the process used to produce hydrogen in the manufacture of ammonia. As a result of this interrelated chemistry, oil and natural gas refineries, and ammonia and methanol plants are often found built into the same facility or very close together to facilitate the easy movement of reactants between the processes.

▶ The first step in the manufacture of methanol is the production of synthesis gas or syngas (this is the same reaction as the first step in the production of hydrogen):

$$CH_{4(g)} + H_2O_{(g)} \rightleftharpoons CO_{(g)} + 3H_{2(g)} \text{ (syngas) } \Delta H \text{ 206 kJ}$$

▶ The syngas is passed over a catalyst made of aluminum pellets coated with copper and zinc oxides.

$$CO_{(g)} + 2H_{2(g)} \rightleftharpoons CH_3OH_{(g)} \quad \Delta H \text{ −91 kJ}$$

10. Imagine you were to build a methanol manufacturing plant. What are the conditions you would need to produce the methanol economically? Remember, heating things costs money, as does producing very high pressures. A slow reaction is very costly because it takes too long for the product to get made.

In groups discuss the conditions and processes you would use to produce methanol. Write down the processes below:

_____

_____

_____

_____

_____

_____

_____

_____

_____

_____

_____

_____

_____

EXPLAIN: Producing ethanol

▶ About 93% of all ethanol is production by fermentation in industrial processes. The other 7% is produced by the direct hydration of the alkene ethene following the equation: $C_2H_{4(g)} + H_2O_{(g)} \rightleftharpoons C_2H_5OH_{(g)} \Delta H$ −45 kJ

▶ Silicon dioxide coated with phosphoric acid is used as a catalyst. The equilibrium sits to the left so excess ethene is added to the mix and ethanol is continually removed. The reaction takes place at around 300°C and a pressure of 70 atmospheres.

11. Explain the reasons for the conditions used in the production of ethanol: _____

_____

_____

_____

_____

_____

_____

©2019 BIOZONE International
ISBN: 978-1-927309-71-1
Photocopying Prohibited

46 | Ocean Chemistry

ENGAGE: Acids and bases

▶ You will be familiar with various acidic substances (such as hydrochloric acid and vinegar) and basic substances (such as sodium hydroxide and ammonia). In this investigation you will test the pH of these and other substances:

INVESTIGATION 6.3: Testing the pH of various substances.   See appendix for equipment list.

⚠ Caution is required when handling acids and bases as they are corrosive. Wear protective eyewear, gloves and clothing.

1. You will need distilled water and 0.1 mol/L hydrochloric acid (HCl), nitric acid (HNO₃), ethanoic acid (CH₃COOH), citric acid (C₆H₈O₇), sodium hydroxide (NaOH), ammonia solution (NH₃), sodium carbonate (Na₂CO₃), and sodium hydrogen carbonate (NaHCO₃).

2. Test the pH of each acid or base by placing a few drops on a watch glass and touching a piece of pH paper to them.

3. Use the color change to identify the pH of the solution and record this in the table below.

Substance	pH
H_2O	
HCl	
HNO_3	
CH_3COOH	
$C_6H_8O_7$	

Substance	pH
NaOH	
NH_3	
Na_2CO_3	
$NaHCO_3$	

EXPLORE: The pH scale

▶ The pH scale ranges from 0 to 14. Substance with a pH of 1 are very acidic, whereas substances with a pH of 14 are very basic. Neutral substances have a pH of 7.

1. The diagram below shows the pH scale. Show the position of the substances you tested above on the scale. Then using books, or the internet find out the pH of a range of household substances and add them to the diagram:

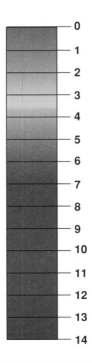

EXPLAIN: pH of acids and bases

▶ The pH scale is based on the concentration of H^+ ions in a solution (H^+ ions actually exist as H_3O^+ in solution). It is a logarithmic scale so that the concentration of H^+ changes by ten times from one pH unit to the next.

▶ pH actually means the hydrogen (H) potential (p) of the solution (p is also stated as power, or *potentia* (capacity)).

▶ Water exists in an equilibrium with the hydronium ion (H_3O^+) and the hydroxide ion (OH^-):

$$2H_2O_{(l)} \rightleftharpoons H_3O^+_{(aq)} + OH^-_{(aq)}$$

What's the $[H^+]$ of a lemon? Find out by testing its pH.

▶ For simplicity H_3O^+ is usually just written as H^+ so:

$$H_2O_{(l)} \rightleftharpoons H^+_{(aq)} + OH^-_{(aq)}$$

▶ The equilibrium lies far to the left, so the concentrations of both H^+ and OH^- are extremely small (1×10^{-7} mol/L).

▶ We can use these concentrations to work out the pH of water. If we take the negative $\log_{10}$ value of the H^+ ion then:

$$-\log_{10} 1 \times 10^{-7} = 7$$

▶ The equation can be written as: **pH = $-\log_{10}[H^+]$** (the square brackets [ ] mean concentration).

▶ If we know the pH of a solution we can also work out the H^+ concentration of that solution using the negative inverse $\log_{10}(10^x)$. So if the pH is 5.3 then: $10^{-5.3} = 5.0 \times 10^{-6}$ mol/L (of H^+ ions).

▶ The equation can be written as **$[H^+] = 10^{-pH}$**

2. Calculate the pH of the following H^+ concentrations:

(a) 1.0×10^{-3} mol/L: _____

(c) 2.3×10^{-9} mol/L: _____

(b) 1.7×10^{-6} mol/L: _____

(d) 6.0×10^{-12} mol/L: _____

3. Calculate the H^+ concentration of a solution with the following pH:

(a) pH 1.0: _____

(c) pH 14.0: _____

(b) pH 3.6: _____

(d) pH 11.4: _____

4. How many times greater is the H^+ concentration in a pH 3 solution than a pH 4 solution? _____

▶ It is useful to note at this stage that as $[H^+]$ increases $[OH^-]$ decreases at the same rate. This can be seen in the equation $[H^+][OH^-] = 1 \times 10^{-14}$. This value is referred to as K_w and is constant.

▶ Thus if $[H^+] = 1.0 \times 10^{-1}$ then $[OH^-] = 1 \times 10^{-14} \div 1.0 \times 10^{-1} = 1.0 \times 10^{-13}$.

5. A solution of NaOH is made up to 0.25 mol/L. Calculate its pH: _____

_____

EXPLAIN: Strong and weak acids

▶ Why do some acids have different pH values to others? Why are some very low and others close to 7? Why do some bases have high pH values and others relatively low?

▶ What actually makes an acid an acid? What makes a base a base?

6. The following substances are acids or bases. The ions they form in solution are shown:

Substance	Acid/base	Ions in solution
HCl	Acid	H^+ Cl^-
HNO_3	Acid	H^+ NO_3^-
CH_3COOH	Acid	H^+ CH_3COO^-
NaOH	Base	$Na+$ OH^-
KOH	Base	$K+$ OH^-
NH_3	Base	NH_4^+ OH^-

(a) What ion(s) do the acids have in common? _____

(b) What ion(s) do the bases have in common? _____

©2019 **BIOZONE** International
ISBN: 978-1-927309-71-1
Photocopying Prohibited

▶ Acids and bases dissociate when placed in water. The more strongly they dissociate, the greater the effect on the pH. For example, when HCl is placed in water, it dissociates completely into H^+ and Cl^- ions: $HCl_{(aq)} \rightarrow H^+_{(aq)} + Cl^-_{(aq)}$

▶ A solution of 0.1 mol/L HCl will produce 0.1 mol/L H^+ ions. Acids that completely dissociate are called **strong acids**.

▶ The same occurs for bases. Bases such as NaOH completely dissociate into ions (Na^+ and OH^-). A 0.1 mol/L solution of NaOH will produce 0.1 mol/L of OH^- ions. Bases that completely dissociate are called **strong bases**.

▶ Some acids and bases, however, do not fully dissociate but instead exist in an equilibrium. For example: $CH_3COOH \rightleftharpoons CH_3COO^- + H^+$.
Because the $[H^+]$ is lower than the concentration of the compound, it will have a higher pH than might be expected. Acids and bases that do not fully dissociate are called weak acids or **weak bases**.

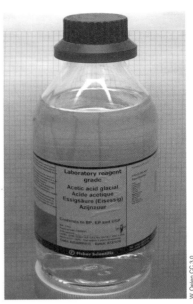

W. Oelen CC 3.0

Ethanoic (acetic) acid, CH_3COOH

7. NH_3 in water reacts to form NH_4^+ in the equilibrium reaction:

$$NH_3 + H_2O \rightleftharpoons NH_4^+ + OH^-$$

(a) Is NH_3 a strong or weak base? _____

(b) Explain why the pH of a NH_3 solution is lower than that of a NaOH solution:

_____

_____

EXPLAIN: Carbon dioxide and pH

▶ Recall that in the carbon cycle the oceans were a large reservoir of carbon by the fact that carbon dioxide from the atmosphere dissolves into them. This is evident in the plot right, which shows how the ocean constantly exchanges CO_2 with the atmosphere.

▶ The effect of carbon dioxide on water can be seen by bubbling it through water containing a pH indicator. Bromothymol blue is an indicator that is blue in basic (alkaline) solutions, blue/green in neutral water and yellow/green in acidic solutions. Adding carbon dioxide to water containing bromothymol blue causes the solution to turn yellow/green as the carbon dioxide dissolves into the water (below).

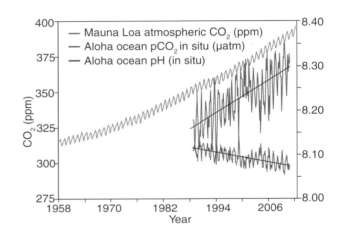

— Mauna Loa atmospheric CO_2 (ppm)
— Aloha ocean pCO_2 in situ (µatm)
— Aloha ocean pH (in situ)

8. (a) Does bubbling carbon dioxide through water cause the water to become acidic or basic?

_____

(b) What does this mean in terms of $[H^+]$ in the water? _____

_____

(c) Does this increase or decrease the pH? _____

(d) What might happen to a piece of calcium carbonate placed in the solution on the far right? _____

_____

©2019 **BIOZONE** International
ISBN:978-1-927309-71-1
Photocopying Prohibited

9. (a) What do you notice about the peak and dips in ocean and atmospheric CO_2 in the graph on the opposite page?

    _____

    (b) What does this pattern indicate? _____

    (c) What is the trend over time in the CO_2 concentration in both reservoirs? _____

    _____

▶ The graphs below show the effect of carbon dioxide on ocean water. The top row shows dissolved CO_2 at three locations and the bottom row shows ocean pH at the same locations. Vertical scales are the same in each case:

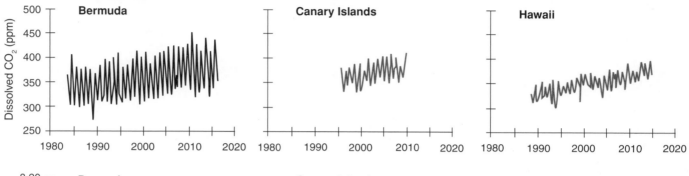

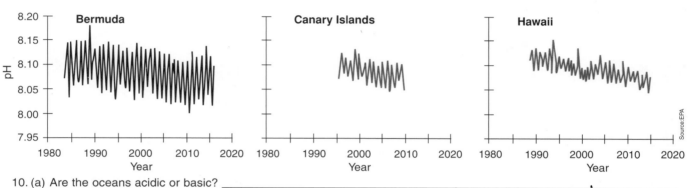

10. (a) Are the oceans acidic or basic? _____

    (b) What is the pattern in the data at each location? _____

    _____

    (c) What does this suggest about the effect of increasing dissolved CO_2 on the pH of the oceans? _____

    _____

    _____

EXPLAIN: Carbon dioxide chemistry

▶ How does carbon dioxide change the pH of water? Acids work by donating protons (e.g. HCl → H^+ + Cl^-). Carbon dioxide reacts with water in the following way:

$$CO_2 + H_2O \rightarrow H_2CO_3$$

▶ Carbonic acid (H_2CO_3) then immediately dissociates to release H^+:

$$H_2CO_3 \rightleftharpoons H^+ + HCO_3^-$$

▶ The increase in H^+ lowers the pH of the water. In seawater a major ion present is the carbonate ion CO_3^{2-}. This reacts with the H^+ ion released from carbonic acid to form another HCO_3^- (bicarbonate, or hydrogen carbonate ion).

▶ The complete reaction can be written as:

$$CO_2 + CO_3^{2-} + H_2O \rightleftharpoons 2HCO_3^-$$

11. (a) For every mole of CO_2 that reacts with seawater, how many moles of CO_3^{2-} are removed? _____

    (b) What is the effect of increasing the concentration of CO_2 on the equilibrium? _____

    _____

    _____

©2019 BIOZONE International
ISBN: 978-1-927309-71-1
Photocopying Prohibited

ELABORATE: Carbon dioxide, temperature, and salinity

▶ The temperature of seawater varies depending on location around the globe. Polar waters have very low temperatures whereas tropical seas have much higher temperatures. How does this affect the amount of carbon dioxide that can dissolve in them?

INVESTIGATION 6.4: The effect of temperature on the solubility of carbon dioxide.   See appendix for equipment list.

1. Set up the following:

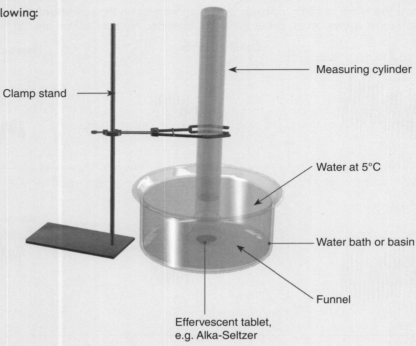

- Measuring cylinder
- Clamp stand
- Water at 5°C
- Water bath or basin
- Funnel
- Effervescent tablet, e.g. Alka-Seltzer

2. Fill the measuring cylinder and invert it underwater as shown so that there is as little air in it a possible.

3. Place a funnel into the mouth of the cylinder to help capture all the CO_2 gas released from the effervescent tablet.

4. Record the starting level of the water in the cylinder. Place the tablet under the funnel and let it continue to fizz until all the tablet has dissolved.

5. Record the new level of water in the measuring cylinder. Calculate the volume of gas captured.

6. Repeat the investigation with water at 45°C water.

Trial number	Volume of gas (mL)	
	Cold water	Warm water
	Temperature =	Temperature =
1		
2		
3		
Average		

12. (a) What is the effect of the water temperature on the volume of gas that accumulated in the measuring cylinder?

_____

_____

   (b) Where did the difference in the volume of gas go? _____

_____

(c) What will be the consequence of a warming ocean? How will this affect the role of the oceans as a CO_2 sink?

_____

_____

_____

(d) Where in the world's oceans would you expect more CO_2 uptake? Where would you expect less?

_____

_____

13. (a) Recall from chapter 2 that the salinity of the oceans also varies from place to place. The average salinity of the oceans is about 35 g/L of sodium chloride. How does this affect the solubility of carbon dioxide in water?

In the space below design an experiment similar to the one you just carried out to test the solubility of carbon dioxide in seawater compared to the freshwater you just tested. Check your design with your teacher, make any changes necessary, then carry out the experiment and write up and discuss the results:

_____

_____

_____

_____

_____

_____

_____

_____

_____

_____

(b) Results: _____

_____

_____

(c) Discussion: _____

_____

_____

_____

_____

▶ The graph below shows how carbon dioxide (CO_2) solubility is affected by depth and salinity:

14. (a) What is the effect of depth on the solubility of CO_2?

_____

_____

_____

(b) What is the effect of salinity on the solubility of CO_2?

_____

_____

_____

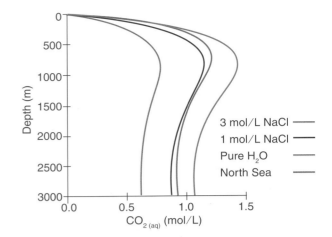

ELABORATE: Carbon dioxide, the oceans, and aragonite

▶ Shell-building marine organisms build their shells from calcium carbonate ($CaCO_3$). The calcium carbonate occurs as calcite or **aragonite**, which have the same molecular formula but different crystal structures. Aragonite is stronger than calcite but more soluble.

▶ Thus marine organisms in high energy environments such as reefs (for example, corals and small sea snails called pteropods) build their shells from aragonite, whereas those that live at depth (e.g. benthic foraminifera) tend to build their shells from calcite. Many marine shell-builders (e.g. bivalve mollusks) use both.

▶ The aragonite-users are crucial to marine ecosystems. Corals build biogenic reefs and pteropods form the basis of many food chains.

▶ What evidence do we have of the effect of CO_2 on marine life? Direct evidence can be obtained by comparing sites where CO_2 seeps naturally from volcanic vents to sites where it does not. Consider the images below:

Reef with carbon dioxide seep: sparse beds of algae.

Reef with no carbon dioxide seep: diverse corals

▶ Recall that in seawater carbon dioxide reacts with water to produce bicarbonate and hydrogen ions. The hydrogen ions then react with carbonate ions in the sea to produce more bicarbonate ions.

▶ From the images above it can be seen that the reef where there is a carbon dioxide seep lacks any corals. The presence of large amounts of dissolved CO_2 clearly affects the ability of these animals to survive. Reef building corals and other marine organisms that build their shells with aragonite are particularly vulnerable to increases in carbon dioxide. We can look at the chemistry of this relationship.

▶ The equilibrium in seawater of aragonite and its ions can be written as:

$$Ca^{2+}_{(aq)} + CO_3^{2-}_{(aq)} \rightleftharpoons CaCO_{3(aq)}$$ Where $CaCO_3$ refers to aragonite

▶ The equation describing aragonite saturation can be written as: $\dfrac{[Ca^{2+}] + [CO_3^{2-}]}{CaCO_3} = \Omega$

▶ When $\Omega = 1$ then the equilibrium is at saturation with aragonite. When $\Omega > 1$ then the water is supersaturated. When $\Omega < 1$ then the water is said to be undersaturated.

©2019 **BIOZONE** International
ISBN:978-1-927309-71-1
Photocopying Prohibited

15. (a) What would adding carbon dioxide to seawater do to the value of Ω? _____

_____

(b) How might this affect the animals that use aragonite to build their shells?_____

_____

_____

▶ The diagrams below show the present aragonite saturation of the oceans and the changes in aragonite saturation since 1880.

Present day aragonite saturation

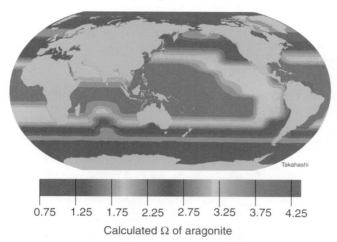

Takahashi

0.75 1.25 1.75 2.25 2.75 3.25 3.75 4.25

Calculated Ω of aragonite

Changes in aragonite saturation 1880-2016

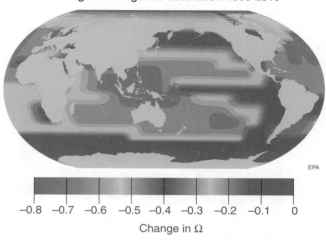

EPA

−0.8 −0.7 −0.6 −0.5 −0.4 −0.3 −0.2 −0.1 0

Change in Ω

16. (a) Which parts of the oceans have the highest aragonite saturation? _____

(b) Which parts of the oceans have the lowest aragonite saturation? _____

(c) Which parts of the oceans have had the greatest change in aragonite saturation? _____

(d) Explain why shell building organisms in the polar oceans are likely to be affected by ocean acidification sooner than those in the tropics:

_____

_____

_____

_____

▶ The increase in carbon dioxide not only favors the dissolution of aragonite from shells but it also affects the ability of shell-making organisms to obtain the CO_3^{2-} ions they need to build and maintain their shells. This causes them to expend more energy on shell building than they would in less carbonated waters. This energy expenditure is ultimately costly because less energy is available to carry out other biological functions, such as growth and reproduction. Warmer waters also cause corals to expel the algae in their tissues causing the coral to whiten or 'bleach'. Corals can survive bleaching events but it indicates stress and results in reduced survival.

Brocken Inaglory CC 3.0

Experiments have shown that larval brittle stars die in less than a week in seawater with higher than normal CO_2. Adults (above) show a loss of muscle mass.

Ocean acidification has been linked to coral bleaching and the reduction in the growth of corals. Rising temperatures may make this even worse.

Ocean acidification (resulting in the reduction of carbonate ions) weakens the shells of mollusks (shellfish). Investigations show fertilization is also affected.

EVALUATE: The biological effects of lower ocean pH

Ocean acidification and crabs

▶ The economy of many countries and livelihoods of many individuals depend on the oceans. The global consumption of seafood is around 143 million tonnes per year. Around 7.5 million tonnes of mollusks (e.g. mussels and clams) are harvested each year.

▶ The effect of future ocean acidification can be measured by changing the pH of seawater in tanks to that predicted by IPCC models (right). Various marine organisms can then be raised in the tanks to study and quantify how pH affects them.

▶ Red king crabs (*Paralithodes camtschaticus*) are native to the Bering Sea. They can have a leg span up to 1.8 meters, a shell width of 28 cm and a weight of 13 kg. They are heavily targeted by fisheries with around 11 million kg being caught per season.

▶ Tanner crabs (*Chionoecetes bairdi*) are also native to the Bering sea and are also heavily targeted by fisheries. Tanner crabs are much smaller than king crabs, weighing up to 2 kg.

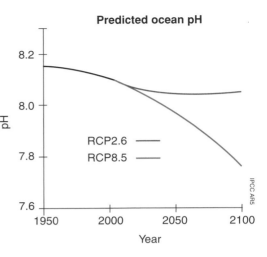

Predicted ocean pH

RCP2.6 ——
RCP8.5 ——

IPCC AR5

▶ The effects of seawater pH on juvenile crabs have been studied with pHs of 8.0, 7.8 (estimated pH by 2100 CE) and 7.3 (estimated pH by 2200 CE). Seawater was acidified by bubbling CO_2 though it.

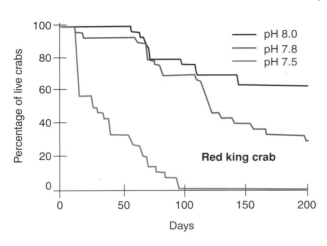

Tanner crab

NOAA

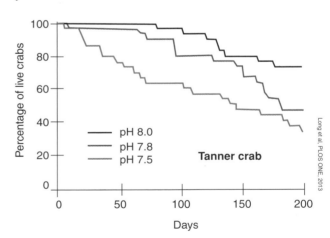

Red king crab

NOAA

Effect of pH on juvenile crabs

pH 8.0
pH 7.8
pH 7.5

Red king crab

pH 8.0
pH 7.8
pH 7.5

Tanner crab

Long et al, PLOS ONE, 2013

▶ The results from the experiment found that pH has a significant effect on the survival of juvenile crabs.

17. (a) What was the effect of decreasing the pH on the survival of the crabs? _____

_____

_____

(b) Which crab was the most affected by the decrease in pH? _____

(c) Which of the pH's tested is a current concern and how did it affect the two crabs? _____

_____

_____

_____

Ocean acidification and mollusks

▶ Pteropods ('wing-foot') are mollusks specialized for life in the open ocean. They are called sea butterflies because of the wing-like structures that help them swim in the oceans. These have evolved from their sea-snail foot.

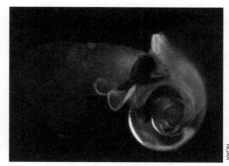

▶ Shelled pteropod species have calcium carbonate shells that are around 5-10 mm in diameter. The species *Limacina helicina* (right) is an Arctic species and is an important part of the ocean food web.

▶ Because these small mollusks have calcium carbonate shells and live in parts of the ocean were the aragonite saturation is close to 1, they are likely to be indicators of the wider effects of ocean acidification. For this reason they are closely studied (along with their close relatives in the Southern Ocean around Antarctica).

▶ The effect of ocean acidification on *Limacina helicina* shell deposition was studied under CO_2 levels equal to 350 ppm (pH 8.09) and 760 ppm (pH 7.78) (as predicted in 2100 CE). Specimens were grown with $^{45}CaCl_2$. ^{45}Ca is radioactive with a half life of 163 days. The rate of $CaCO_3$ shell deposition was estimated from the radioactivity in each shell after incubation with ^{45}Ca.

▶ The table below shows the conditions of the study:

Conditions	pH	pCO₂ (ppm)	Ω	Temperature
Normal pH (as per 1990 average)	8.09	350	1.90	5
Low pH (predicted 2100)	7.78	765	1.00	5
Fjord where collected	8.12	320	1.81	2.2

▶ The graph shows the effect on $CaCO_3$ shell deposition:

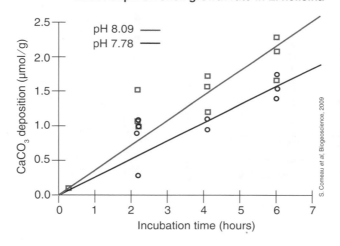

Effect of pH on shell growth rate in *L. helicina*

pH 8.09 ——
pH 7.78 ——

x-axis: Incubation time (hours)
y-axis: $CaCO_3$ deposition (µmol/g)

S. Comeau *et al*, Biogeoscience, 2009

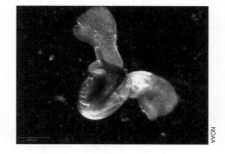

18. (a) What was the effect of decreasing pH on the shell deposition of $CaCO_3$ in *Limacina helicina*?

_____

(b) How would this affect the possible survival of *Limacina helicina*? _____

_____

_____

(c) Why is *Limacina helicina* a good indicator species of the effects of increased CO_2 absorption in the oceans?

_____

_____

_____

_____

Carbon dioxide

▸ The burning of fossil fuels produces energy for humans needs but also vast quantities of carbon dioxide, some of which is absorbed by the oceans.

▸ The natural alkalinity of the oceans acts to a certain degree as a buffer against the acidifying nature of CO_2. Continued absorption of CO_2 shifts the carbonate-bicarbonate equilibrium in favor of bicarbonate.

Ocean acidification and fish

▸ A lower ocean pH does not only affect animals that build shells. New studies on fish show that increased CO_2 can affect their behavior and ultimately their chances of survival.

▸ A study of the behavior of clownfish (*Amphiprion percula*) (right) was carried out by raising larval clownfish in seawater at ambient CO_2(390 ppm), 550 ppm, 700 ppm and 850 ppm CO_2.

▸ At each CO_2 concentration, the larval fish were given a choice of water streams. One contained the chemical cue of a natural predator and the other did not. The results are shown in the graph below. For each set of trials, there was also an untreated control, where both water streams lacked the predator cue (purple bars).

Effect of CO_2 concentration on predator avoidance in larval clownfish

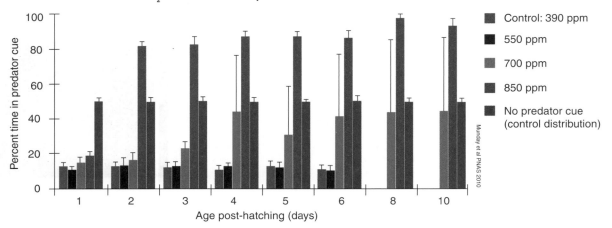

Munday et al PNAS 2010

Control: 390 ppm
550 ppm
700 ppm
850 ppm
No predator cue (control distribution)

▸ The clown fish were tested for predator avoidance again at the settlement stage (transformation to a juvenile). These were compared to wild caught damselfish (*Pomacentrus wardi*) that were also treated with the same levels of CO_2. The graph below shows their behavior at different levels of CO_2.

Effect of CO_2 concentration on predator avoidance in juvenile fish

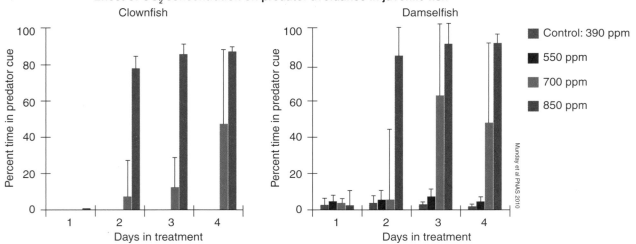

Munday et al PNAS 2010

Control: 390 ppm
550 ppm
700 ppm
850 ppm

▸ Finally the control damselfish and those treated at 700 ppm and 850 ppm were transplanted back to the coral reef. Here they appeared more active and showed riskier behavior than previously. This led to changes in their survival (below).

▸ Although damselfish whose behavior appeared unaffected in the lab displayed less riskier behavior than damselfish that appeared affected, their behavior was still significantly more risky than that of the control fish.

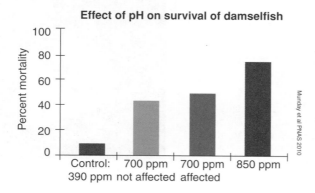

Effect of pH on survival of damselfish

Percent mortality (y-axis: 0 to 100)

x-axis categories: Control: 390 ppm, 700 ppm not affected, 700 ppm affected, 850 ppm

Munday et al PNAS 2010

Pomacentrus vaiuli

There are many species of damselfish. Many live in and around tropical reefs.

19. (a) Describe the effect of increasing CO_2 on the behavior of larval clownfish: _____

_____

_____

(b) Did this effect change over time? _____

_____

(c) What was the purpose of the no predator test? _____

_____

_____

20. (a) Describe the effect of increasing CO_2 on the behavior of juvenile clownfish and damselfish. Was there any difference in behavioral response between the two fish species?

_____

_____

_____

_____

(b) What does this say about the significance of the result? _____

_____

_____

_____

21. (a) How did the change in behavior of the damselfish affect their survival? _____

_____

_____

(b) Was survival affected by the level of CO_2? _____

22. What is the possible significance of these result to the fishing industry? _____

_____

_____

_____

47 Seashells by the Seashore Revisited

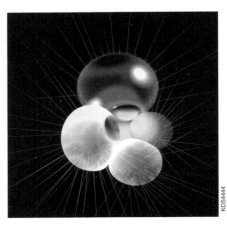

KDS4444

▶ At the beginning of this chapter you were shown some evidence that seashells contained calcium carbonate. You were also shown data that showed the shells of certain shell-making marine organisms were becoming thinner over time.

▶ During this chapter you will have become familiar with the concept of equilibrium and how it can be applied to ocean chemistry.

▶ You should now be able to explain exactly why the shells of some marine organisms are becoming thinner and where this phenomenon is likely to have the greatest impact.

1. Explain to your class why the shells of calcium carbonate shell-building marine organisms are likely to become thinner in coming decades. Discuss the chemistry around this phenomenon, and what conditions seem to affect it. Discuss how this shell thinning phenomenon might affect the survival of shell-building creatures. If you prefer, you can present your discussion as a slide presentation or poster.

2. Ocean acidification may not affect only shell-building creatures. How might ocean acidification affect the wider marine community? Use the resources on the **BIOZONE Resource Hub** to help you research a more detailed discussion.

ESS2.D CE SC

©2019 **BIOZONE** International
ISBN:978-1-927309-71-1

48 Summative Assessment

1. When ammonia dissolves in water the following equilibrium occurs: $NH_{3(g)} + H_2O_{(l)} \rightleftharpoons NH_4^+{}_{(aq)} + OH^-{}_{(aq)}$

   (a) Describe a simple method for detecting the **ammonia**: _____

   _____

   _____

   (b) How could you show OH^- ions were present? _____

   _____

2. A scientist on a internet video share site shows the effect of ocean acidification by placing a shell in a cup of vinegar. The shell dissolves over time and the scientist explains that this is what will happen if we keep adding carbon dioxide to the oceans.

   Explain why this explanation is incorrect and misleading: _____

   _____

   _____

   _____

   _____

   _____

   _____

   _____

3. Explain what is meant by a **dynamic equilibrium**. Use the equation $PCl_{5(g)} \rightleftharpoons PCl_{3(g)} + Cl_{2(g)}$ to help your explanation.

   _____

   _____

   _____

   _____

   _____

4. Consider the following equation: $2O_{3(g)} \rightleftharpoons 3O_{2(g)}$ $\Delta H= -285$ kJ. Describe the effect of the following changes in conditions on the number of $O_{2(g)}$ molecules in the system:

   (a) The pressure is increased: _____

   (b) The temperature is increased: _____

   (c) O_3 is removed from the system: _____

5. The bicarbonate buffer system in the blood is a system evolved to reduce the change in the blood's pH. The system is based around the bicarbonate ion (HCO_3^-). The equilibrium is: $CO_2 + H_2O \rightleftharpoons H_2CO_3 \rightleftharpoons HCO_3^- + H^+$.

   (a) What would be the effect of adding an acid (H^+) to the system? _____

   _____

   (b) How does adding the acid affect the blood's pH? _____

   _____

   (c) How is any acid added to the system ultimately removed? Explain your answer: _____

   _____

   _____

   _____

SC ESS2.D ESS2.A PS1.B

6. Consider the two acids HCl and CH_3COOH. When in (separate) solutions they react in the following way:

$$HCl \rightarrow H^+ + Cl^-$$
$$CH_3COOH \rightleftharpoons H^+ + CH_3COO^-$$

- The pH of the HCl was measured at 1. The pH of the CH_3COOH was measured at 2.88.
- 25 mL 0.1 mol/L of each acid was reacted with an excess of sodium carbonate (Na_2CO_3). The reaction between HCl and Na_2CO_3 was vigorous. The reaction between CH_3COOH and Na_2CO_3 was much slower.
- Each reaction produced the same amount of CO_2 gas.

    (a) Which acid has the greatest concentration of H^+ ions in solution? _____

    (b) Explain why the same amount of CO_2 gas was produced despite the pH of the acids being different:

    _____

    _____

    _____

7. A student set up an equilibrium by dissolving the slightly soluble solid calcium hydroxide in water:

$$Ca(OH)_{2(s)} \rightleftharpoons Ca^{2+}_{(aq)} + OH^-_{(aq)}$$

The student wishes to shift the equilibrium so that more calcium hydroxide dissolves into the solution. He has the following available: nitric acid (HNO_3) and calcium nitrate ($Ca(NO_3)_2$).

Which of these solutions should the student use and why? _____

_____

_____

_____

8. Sodium carbonate (Na_2CO_3) placed in water forms a basic solution. Carbonic acid (H_2CO_3) in water forms an acidic solution. Use equations to explain these results:

_____

_____

_____

_____

9. The graph below shows the changes in carbon dioxide and carbonate ions with pH.

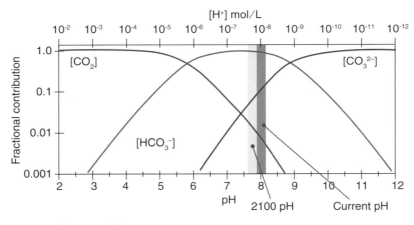

(a) What is the current range of ocean pH? _____

(b) What happens to the relative HCO_3^- and CO_3^{2-} contributions as pH decreases ($[H^+]$ increases) over the next 100 years? How will this affect shell-building marine organisms?

_____

_____

_____

©2019 **BIOZONE** International
ISBN:978-1-927309-71-1
Photocopying Prohibited

10. (a) On page 175 you developed a quantitative model of the carbon cycle. Using your model, as well as the information in this chapter, draw a diagram to represent a cause and effect chain illustrating how burning fossils fuels can affect natural systems.
   (b) One change to an Earth system can create feedbacks that cause changes to other systems. Add information to your diagram to show how climate feedback can affect other systems.

©2019 **BIOZONE** International
ISBN: 978-1-927309-71-1

SEP support

Basic Skills for Chemistry Students

Science and engineering practices

Background in activities as noted. Covered in earlier chapters in context.

Asking questions and defining problems

☐ 1 Demonstrate an understanding of science as inquiry. Appreciate that unexpected results may lead to new questions and to new discoveries.   **49**

☐ 2 Ask and evaluate questions that you are able to investigate with the resources you have available. Ask questions that arise from observation or examining models or theories, or to find out more information, determine relationships, or refine a model.   **49 51**

Developing and using models

☐ 3 Develop and use models to describe systems or their components and how they work, to explain or make predictions about phenomena, or to generate data to support explanations or solve problems.   **50**

☐ 4 Develop a model that allows you to manipulate and test a system or process.   **50**

Planning and carrying out investigations

☐ 5 Plan and carry out investigations to provide data to test a hypothesis, support an explanation, or test a solution to a problem. Identify and evaluate the importance of any assumptions in the design of your investigation.   **51 52**

☐ 6 Use appropriate tools to collect, record, analyze, and evaluate data.   **53-59**

☐ 7 Make and test hypotheses about the effect on a dependent variable when an independent variable is manipulated. Understand and use blanks, controls, and trial runs appropriately.   **54**

☐ 8 Consider and evaluate the accuracy and precision of the data that you collect.   **55**

Analyzing and interpreting data

☐ 9 Analyze data in order to make valid and reliable scientific claims. Consider limitations of data analysis (e.g. measurement error, bias) when analyzing and interpreting data.   **57-60**

☐ 10 Apply concepts of statistics and probability to answer questions and solve problems.   **61**

Use mathematics and computational thinking

☐ 11 Demonstrate an ability to use mathematics and computational tools to analyze, represent, and model data. Recognize and use appropriate units in calculations and demonstrate an ability to apply unit conversions.   **57**

☐ 12 Create and use simple computational simulations based on mathematical models.   **50**

☐ 13 Demonstrate an ability to apply ratios and proportional reasoning when mixing solutions with specific molarities, making dilutions, and analyzing molecular structure. Calculate rates and use algebra and graphs to analyze reaction rates. Understand the use of logarithms, e.g. as in pH scale.   **57 58 60**

Construct explanations and design solutions

☐ 14 Apply scientific evidence, ideas, and principles to explain phenomena and solve problems.   **49**

Engage in argument from evidence

☐ 15 Use evidence to defend and evaluate claims and explanations about science.   **49**

☐ 16 Provide and/or receive critiques on scientific arguments by using scientific methodology.   **49**

Obtain, evaluate, and communicate information

☐ 17 Evaluate the validity and reliability of designs, methods, claims, and/or evidence. Communicate scientific and/or technical information in multiple formats.   **55 56 60**

☐ 18 Demonstrate an ability to read critically and compare, integrate, and evaluate sources of information in different media and formats.   **49**

49 The Nature of Science

▸ Science is a way of understanding the universe we live in: where it came from, the rules it obeys and how it changes over time. Science distinguishes itself from other ways of understanding the universe by using empirical standards, logical arguments, and skeptical review. What we understand about the universe changes over time.

▸ Science is a human endeavor and requires creativity and imagination. New research and ways of thinking can be based on the well argued idea of a single person. It could be said that the scientific method is '*the art of embracing failure*', because apparent failures can lead to new discoveries and ways of thinking.

▸ Science influences and is influenced by society and technology, both of which are constantly changing. Scientists build on the ideas and work of their contemporaries and those that went before them.
"If I have seen further it is by standing on the shoulders of Giants".....*Isaac Newton*

▸ Science can never answer questions about the universe with absolute certainty. It can be confident of certain outcomes, but only within the limits of the data. Science might help us predict with 99.9% certainty a system will behave a certain way, but that still means there's one chance in a thousand it won't.

Science is a way of exploring the world

Science is not linear. Results may answer some questions and raise others. Collaborators bring new ways of thinking and new directions of research. We can make new discoveries by accident or because of unexpected results. Can you think of other words to add to this word map?

Observing
Observations cause questions; Iron appears to lose mass when rusting (rusted objects are crumbly and worn). Where does the mass go?

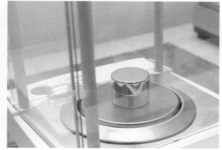

Carrying out investigations
Investigations seek to answer a question, or part of it. An iron object kept in a container can be weighed before and after rusting. Mass is **gained** during rusting.

Interpreting results, exploring further
How does the result change our understanding of iron and rusting? Why is it apparently different to what we think we see? What process is occurring here?

©2019 **BIOZONE** International
ISBN: 978-1-927309-71-1
Photocopying Prohibited

The nature of science: a brief overview of atomic theory

What is our world made of?

The ideas of the Greek philosophers were proposed based on observation and thought. No experimentation was carried out.

Empedocles (450 BC) proposed all matter was made up of four elements (earth, air, fire, and water) and two forces (love and strife), could mix and separate the elements.

Around 400 BC **Democritus** proposed that matter was made of particles and could be cut up until the particles were so small they could no longer be divided. He named the particles "atomos".

Philosophers at the time thought that problems could be solved simply by thinking about them.

Religion heavily influenced theories and many ideas that were at odds with social beliefs were not accepted nor discussed openly.

Plato (340 BC) disagreed with Democritus about the presence of atomos. Plato proposed that the four elements were regular solids composed of triangles. The triangles could combine to form different materials and states. He did not think they could be divided into smaller particles. This theory was widely accepted for a long time.

Aristotle (300 BC) also disagreed with Democritus and believed everything was a combination of the four elements. He believed the gods could divide an element into something smaller if they wanted to. Most people agreed with his ideas until the 17th century.

A practice of experimentation and scientific observation began to arise and become common.

Gathering evidence allowed new ideas to be formed and redefined as new knowledge came to light.

Robert Boyle (1600s) wrote the "Skeptical Chemist" urging scientists to abandon the view that elements were mystical substances. He argued Earth could not be an element as it contained other substances (e.g. gold and iron). He helped to pioneer the scientific method.

In the 1700s chemists **Joseph Priestly** and **Antoine Lavoisier** began to explain chemical behavior in terms of the atom. They showed that substances could combine to form new materials.

John Dalton (1803) developed an atomic theory covering five main principles. It was the first attempt to describe all matter in terms of atoms and their properties. His work was generally accepted because it provided logical answers to many questions.

The scientific evidence for atomic theory become widely accepted.

The atomic theory was refined and became more sophisticated as technology improved and new evidence was gathered.

Through the 1800s and 1900s, many scientists made discoveries that helped to refine Dalton's atomic theory. For example, Dalton proposed that atoms could not be divided into smaller parts. However, subsequent research showed that atoms are made up of smaller components. In 1904 **J.J. Thomson** discovered atoms contained electrons and proposed the "plum pudding model". A few years later, **Ernest Rutherford** carried out a gold foil experiment and described the presence of a nucleus. He developed the planetary model. Further refinements, including the position and movement of electrons (**Niels Bohr**) and the discovery of neutrons (**James Chadwick**) contributed to the model of the atom accepted today. Many of these discoveries were aided by improvements in technology allowing researchers to build on the knowledge of other scientists.

Fire   Water

Air   Earth

Empedocles and others

Dalton

Thomson: Plum pudding model

Rutherford: Planetary model

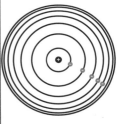

Bohr

1. Work in groups to discuss how the nature of science was important in the development of the atomic theory. You should include the following in your discussion:

▸ How was the theory's progress affected by the beliefs of the day (e.g. societal and religious ideas)?

▸ How did the switch from thinking about a problem (philosophizing) to experimental based evidence affect progress?

▸ What role did technological advancement play?

▸ Why was the work of earlier scientists important to those who came afterwards?

©2019 **BIOZONE** International
ISBN: 978-1-927309-71-1
Photocopying Prohibited

50 Systems and System Models

▶ A system is an interacting set of matter and energy. If, for example, reactions are occurring in a beaker, the beaker and everything inside it is the system. Everything outside the beaker is the surroundings.

▶ Most systems are open systems and exchange energy and matter with their surroundings.

▶ Closed systems exchange energy with their surroundings, but not matter. For example, a boiling pot with a tightly fitting lid represents a closed system. If the lid is lifted, the system can exchange both energy and matter with its environment (open). The Earth itself is essentially a closed system also.

▶ An isolated system does not exchange energy or matter with its surroundings. No isolated systems are known to exist but a thermos flask approximates an isolated system for a short time.

Open

Closed

Isolated?

Models vary in complexity

▶ Models are extremely important when trying to understand how a system operates. A model is a representation of an object or system that shares important characteristics with the object or system being studied.

▶ A model is a useful way to break a system down into smaller, more manageable parts, which are often modeled separately. The model does not have to incorporate all the features of the system to be useful. As understanding of the system increases, the model can include more information so that it more closely represents the real system. One example is the use of models to represent atoms. The models below become more complex from left to right.

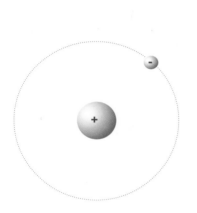

Rutherford's atomic model showing position of charge

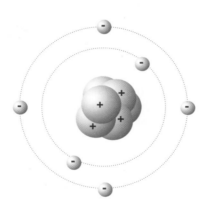

Bohr atomic model showing electron orbitals (2D)

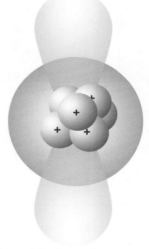

Atomic model using quantum mechanics to show 3D electron clouds.

1. (a) In your own words explain what a system is and give your own example: _____

    _____

    _____

    (b) In your own words explain what a model is and give your own example: _____

    _____

    _____

2. Describe how the atomic models above become more complex: _____

    _____

    _____

    _____

©2019 **BIOZONE** International
ISBN: 978-1-927309-71-1

SSM

Examples of models

▶ Models are commonly used in science to understand a system better and describe it more accurately.

▶ Some models are predictive. A model can be used to predict what will happen if a specific change is made to a system. The information can be used to determine how all the components (living and non-living) within the system may be affected. Examples of predictive models are those used to develop new pharmaceuticals, and to study weather patterns and the effect of increased levels of carbon dioxide on ocean pH.

▶ There are many different ways to model systems (e.g. mathematical or visual models). Often seeing data presented in different ways can help us to understand it better.

Modeling changes in the ocean
The oceans act as a carbon sink, absorbing much of the carbon dioxide produced from burning fossil fuels. The increasing amount of carbon dioxide in the atmosphere is reducing the pH of the ocean. Scientists use models to predict change in ocean pH over time. They use this data to determine how ocean organisms could be affected.

Modeling the Earth's structure
The Earth's structure can be modeled using data from earthquakes, Earth's magnetic field, and volcanic activity. The Earth's magnetic field suggests an iron core surrounded by molten material. The bending of earthquake waves suggests a thin solid crust. Volcanic activity shows there is molten material below the crust.

Modeling the effects of medicines
Predictive models are central to the development of new drugs and medicines. Using predictive models speeds up the drug development process by reliably predicting the attributes (and effects) of potential new compounds on the basis of their molecular structure. Models can also evaluate how medicines will interact with each other.

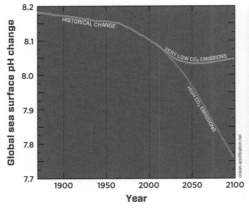

3. (a) Explain why models are never 100% accurate representations of the system being studied: _____

_____

_____

_____

(b) Discuss the advantages and disadvantages of using models to explain a system: _____

_____

_____

_____

_____

_____

(c) Why is it easier to use a series of simple models to explain a complex system than one complex model?

_____

_____

_____

_____

_____

_____

©2019 **BIOZONE** International
ISBN: 978-1-927309-71-1
Photocopying Prohibited

51 Observations and Assumptions

Observations and hypotheses

▶ An observation is watching or recording what is happening. Observation is the basis for forming hypotheses and making predictions. An observation may generate a number of hypotheses (tentative explanations for what we see). Each hypothesis will lead to one or more predictions, which can be tested by investigation.

▶ A hypothesis can be written as a statement to include the prediction: "If X is true, then if I do Y (the experiment), I expect Z (the prediction)". Hypotheses are accepted, changed, or rejected on the basis of investigations. A hypothesis should have a sound theoretical basis and should be testable.

Observation 1: Iron-containing steel chain rusted (developed a brown-red flaky coating) when it was left exposed to air and moisture for several months.

Observation 2: An iron-containing steel chain was coated with a varnish before being placed outside. After several months exposed to air and moisture its appearance remained unchanged.

Assumptions

Any investigation requires you to make **assumptions** about the system you are working with. Assumptions are features of the system you are studying that you assume to be true but that you do not (or cannot) test. Some assumptions about the two observations above are:

▶ The steel chain in both observations is exposed to the same environmental conditions (moisture, air, temperature).

▶ Exposure to certain environmental conditions causes the iron in steel to undergo a chemical reaction.

▶ The chemical reaction results in the formation of rust.

1. Read the two observations above and then answer the following questions:

   (a) Generate a hypothesis to explain why rusting did not occur when the steel chain was coated in varnish:

   Hypothesis: _____

   _____

   _____

   _____

   (b) Describe one of the assumptions being made in your hypothesis: _____

   _____

   _____

   (c) Generate a prediction about the extent of rusting that would occur if treated and untreated steel were left outside for several years:

   _____

   _____

   _____

   _____

Occam's razor

▶ Occam's razor is a problem solving method. At its simplest, it states that the simplest explanation is usually likely to be correct. Among competing hypotheses, the one with the least number of assumptions should be used. Occam's razor helps rule out hypotheses or explanations that contain too many assumptions.

▶ Let's look at an everyday example to see Occam's razor in use. You return home from school, turn off the house alarm and go into the kitchen. You see an element on your cook top is on. You cooked eggs for breakfast in the morning but you are surprised the element is still on because you always turn it off.

▶ One explanation is that you simply forgot to turn it off. Another explanation could be that someone broke into your home and turned the cook top on. The second explanation is more complicated. It means someone broke into your home, cracked the alarm code, turned on the cook top and left again after resetting the alarm. It is far more likely you simply forgot to turn it off in your hurry to get to school!

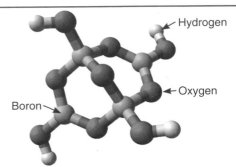

Boron molecules come is various different shapes (configurations). Occam's razor was used to help narrow down how the tetrahedral boron molecule forms (above).

One group proposed a very complicated theory where bonds were not broken but simply rearranged. However, it is far more likely the formation of the tetraborate is more straightforward and results from the breaking and rearrangement and bonds.

Assumptions and the wider universe

For us to understand the universe, we have to assume certain ideas hold true everywhere and, if they don't, we have to be able to explain why not. There are essentially two rules that are assumed to be true in science.

1   All of existence (i.e. the universe) is governed by rules (laws) that are the same everywhere. They are inviolable (they cannot be broken).

▶   This is essential for us to discover and understand the laws of the universe. There can't be one set of laws that apply in our universe today and a different set of laws tomorrow. Nor can there be different laws that apply to different parts of the universe. For example, the movement of light in a vacuum must behave the same way today, as it did yesterday, as it does everywhere in the universe.

2   These laws can be determined by observation of the universe around us.

▶   The second rule is equally important. What if the laws governing the universe could not be understood? What if the number of laws was essentially infinite? No matter how carefully you observed something or how general your equations, you would never be able to write down a law that could be applied reliably to more than one situation.

2. (a) How does Occam's razor help to simplify explanations? _____

    _____

    _____

    (b) Two students observed that two trees had toppled over in the night and that the grass around the trees was apparently undisturbed. Student A hypothesized that the wind had blown them over. Student B hypothesized that the trees had been knocked over by a large truck and the grass repaired after the truck had been removed.

    Decide which of these two hypotheses is more likely and explain your choice: _____

    _____

    _____

    _____

3. Explain why it is important in science to assume that the laws of nature are universal, behaving in the same way everywhere and at every time:

    _____

    _____

    _____

©2019 **BIOZONE** International
ISBN: 978-1-927309-71-1
Photocopying Prohibited

52 Useful Concepts in Chemistry

Temperature

▸ Temperature is a measure of the energy of an object. Molecules constantly vibrate (kinetic energy) and temperature is a measure of these vibrations. The faster and larger the vibrations the higher the object's temperature. Temperature rises as heat is added to a system and lowers when heat is removed.

▸ There are many temperature scales used throughout the world, but the most common are the Celsius, Fahrenheit, and Kelvin scales. The Kelvin scale is commonly used in science, although because it uses the same magnitude of scale as the Celsius scale, Celsius is also commonly used.

Scale	Basis	Freezing/boiling point of water
Celsius	Boiling and freezing points of pure water.	Freezing 0°C Boiling 100°C
Fahrenheit	Zeroed on a mixture of ice and salt. Original scale set freezing point of water at 30°F and body temperature at 90°F.	Freezing 32°F Boiling 212°F
Kelvin	Absolute zero; the point at which all vibrations stop. Same scale as Celsius. An absolute scale so no degree symbol is used.	Freezing 273 K Boiling 372 K

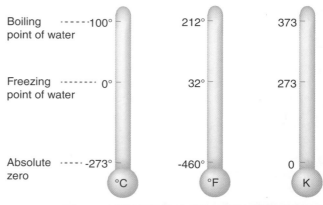

Boiling point of water ----- 100° | 212° | 373

Freezing point of water -------- 0° | 32° | 273

Absolute zero ----- -273° | -460° | 0

°C | °F | K

▸ Temperature can be inferred from color. A heated piece of iron will initially glow red, then orange-yellow as it gets hotter, then white.

▸ In chemistry, the color of a Bunsen flame gives an indication of temperature. A yellow (or safety) flame is the coolest at 1000°C. With increasing oxygen supply, a hotter blue flame is produced, with a temperature of ~1600°C (right). A blue-colored flame indicates that there is no soot (uncombusted material) in the flame. Many metals also produce a characteristic color when heated, e.g. sodium produces an intense yellow flame and lithium a crimson red flame.

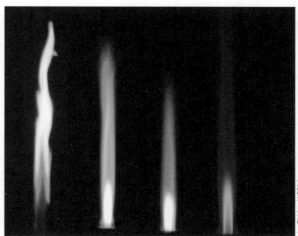

Jan Fjaldowski CC3.0

1. What is temperature measuring? _____

_____

_____

_____

2. How can flame color be used to predict temperature? _____

_____

_____

_____

3. For each of the temperature scales above, write down the temperature at which the following occurs:

(a) The boiling point of water:

(°C) _____ (°F) _____ (K) _____

(b) The freezing point of water:

(°C) _____ (°F) _____ (K) _____

Pressure

▸ Pressure is an important concept in the physical sciences. Pressure is a measure of the force being applied per unit surface area. The pressure of the air pressing on the surface of the Earth is 101.3 Pa (pascals).

▸ Pressure is one of the most measurable properties of a gas. The pressure (P), volume (V), number of moles, and temperature (T) of an ideal gas are related by a simple formula called the ideal gas law. This equation allows us to predict the behavior of a gas given certain conditions. For example, if you keep the volume constant and heat a gas, the pressure increases is a linear way. $P \propto T$ for a given mass and volume of gas. $\propto$ means proportional to.

Low temperature - slow movement of gas particles

High temperature - fast movement of gas particles

Density

▸ The density of a substance is the relationship between the mass of the substance and how much space it takes up (volume). In other words, density is the amount of matter contained in a particular volume. An element such as lead is very dense because its particles are very close together.

▸ Density can be used to identify pure substances and to determine the composition of mixed substances.

▸ Water and oil are an provide an easy example of observing differences in density (right). An object's relative density to water will determine whether it floats or sinks. Oil has a lower density than water so it floats above the water. An object with a higher density will sink. In glass A to the right, the density of the water is greater than that of the cork, but less than that of the metal.

Oil

Water

A

B

4. What is pressure?_____

_____

_____

5. (a) Explain why the pressure in a sealed container of gas increases when heat is added to the system: _____

_____

_____

_____

(b) Explain why the pressure in a sealed container of gas decreases when the system is cooled: _____

_____

_____

_____

6. Fresh water has a density of 1000 kg/m³. Will the following objects sink or float if placed in it?

(a) A cork (density = 240 kg/m³): _____

(b) A piece of lead (density = 11,340 kg/m³): _____

(c) Air (density = 1.2 kg/m³): _____

7. In glass B (above right) what can you say about the densities of the three substances present? _____

_____

_____

53 Standard Chemistry Equipment

▶ Most high school chemistry experiments can be carried out using just a few basic pieces of laboratory equipment. In addition to the laboratory supplies, it is important that personal protective equipment (PPE) is worn at all times.

NEED HELP? See activity 2

▶ Some basic laboratory equipment is shown below. It is important that you know how to use it correctly and also how to maintain and clean it so that it works properly. Clearly label any containers so you know what is in them and at the end of the experiment dispose of the waste correctly. Clean your equipment thoroughly after use. This prolongs the life of the equipment and prevents contamination when the equipment is used next.

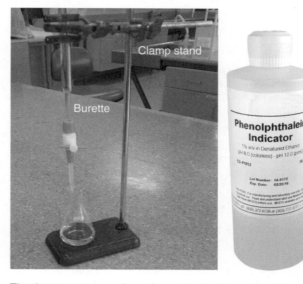

Laboratories have an assortment of glassware in a variety of sizes. This includes beakers, conical flasks, volumetric flasks and measuring cylinders (L→R above). They all measure liquids, but their accuracy varies.

Titrations are commonly performed in the laboratory. They require several pieces of equipment including a burette, clamp stand, conical flask, funnel, and chemical indicator. Phenolphthalein is a commonly used indicator. It changes color when the end point is reached (above).

Balances, pH meters (or indicator paper) and thermometers are used in nearly every chemistry experiment. Remember if you are using pH meters you must calibrate them with standards first. This will tell you if the machine is working correctly. There are many different types of balances, make sure you choose the correct one for the mass of sample you want!

Make sure you know how to use each piece of equipment properly *before you begin your experiment*. If you are trying to figure out how to use equipment while carrying out your experiment the chances of mistakes (and collecting unreliable data) are high. Correct use also keeps you and your classmates safe.

1. Work in pairs or small groups to identify the chemistry equipment you use most frequently. Take some time to ask yourself if you know how to use it correctly? Are there any special instructions you need to know before you use it? Write your ideas here (you many want to use extra paper and staple it to this page):

_____

_____

_____

_____

©2019 **BIOZONE** International
ISBN: 978-1-927309-71-1
Photocopying Prohibited

54 Experimenting in Chemistry

▶ Chemistry is an experimental science and all chemical statements are based on experiment. In your study of chemistry, you will investigate the properties of substances and the interactions between different types of matter. Chemistry helps you to understand how things work.

▶ You can investigate in two broad ways: by using experimentation to explore the properties of a substance or substances and by conducting controlled experiments. In a controlled experiment you alter just one variable at a time in order to answer a question you have asked about a phenomenon.

▶ A variable is a factor that can be changed during an experiment (e.g. temperature, mass, pressure). Investigations often look at how changing one variable affects another.

Variables and controls

▶ The independent variable is set by the experimenter. It is the variable that is deliberately altered and is recorded on the x axis of a graph. Where a response is recorded over time, the independent variable is time.

▶ The dependent variable is the response variable, measured during the course of the experiment It is recorded on the y axis of a graph.

▶ Controlled (or constant) variables are variables that you keep the same during your experiment.

▶ To be a fair test, an experiment should alter only one variable at a time and there should be a control, which acts as a standard or reference treatment. A control is identical to the original experiment except it lacks the altered variable, so it provides confidence that the analytical method is working correctly.

▶ A blank is often used in chemistry. This is a solution containing little to no analyte of interest. It is used to give a baseline reading and calibrate instruments such as a colorimeter. A blank allows you to trace unidentified sources of contamination.

Cooking is chemistry!

A chemistry experiment is not unlike a recipe. Ingredients are added in specific proportions and, given certain conditions, there is a result.

▶ In bread-making, dried baker's yeast is activated by adding it to a mix of warm water and sugar, and then mixed with flour to form a dough.

▶ The dough is worked (kneaded) for 5-10 minutes and then incubated at around 25-27°C. The growing yeast produces CO_2, which causes the dough to rise.

▶ Imagine you wanted to find out if the amount of yeast added affected the doubling time of the dough (the time taken for the volume of dough to double in size).

New dough, beginning to rise The dough, 40 minutes later

Photos: ElinorD cc 3.0

1. In the experiment to investigate the effect of added yeast mass on the doubling time of dough (above right):

   (a) Identify the independent variable: _____

   (b) Identify the dependent (response) variable: _____

   (c) What would the controlled (constant) variables be?_____

   _____

   _____

   (d) What would the control be?_____

2. In the space right, draw and label the axes on which you could plot your results.

3. What difficulties or sources of error are most likely to interfere with obtaining a reliable result in this cooking experiment?

   _____

   _____

   _____

   _____

©2019 **BIOZONE** International
ISBN: 978-1-927309-71-1
Photocopying Prohibited

55 Accuracy and Precision

▶ **Accuracy** refers to how close a measured or derived value is to its true value. Simply put, it is the correctness of the measurement. The accuracy of a measurement can be increased by increasing the number of measurements taken. For example, the accuracy of determining the concentration of an analyte in a solution can be increased by increasing the number of titrations carried out.

▶ **Precision** refers to how close repeated measurements are to each other, i.e. the ability to be exact. A balance with a fault in it could give very precise (repeatable) but inaccurate (untrue) results. Data can only be reported as accurately as the measurement of the apparatus allows. It is often expressed as significant figures (the digits in a number which express meaning to a degree of accuracy).

▶ The precision of a measurement relates to its repeatability. In most laboratory work, we assume a piece of equipment (e.g. a pipette) performs accurately, so making precise measures is the most important consideration. We can test precision by taking repeated measurements from individual samples. Precision and reliability are synonymous and describe how dependably an observation is the same when repeated.

A digital device such as the pH meter (above left) will deliver precise measurements, but its accuracy will depend on correct calibration.

The precision of measurements taken with instruments such as reading the level in a burette (above right) will depend on the skill of the operator. Precise measurements give reliable data.

Accuracy and equipment

You will need to take into account the accuracy of the measuring equipment when reporting values. For example, electronic balances may give readings to one or more decimal places based on their accuracy (laboratory balances may read to a hundred thousandths of a gram).

The table below illustrates the difference between a balance weighing to 0.1 of a gram and one weighing to 0.01 of a gram.

Sample	1	2	3	4	5	Mean
Mass (g) (2 s.f)	1.1	1.2	1.4	1.2	1.3	1.2
Mass (g) (3 s.f)	1.12	1.23	1.44	1.19	1.28	1.25

The difference in mean mass is slight (just 0.05 g) but over larger samples or larger masses the differences can add up.

The table above also shows the importance of significant figures (s.f.). The actual numerical mean for the second row is 1.252. However because we are measuring to three significant figures we cannot be sure of the final number thus the answer must be given in the same significant figures as the measurements.

1. Distinguish between accuracy and precision: _____

_____

_____

_____

_____

_____

_____

2. Describe why it is important to take measurements that are both accurate and precise:

_____

_____

_____

_____

_____

3. A researcher is trying to determine the melting point of a substance. Their temperature probe is incorrectly calibrated. How would this affect the accuracy and precision of the data collected?

_____

_____

_____

4. A bulls-eye target analogy is often used to represent the difference between accuracy and precision (assuming the bulls-eye is the true value or point). Draw dots on each of the four targets below to describe the four situations:

(a) Accurate but imprecise	(b) Inaccurate and imprecise	(c) Precise but inaccurate	(d) Accurate and precise

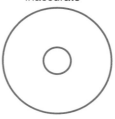

56 Measurement and Quantitative Analysis

▸ In experimental work, we use the term 'experimental error' to describe the uncertainty created by variations in the data. These are often systematic errors (consistent over- or underestimation), which arise because of instrument errors or errors in the technique of the experiment.

▸ Systematic errors can be reduced by choosing apparatus that is appropriate for the experiment or analysis and calibrating and using it correctly. Calibration ensures that the equipment is delivering the correct response. This is done by measuring the actual response against a standard that you know to be accurate (true).

▸ Inaccurate results are produced if equipment is not calibrated. In a high school laboratory, inaccurate results are annoying but in industry they could have serious effects. For example, a faulty pH meter in a food processing plant may result in not enough acid being added to a food, which could result in spoilage and costly product recalls.

Selecting the correct equipment

It is important that you choose equipment that is appropriate for the type of measurement you want to take. For example, which of the glassware would you use if you wanted to measure 225 mL?

The 500 mL graduated cylinder has graduations every 5 mL whereas the 500 mL beaker has graduations every 50 mL. It would be more accurate to measure 225 mL in a graduated cylinder.

Different types of **graduated glassware** have different accuracies. A beaker is less accurate than a measuring cylinder and a measuring cylinder is less accurate than a pipette. Volumetric glassware is the most accurate. Can you think why?

What about pipettes?

Pipettes are a common tool for volumetric work in chemistry and you are likely to come across several different types, from simple, single unit glass pipettes (right) to adjustable micropipettes for delivering very small volumes (up to 1 mL). In titrations, you will frequently use a volumetric pipette of 10-25 mL volume.

Volumetric pipettes have a large bulb and a long narrow part above that has one graduation mark. They are calibrated to deliver accurately a fixed volume of liquid (just like a volumetric flask). Different devices, such as bulbs, are used to draw the liquid into the pipette.

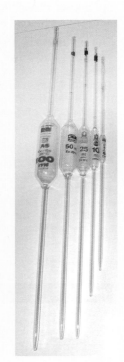

Percentage errors

Percentage error allows you to express how far your result is from the ideal (expected) result. The equation for calculating percentage error is:

$$\frac{\text{experimental value} - \text{ideal value}}{\text{ideal value}} \times 100$$

Example: To determine the accuracy of a 10 mL pipette, dispense 10 mL of water from the pipette and weigh the dispensed volume. The mass (g) = volume (mL). Imagine the volume is 10.02 mL.

$$\frac{10.02 - 10.0}{10.0} \times 100$$

The percentage error = 0.2% (the pipette is dispensing **more** than it should).

1. Assume that you have the following measuring devices available: 50 mL beaker, 50 mL cylinder, 50 mL volumetric pipette, 25 mL cylinder, 10 mL pipette, 10 mL beaker, 25 mL volumetric pipette. What would you use to most accurately measure:

   (a) 21 mL: _____

   (b) 48 mL: _____

   (c) 9 mL: _____

   (d) 25 mL: _____

   (e) 50 mL: _____

2. Calculate the percentage error for the following situations (show your working):

   (a) A 1 mL pipette delivers a measured volume of 0.98 mL:

   _____

   (b) A 5 mL pipette delivers a measured volume of 4.98 mL:

   _____

   (c) A 50 mL volumetric pipette delivers a measured volume of 50.025 mL:

   _____

©2019 **BIOZONE** International
ISBN: 978-1-927309-71-1
Photocopying Prohibited

Deluxecheese cc 4.0

Using titration in chemistry

▶ Chemistry often involves titration. As this involves using solutions, it is also called volumetric analysis. During a titration, a solution of known concentration (called a **standard solution**) is used to determine the concentration of a solution with an unknown concentration.

▶ A standard solution contains a known and accurate amount of a substance or element and is made by dissolving a **primary standard** in a suitable solvent (often distilled water). A primary standard is typically a soluble solid compound that is very pure, with a consistent formula and a relatively high molar mass.

▶ The solution being added from the burette is called the titrant. The solution in the receiving conical flask contains 1-2 drops of **indicator** that changes color at a known point (e.g. pH). The concentration of the unknown can be calculated from how much titrant was added to reach an end point (usually neutralization in an acid-base titration).

▶ The end color depends on the indicator. Methyl orange and phenolphthalein are common indicators for acid-base titrations. The titration is repeated several times to obtain values within 0.5 mL and then a mean value is calculated.

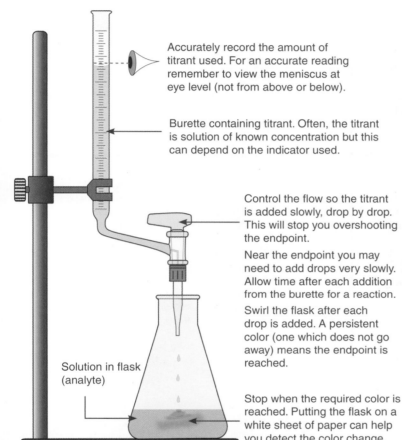

Accurately record the amount of titrant used. For an accurate reading remember to view the meniscus at eye level (not from above or below).

Burette containing titrant. Often, the titrant is solution of known concentration but this can depend on the indicator used.

Control the flow so the titrant is added slowly, drop by drop. This will stop you overshooting the endpoint.

Near the endpoint you may need to add drops very slowly. Allow time after each addition from the burette for a reaction.

Swirl the flask after each drop is added. A persistent color (one which does not go away) means the endpoint is reached.

Solution in flask (analyte)

Stop when the required color is reached. Putting the flask on a white sheet of paper can help you detect the color change.

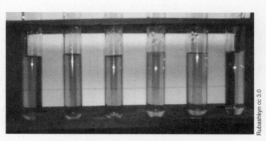

Methyl orange shows a red color below pH 3.1 and a yellow color above pH 4.4.

The phenolphthalein molecule is colorless but the ion is pink. When a base is added to a solution containing phenolphthalein, more of it becomes ionized and the solution turns pink. Titrate just to the end point (color change), no further!

3. Indicators themselves are weak acids or weak bases. Why do you think then that only a 1-2 drops of indicator is used in an acid-base titration?

_____

4. Why do you think a primary standard typically has a high molar mass? _____

_____

5. With your lab partners, discuss potential sources of error during a volumetric analysis (from making the standard solution to performing the titration). Name them and describe how you would minimize them. Use more paper if you need to:

_____

_____

_____

_____

_____

©2019 **BIOZONE** International
ISBN: 978-1-927309-71-1
Photocopying Prohibited

57 Working with Numbers

▶ Mathematics is used to analyze, interpret, and compare data. It is important that you are familiar with mathematical notation (the language of mathematics) and can confidently apply some basic mathematical principles and calculations to your data.

Log transformations

▶ A log transformation can make very large numbers easier to work with.

▶ The log of a number is the exponent to which a fixed value (the base) is raised to get that number. So $\log_{10} (1000) = 3$ because $10^3 = 1000$.

▶ Both $\log_{10}$ and $\log_e$ (natural logs or *ln*) are commonly used.

▶ Log transformations are useful for data where there is an exponential increase or decrease in numbers. In this case, the transformation will produce a straight line plot.

▶ To find the $\log_{10}$ of a number, e.g. 32, using a calculator, key in log 32 = . The answer should be 1.51.

▶ An example of a log scale is the pH scale. The pH scale measures how acidic or basic a substance is and ranges from pH 0-14. Each whole unit represents a 10 times magnitude. For example pH 4 is 10 times more acidic than pH 5. pH 9 is 100 times more alkaline than pH 7.

Multiples

Multiple	Prefix	Symbol	Example
10^9	giga	G	gigawatt (GW)
10^6	mega	M	megawatt (MW)
10^3	kilo	k	kilogram (kg)
10^2	hecto	h	hectare (ha)
10^{-1}	deci	d	decimeter (dm)
10^{-2}	centi	c	centimeter (cm)
10^{-3}	milli	m	millimeter (mm)
10^{-6}	micro	μ	microsecond (μs)
10^{-9}	nano	n	nanometer (nm)
10^{-12}	pico	p	picosecond (ps)

Decimal and standard form

Decimal form (also called ordinary form) is the longhand way of writing a number (e.g. 15,000,000). Very large or very small numbers can take up too much space if written in decimal form and are often expressed in a condensed standard form. For example, 15,000,000 is written as 1.5×10^7 in standard form.

In standard form a number is always written as $A \times 10^n$, where A is a number between 1 and 10, and n (the exponent) indicates how many places to move the decimal point. n can be positive or negative.

For the example above, A = 1.5 and n = 7 because the decimal point moved seven places (see below).

$$1.5\,0\,0\,0\,0\,0\,0 = 1.5 \times 10^7$$

Small numbers can also be written in standard form. The exponent (n) will be negative. For example, 0.00101 is written as 1.01×10^{-3}.

$$0.0\,0\,1\,0\,1 = 1.01 \times 10^{-3}$$

Adding numbers in standard form

Numbers in standard form can be added together so long as they are both raised to the same power of ten.
e.g: $1 \times 10^4 + 2 \times 10^3 = 1 \times 10^4 + 0.2 \times 10^4 = 1.2 \times 10^4$

Rates

Rates are expressed as a measure per unit of time and show how a variable changes over time. Rates are used to provide meaningful comparisons of data that may have been recorded over different time periods.

Often rates are expressed as a mean rate over the duration of the measurement period, but it is also useful to calculate the rate at various times to understand how rate changes over time. The table below shows the reaction rates for a gas produced during a chemical reaction. A worked example for the rate at 4 minutes is provided below the table.

Time (Minute)	Cumulative gas produced (cm^3)	Rate of reaction (cm^3/min)
0	0	0
2	34	17
4	42	4*
6	48	?
8	50	?
10	50	0

* Gas produced between 2-4 min: $42\,cm^3 - 34\,cm^3 = 8\,cm^3$
  Rate of reaction between 2-4 min: $8 \div 2\,min = 4\,cm^3/min$

---

1. Use the information above to complete the following calculations:

    (a) Write 6,340,000 in standard form: _____ (b) Write 7.82×10^7 as a number: _____

    (c) Write 0.00103 in standard form: _____ (d) $4.5 \times 10^4 + 6.45 \times 10^5$: _____

2. How many times greater is the hydrogen ion concentration of a pH 2 solution than a pH 6 solution? _____

3. Using the table (above right) calculate the rate of gas produced between:

    (a) 4 and 6 minutes: _____

    (b) 6 and 8 minutes: _____

©2019 **BIOZONE** International
ISBN: 978-1-927309-71-1

58 Ratio and Proportion in Chemistry

▶ Ratio and proportion are important concepts in chemistry. A ratio compares quantities of two different categories, e.g. in a bread recipe, we use 2 cups of flour for every 1 cup of water. The ratio of flour to water is 2 : 1. We use ratios a lot in chemistry where atoms and reagents are found in fixed proportions (they are proportional).

▶ Proportion is a mathematical concept, which states **the equality of two ratios or fractions**. You use proportions every time you double or halve a recipe because the ingredients go up or down in proportion. You do the same thing in chemistry!

Try it out!

A box of pancake mix gives instructions for mixing the pancakes (right):

Pancakes	Volume of mix	Volume of water
6	1 cup	0.75 cup
12	2 cups	1.5 cups
18	3 cups	2.25 cups

1. What is the ratio of mix to water in each case? _____

2. How can we work out how much mix we need to make 30 pancakes? The answer is we cross multiply using the ratio of mix to pancakes (1 : 6):

$$\frac{1}{6} \times = \frac{x}{30} \qquad 30 = 6x \qquad \text{Answer = 5 cups}$$
$$5 = x$$

Now use the ratio of mix to water to calculate the amount of water needed:

_____

_____

Now let's apply these basic principles to some important aspects of chemistry.

Ratios in stoichiometry

Example 1

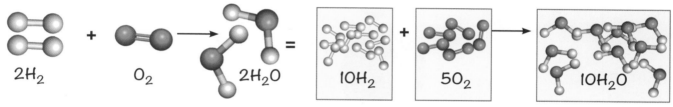

$$2H_2 \qquad O_2 \qquad 2H_2O \qquad IOH_2 \qquad 5O_2 \qquad IOH_2O$$

If you know the reactants and products in a reaction, you can write an unbalanced equation by putting the reactants on one side and the products on the other. Both sides of the equation must have the same number of atoms (the law of conservation of mass). The multiplication factors required to balance the equation tells you the mole ratios of each of the compounds in the reaction. In the reaction above, 2 moles H_2 and 1 mole O_2 give 2 moles of water.

Example 2

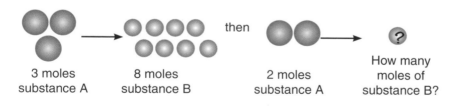

3 moles substance A → 8 moles substance B then 2 moles substance A → ? How many moles of substance B?

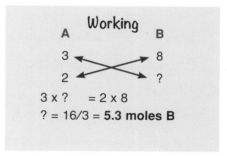

Working

A   B

3   8

2   ?

$3 \times ? = 2 \times 8$

$? = 16/3 = $ **5.3 moles B**

Example 3

▶ Consider the formula for propanol: C_3H_5OH. The ratio of carbon to hydrogen atoms is 3:6. The mass ratios will be in proportion.

▶ First we use molar mass (M) in mol/g and the equation **n=m/M** to convert the mass (m) to number of moles (n). We can then cross multiply to calculate that if there is 8 g C in a propanol sample, there will be 1.33 g of H.

▶ Note that the units mol and mol/g cancel, leaving the final unit (grams).

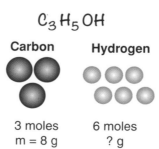

C_3H_5OH

Carbon — 3 moles, m = 8 g

Hydrogen — 6 moles, ? g

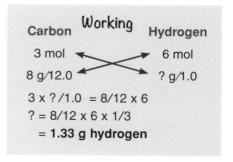

Working

Carbon   Hydrogen

3 mol   6 mol

8 g/12.0   ? g/1.0

$3 \times ?/1.0 = 8/12 \times 6$

$? = 8/12 \times 6 \times 1/3$

$= $ **1.33 g hydrogen**

Using ratios to concentrations and pressures

▶ Now you can apply your understanding of ratios and proportions to some other common situations.

3. **Concentration**: If a solution of the desired concentration contains 5 g of a salt in 30 mL of water, how many grams of salt would you dissolve in 75 mL to have the same concentration? If you want, draw arrows on the diagram to help you.

5 g

? g

30 mL

75 mL

Working

g   mL

4. **Pressures**: A pressure of 759 mm Hg gives 101.2 kPa. If a balloon is inflated to 60 kPa, what is the pressure in mm Hg? If you want, draw arrows on the diagram to help you.

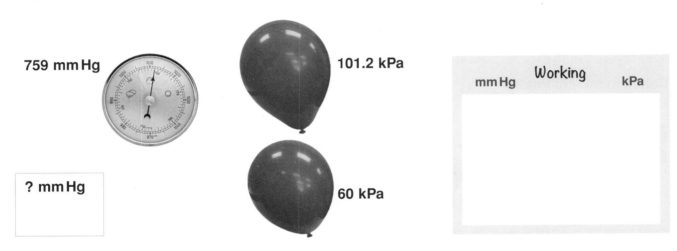

759 mm Hg

? mm Hg

101.2 kPa

60 kPa

Working

mm Hg   kPa

5. Ammonia (NH_3) is a compound with 1 : 3 ratio of nitrogen to hydrogen atoms.

   (a) If a sample of ammonia contains 1500 nitrogen atoms, determine the number of hydrogen atoms present?

   _____

   (b) If a sample of ammonia contains 1410 hydrogen atoms, determine the number of nitrogen atoms present?

   _____

6. Methane (CH_4) is a gas.

   (a) What is the ratio of carbon to hydrogen atoms? _____

   (b) If a methane sample contains 1575 atoms, how many carbon and hydrogen atoms are present? Show your working:

   _____

   _____

   (c) Can a sample of methane contain 1577 atoms? Explain your answer: _____

   _____

7. The mass to charge ratio of an isotope was found to be 2.0×10^{-7} kilograms per coulomb. If the charge on the isotope is 1.6×10^{-19} coulombs, what is the mass of the isotope? HINT: Determine the ratio and cross multiply as usual.

   _____

   _____

©2019 **BIOZONE** International
ISBN: 978-1-927309-71-1
Photocopying Prohibited

59 Logbooks and Tables

Recording your results accurately is very important in any type of scientific investigation. If you have recorded your results accurately and in an organized way, it makes analyzing and understanding your data easier. Log books and dataloggers are two methods by which data can be recorded.

Log books

▶ A log book records your ideas and results throughout your scientific investigation. It also provides proof that you have carried out the work.

▶ A lined exercise book is a good choice for a log book. It gives enough space to write ideas and record results and provides space to paste in photos or extra material (such as printouts).

▶ Each entry must have the date recorded.

▶ Your log book is a full record of your work. Include any mishaps, failed experiments, or changes in methodology in your logbooks. Where possible, explain the reasons for the failure or change. Sometimes failed experiments can be just as valuable as successful experiments in understanding a result.

▶ Make sure that you can read what you write at a later date. A log book entry is meaningless if it is incomplete or cannot be read.

Dataloggers

Another way to collect data is using a datalogger. A datalogger is an electronic device that automatically records data over time.

▶ Dataloggers can measure different physical properties. Common properties include light, temperature, pH, conductivity, and humidity.

▶ Information collected by the datalogger can be downloaded to a computer so that the data can be accessed and analyzed.

Tables

A table (below) is a good way to record and present results. Patterns, trends, or anomalies can be easier to see. You may want to change your experimental conditions as a result of emerging trends. For example, increase the frequency of data collection if a reaction is proceeding quickly.

02 / 10 / 2019

Volume of CO_2 gas collected when $CaCO_3$ is added to HCl

Time (min)	Volume CO_2 (mL)
0	0
1	3
2	10
3	29
4	48
5	51
6	52
7	52

▶ Title, and row and column headings must state clearly and accurately what the table is about.

▶ Tables allow you to systematically record and condense a large amount of information. They provide an accurate record of your data.

▶ Columns can be added for calculated values such as density, rate, and summary statistics (e.g. mean).

▶ Summary statistics make it easier to identify trends and compare treatments. Rates are useful in comparing multiple data sets, e.g. if recordings were made over different time periods.

1. Why is it important to keep a detailed logbook during a scientific investigation?_____

_____

_____

_____

_____

2. What are two advantages of using a table format for data presentation?

(a) _____

_____

(b) _____

_____

60 Drawing and Interpreting Graphs

▶ Graphs are a good way of visually showing trends, patterns, and relationships without taking up too much space. Complex data sets tend to be presented as a graph rather than a table.

▶ You should plot your data as soon as possible, even during your experiment, as this will help you to evaluate your results as you proceed and make adjustments as necessary (e.g. to the sampling interval).

▶ Give your graph a title and appropriately labeled axes so the information displayed is clearly communicated.

Line graph	Scatter plot
▶ The data must be continuous for both variables (i.e. not counts and not categories).	▶ The data must be continuous for both variables (i.e. not counts and not categories).
▶ The response variable is dependent on the independent variable. The independent variable is often time or the experimental treatment.	▶ There is no manipulated (independent) variable but the variables are often correlated, i.e. they vary together in a predictable way.
▶ The points are connected point to point.	▶ The points on the graph should not be connected but a **line of best fit** can be drawn through the points. A line of best fit should follow the trend of the data with roughly half the data points above the line and half below.
▶ Used to illustrate the response to a manipulated variable, e.g. reaction time against temperature.	▶ Used to show the relationship between two correlated variables, e.g. atomic number vs atomic radius.

1. Copper ions react with ammonia to form a dark blue copper-containing solution. The absorbance of the solution can be read using a spectrophotometer. A student produced a standard curve for this system so they could measure the amount of copper in an unknown sample. Their results are presented in the table (right).

Concentration of Cu^{2+} (mol/L)	Absorbance (610 nm)
0.001	0.042
0.002	0.083
0.004	0.165
0.006	0.250
0.008	0.330
0.012	0.502

(a) Give the student's table an appropriate title:

_____

_____

_____

_____

(b) Plot the data points on the grid provided:

(c) Would you join the points (producing a line graph) or plot a line of best fit (producing a scatter plot)?

_____

(d) Explain your reasoning: _____

_____

_____

_____

_____

_____

_____

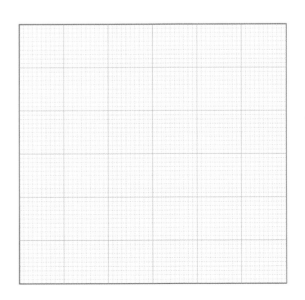

©2019 **BIOZONE** International
ISBN: 978-1-927309-71-1

A line may have a positive, negative, or zero slope

The graph on the right illustrates three types of gradients for a line graph.

▶ **Positive gradients** (blue line): the line slopes upward to the right (y is increasing as x increases).

▶ **Negative gradients** (red line): the line slopes downward to the right (y is decreasing as x increases).

▶ **Zero gradients** (green line): the line is horizontal (y does not change as x increases).

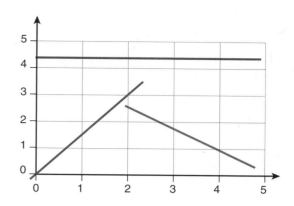

Measuring gradients and intercepts

▶ Data plotted as a linear (straight) line can give us information about the system we are observing.

▶ A linear line can be described by the equation: **y = mx + c**.

▶ The equation can be used to calculate the gradient (slope) of a straight line and tells us about the relationship between x and y (how fast y is changing relative to x). For a straight line, the rate of change of y relative to x is always constant.

The equation for a straight line is written as:

y = mx + c

Where :

y = the y-axis value

m = the slope (or gradient)

x = the x-axis value

c = the y intercept (where the line crosses the y-axis).

Determining "m" and "c"

To find "c" just find where the line crosses the y-axis.

To find m:

1. Choose any two points on the line.

2. Draw a right-angled triangle between the two points on the line.

3. Use the scale on each axis to find the triangle's vertical length and horizontal length.

4. Calculate the gradient of the line using the following equation:

$$\frac{\text{change in y}}{\text{change in x}}$$

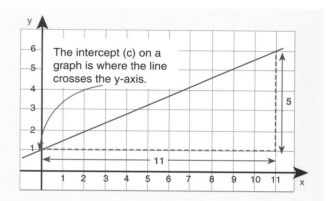

The intercept (c) on a graph is where the line crosses the y-axis.

For the example above:

c = 1

m = 0.45 (5 ÷11)

Once c and m have been determined you can choose any value for x and find the corresponding value for y.

For example, when x = 9, the equation would be:

y = 9 x 0.45 + 1

y = 5.05

2. The graph on the right shows the decomposition of nitrogen pentoxide (N_2O_5) in carbon tetrachloride solvent over time. A line of best fit has been drawn through the data points.

(a) Determine c (the y intercept): _____

(b) What type of gradient is represented by this reaction?

_____

_____

(c) Determine m (the gradient):

_____

_____

(d) Determine the concentration of N_2O_5 at 450 seconds. Show your working:

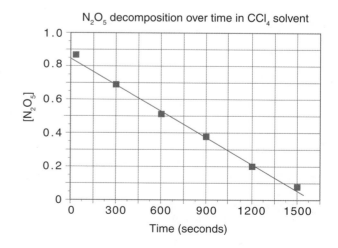

N_2O_5 decomposition over time in CCl_4 solvent

_____

_____

©2019 **BIOZONE** International
ISBN: 978-1-927309-71-1
Photocopying Prohibited

61 Describing the Data

Most data shows variability. Descriptive statistics (e.g. mean and standard deviation) are used to summarize important features of a data set such as central tendency (the mid-point of the data's distribution) and how the data values are distributed around this value.

Mean

The mean is a single value representing the central position in a set of data with a normal distribution (see plot below).

In biology, the mean is often used to describe a variable in a population (e.g. mean height). Data sets are often large.

In chemistry, the mean is most often applied to smaller data sets (e.g. the mean of three titration values during an experiment, or mean atomic mass).

It is not always appropriate to calculate a mean. Do not calculate a mean if:

▶ The values are already means (averages) themselves.

▶ The data are ratios, such as percentages.

▶ The measurement scale is not linear (e.g. pH units).

The sample mean ($\bar{x}$) is calculated by summing all the data values (x) and dividing them by the total number of data points (n). Outliers (very extreme values) are usually excluded from calculations of the mean. For very skewed data sets, it is better to use the median as a measure of central tendency. This is the middle value when the data values are placed in rank order. If two values share the central position, the sum of the two values is divided by two.

Nitrate concentrations in a water supply over 2 days

Sample number	Nitrate (mg/L) Day 1	Nitrate (mg/L) Day 2
1	2.71	2.78
2	2.52	3.15
3	3.07	9.63
4	3.35	2.97
5	2.89	3.30
Sum (Σ)		
Mean ($\bar{x}$)		

1. Write a mathematical expression for how to calculate a mean: _____

2. The use of nitrates in industry and agriculture can pollute drinking water. Nitrates can cause health issues if they exceed 10 mg/L in drinking water. An environmental technician took 5 samples (n=5) from a public water supply on two consecutive days. The nitrate levels are recorded in the table above.

   (a) Complete the table above (include all the data points):

   (b) Identify the anomalous data point: _____

   (c) Recalculate the mean without the anomalous data point. How did the anomalous value affect the mean? _____

   _____

   _____

   _____

3. (a) Calculate the median value for the 'day 2' data set: _____

   (b) Which is the better measure of central tendency for this data set, mean or median? _____

Standard deviation

While it is important to know the mean of a data set, it is also important to know how much spread there is within the data. For normally distributed data (right) this is measured using standard deviation. It provides a way to evaluate the reliability of estimates of the true mean.

▶ Sample standard deviation (s) is usually presented as $\bar{x} \pm s$. In normally distributed data, 68% of all data values will lie within one standard deviation (1s) of the mean and 95% of all values will lie within two standard deviations (2s) of the mean (right).

▶ The lower the standard deviation, the more closely the data values cluster around the mean.

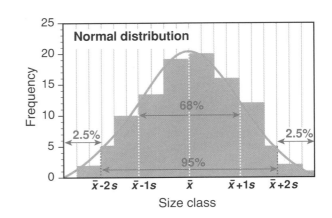

©2019 **BIOZONE** International
ISBN: 978-1-927309-71-1
Photocopying Prohibited

Sample standard deviation is very easily calculated using the equation on the right. It is often calculated using a spreadsheet by entering the data into columns and typing the formula using standard spreadsheet formula rules (see the **Resource Hub**).

Two students tested to see how pipette accuracy is affected by pipette size. Both students dispensed 200 µL 50 times and weighed the dispensed volume each time. Student A used a 200 µL pipette, student B used a 1000 µL pipette. Their results are shown below.

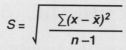

$$S = \sqrt{\frac{\sum(x - \bar{x})^2}{n-1}}$$

$\sum(x - \bar{x})^2$ = the sum of squared deviations from the mean

n = sample size (number of data values).

n-1 provides a unbiased s for small sample sizes (large samples can use n).

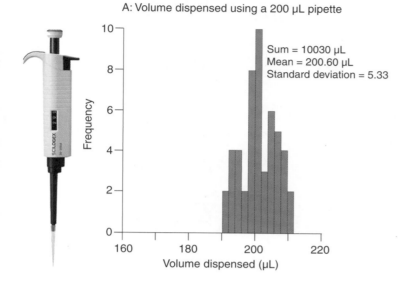

A: Volume dispensed using a 200 µL pipette

Sum = 10030 µL
Mean = 200.60 µL
Standard deviation = 5.33

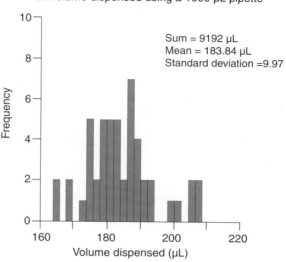

B: Volume dispensed using a 1000 µL pipette

Sum = 9192 µL
Mean = 183.84 µL
Standard deviation =9.97

4. (a) Use the calculated statistics for each data set to comment on how pipette size affected the dispensing accuracy:

_____
_____
_____
_____

(b) Set A has a lower standard deviation than set B. What does this tell us about the reliability of the data?

_____
_____

(c) How could you use this information to select the appropriate equipment for your experiments? _____

_____
_____

5. Calculating a 95% confidence interval (95% CI) provides a good estimate of how close the sample mean is to the true mean. The mean ± the 95% CI gives the 95% confidence limits. On average, 95 times out of 100, the true population mean will lie within the confidence limits. The 95% CI can be plotted onto graphs to determine significance. If they overlap there is no significant difference between the data.

The 95% CI for student A is 1.27 and for student B is 2.37 at p=0.05.

(a) Plot the mean dispensing volume and 95% CI for both sets of data on the grid right). Plot as a column graph with error bars.

(b) Is the difference significant? Why or why not? _____

_____
_____

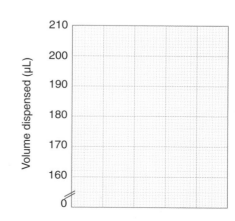

©2019 **BIOZONE** International
ISBN: 978-1-927309-71-1
Photocopying Prohibited

Legend (key)

- Atomic number → 26
- Chemical symbol → Fe
- Name → Iron
- Relative atomic mass → 55.845
- Electronegativity → 1.83
- * = unknown

STATE OF MATTER: SOLID GAS LIQUID UNKNOWN

Categories: nonmetals · alkali metals · alkaline earth metals · transition metals · metalloids · post-transition metals · halogens · noble gases · lanthanoids · actinoids

Periodic Table (atomic number, symbol, name, relative atomic mass, electronegativity)

Group	Period 1	Period 2	Period 3	Period 4	Period 5	Period 6	Period 7
1	1 H Hydrogen 1.00794 (2.20)	3 Li Lithium 6.941 (0.98)	11 Na Sodium 22.98976 (0.93)	19 K Potassium 39.0983 (0.82)	37 Rb Rubidium 85.4678 (0.82)	55 Cs Caesium 132.9054 (0.79)	87 Fr Francium (223) (0.7)
2		4 Be Beryllium 9.012182 (1.57)	12 Mg Magnesium 24.3050 (1.31)	20 Ca Calcium 40.078 (1.0)	38 Sr Strontium 87.62 (0.95)	56 Ba Barium 137.327 (0.89)	88 Ra Radium (226) (0.9)
3				21 Sc Scandium 44.95591 (1.36)	39 Y Yttrium 88.90585 (1.22)	57–71	89–103
4				22 Ti Titanium 47.867 (1.54)	40 Zr Zirconium 91.224 (1.33)	72 Hf Hafnium 178.49 (1.3)	104 Rf Rutherfordium (261)
5				23 V Vanadium 50.9415 (1.63)	41 Nb Niobium 92.90638 (1.6)	73 Ta Tantalum 180.9478 (1.5)	105 Db Dubnium (262)
6				24 Cr Chromium 51.9962 (1.66)	42 Mo Molybdenum 95.96 (1.9)	74 W Tungsten 183.84 (2.36)	106 Sg Seaborgium (266)
7				25 Mn Manganese 54.93804 (1.55)	43 Tc Technetium 98.907 (1.9)	75 Re Rhenium 186.207 (1.9)	107 Bh Bohrium (264)
8				26 Fe Iron 55.845 (1.83)	44 Ru Ruthenium 101.07 (2.2)	76 Os Osmium 190.23 (2.2)	108 Hs Hassium (277)
9				27 Co Cobalt 58.93319 (1.88)	45 Rh Rhodium 102.9055 (2.28)	77 Ir Iridium 192.217 (2.20)	109 Mt Meitnerium (268)
10				28 Ni Nickel 58.6934 (1.91)	46 Pd Palladium 106.42 (2.20)	78 Pt Platinum 195.084 (2.28)	110 Ds Darmstadtium (271)
11				29 Cu Copper 63.546 (1.90)	47 Ag Silver 107.8682 (1.93)	79 Au Gold 196.9665 (2.54)	111 Rg Roentgenium (272)
12				30 Zn Zinc 65.38 (1.65)	48 Cd Cadmium 112.441 (1.69)	80 Hg Mercury 200.59 (2.0)	112 Cn Copernicium (285)
13		5 B Boron 10.811 (2.04)	13 Al Aluminium 26.98153 (1.61)	31 Ga Gallium 69.723 (1.81)	49 In Indium 114.818 (1.78)	81 Tl Thallium 204.3833 (1.62)	113 Nh Nihonium (284)
14		6 C Carbon 12.0107 (2.55)	14 Si Silicon 28.0855 (1.90)	32 Ge Germanium 72.64 (2.01)	50 Sn Tin 118.710 (1.96)	82 Pb Lead 207.2 (2.33)	114 Fl Flerovium (289)
15		7 N Nitrogen 14.0067 (3.04)	15 P Phosphorus 30.97696 (2.19)	33 As Arsenic 74.92160 (2.18)	51 Sb Antimony 121.760 (2.05)	83 Bi Bismuth 208.9804 (2.02)	115 Mc Moscovium (288)
16		8 O Oxygen 15.9994 (3.44)	16 S Sulfur 32.065 (2.58)	34 Se Selenium 78.96 (2.55)	52 Te Tellurium 127.60 (2.1)	84 Po Polonium 208.982 (2.0)	116 Lv Livermorium (293)
17		9 F Fluorine 18.998403 (3.98)	17 Cl Chlorine 35.453 (3.16)	35 Br Bromine 79.904 (2.96)	53 I Iodine 126.9044 (2.66)	85 At Astatine 209.987 (2.2)	117 Ts Tennessine (294)
18	2 He Helium 4.002602	10 Ne Neon 20.1797	18 Ar Argon 39.948	36 Kr Krypton 83.798 (3.0)	54 Xe Xenon 131.293 (2.6)	86 Rn Radon 222.018 (1.27)*	118 Og Oganesson (294)

Lanthanoids (57–71)

57 La Lanthanum 138.9054 (1.10)	58 Ce Cerium 140.116 (1.12)	59 Pr Praseodymium 140.9076 (1.13)	60 Nd Neodymium 144.242 (1.14)	61 Pm Promethium (145)	62 Sm Samarium 150.36 (1.17)	63 Eu Europium 151.964	64 Gd Gadolinium 157.25 (1.2)	65 Tb Terbium 158.9253	66 Dy Dysprosium 162.500 (1.22)	67 Ho Holmium 164.9303 (1.23)	68 Er Erbium 167.259 (1.24)	69 Tm Thulium 168.9342 (1.25)	70 Yb Ytterbium 173.054	71 Lu Lutetium 174.9668 (1.27)

Actinoids (89–103)

89 Ac Actinium (227) (1.1)	90 Th Thorium 232.0380 (1.3)	91 Pa Protactinium 231.0358 (1.5)	92 U Uranium 238.0289 (1.38)	93 Np Neptunium (237) (1.36)	94 Pu Plutonium (244) (1.28)	95 Am Americium (243) (1.3)	96 Cm Curium (247)	97 Bk Berkelium (247) (1.3)	98 Cf Californium (251) (1.3)	99 Es Einsteinium (252) (1.3)	100 Fm Fermium (257) (1.3)	101 Md Mendelevium (258) (1.3)	102 No Nobelium (259) (1.3)	103 Lr Lawrencium (262)

©2019 **BIOZONE** International
ISBN: **978-1-927309-71-1**
Photocopying Prohibited

Appendix: Equipment list

The equipment list provides the material and equipment needed per student, pair, or group.

IS 1: Combustion and Energy Transfer

INVESTIGATION 1.1
100 mL measuring cylinder

INVESTIGATION 1.2
100 mL beaker
Balance
Thermometer
Tripod
Stopwatch
Bunsen burner

Crushed ice

INVESTIGATION 1.3
Polystyrene cup
Bunsen burner
Thermometer
Stirring rod
Balance

Ice cubes

INVESTIGATION 1.4
50 mL measuring cylinder
100 mL conical flask
Thermometer
Filter paper (any will do)
Balance

50 mL 1.0 M HCl solution
2 g sodium hydrogen carbonate ($NaHCO_3$)

INVESTIGATION 1.5
50 mL measuring cylinder
100 mL conical flask
Balloon
Balance

50 mL 1.0 M HCl solution
2 g Sodium bicarbonate

INVESTIGATION 1.6
100 mL beaker
Heating plate (hot plate) or Bunsen burner
Tripod
Thermometer
Stopwatch

50 mL vegetable oil

IS 2: Heat and Energy Transfer in the Earth System

INVESTIGATION 2.1
Moldable wax
Clamp stand and clamp
Bunsen burner
Steel rod
Copper rod
Aluminium rod
Stopwatch

INVESTIGATION 2.2
Large beaker (~250 mL)
Small beaker (~50 mL)
Thermometer
Insulated box or insulation

50 mL cooking oil

INVESTIGATION 2.3
2 x 500 mL beakers
Thermometer

INVESTIGATION 2.4
2 x 250 mL beakers

A few crystals of potassium permanganate ($KMnO_4$) or food coloring

INVESTIGATION 2.5
Needle
Micropipette and tip
Coverslip
Light microscope

Milk or oil

INVESTIGATION 2.6-2.8
Computers and online access to Energy 2D software
http://energy.concord.org/energy2d/index.html

INVESTIGATION 2.9
Balance
Large graduated cylinder

Selection of rocks (e.g. volcanic, sedimentary)

IS3: Atoms, Elements and Molecules

INVESTIGATION 3.1
6 x petri dishes or
6 x filter paper (any will do)
Balance

Sodium chloride (NaCl)
Sulfur (S)
Copper chloride ($CuCl_2.2H_2O$)
Iron oxide (FeO)
Carbon (C)
Glucose ($C_6H_{12}O_6$)

INVESTIGATION 3.2
Crucible and lid
Balance
Tripod
Clay triangle
Bunsen burner
Tongs

Magnesium ribbon (10 cm)

INVESTIGATION 3.3
Crucible and lid
Balance
Tripod
Clay triangle
Bunsen burner
Tongs

6 g hydrated copper sulfate

INVESTIGATION 3.4
Filter paper (any will do)
Balance
2 x test tubes
Rubber cork
Delivery tube
Clamp stand and clamp
Glass beaker (big enough to fit the test tube)
Bunsen burner
100 mL beaker
Glass stirring rod
Steel wool or sandpaper
Large iron nail
Buchner funnel
Drying oven (optional)

2 g copper II carbonate ($CuCO_3$)
Limewater
80 mL 1 mol/L sulfuric acid solution

INVESTIGATION 3.5
Small beaker
250 mL volumetric flask
Glass funnel
Dropper

1.3 g anhydrous Na_2CO_3
Distilled water

INVESTIGATION 3.6
100 mL beaker
25 mL pipette
250 mL volumetric flask
50 mL burette
Clamp stand and clamps
4 x 100 mL conical flasks

50 mL 1 mol/L HCl solution
Na_2CO_3 solution (prepared in investigation 3.5)
Methyl orange indicator
Distilled water

INVESTIGATION 3.7
100 mL beaker
250 mL volumetric flask
25 mL pipette
Balance
50 mL burette
20 mL pipette
Clamp stand and clamps
4 x 100 mL conical flask

50 mL 1 mol/L NaOH solution or 1 g NaOH
80 ml standardized HCl solution
Phenolphthalein indicator

INVESTIGATION 3.8
50 mL burette
Clamp stand and clamps
25 mL pipette
100 mL volumetric flask
4 x 100 mL conical flask

50 mL standardized NaOH solution
25 mL vinegar (any will do)
Phenolphthalein indicator

IS4: Chemical Reactions

INVESTIGATION 4.1
4 x balloons
Marker pen

INVESTIGATION 4.2
11 x watch glasses
11 x 50 mL beakers
Conductivity meter
Stirring rod
Test tube
2 x deflagrating spoon
Bunsen burner
Small heat resistant pad or glass plate
Glass jar

1 g sodium chloride (NaCl),
1 g magnesium (Mg)
1 g magnesium sulfate ($MgSO_4$)
1 g sulfur (S)
1 g iron (Fe)
1 g copper (Cu
1 g copper sulfate ($CuSO_4$)
Distilled water
Ice
1 mL cyclohexane (C6H12)
1 g quartz or glass (SiO2)

INVESTIGATION 4.3
2 x 50 mL burettes
100 mL beaker
Glass rod
Silk cloth or polyester towel

50 mL distilled water
50 mL cyclohexane

INVESTIGATION 4.4
Balance
Alcohol burner
Soda can (empty)
Thermometer
Ring stand
Wire gauze or clamp stand
Ring clamp and clamp
Stopwatch

Methanol (CH_3OH)
Ethanol (CH_3CH_2OH)
Propan-1-ol ($CH_3CH_2CH_2OH$)
Distilled water

INVESTIGATION 4.5
3 x 25 mL beakers
Watch glass
Thermometer

Sodium hydroxide (solid)
Ammomium chloride (solid)
1 M HCl solution
1 M NaOH solution
Ammonium thiocyanate (solid)
Barium hydroxide (solid)
Distilled water

INVESTIGATION 4.6
Styrofoam cup
100 mL measuring cylinder
Thermometer

100 mL 0.1 mol/L copper sulfate solution
Zinc powder

INVESTIGATION 4.7
5 x 50 mL measuring cylinders
5 x test tubes
Colorimeter
Stopwatch

Bleach (sodium hypochlorite, NaClO)
Food coloring

INVESTIGATION 4.8
3 x boiling tubes
Ice bath
Water bath (50°C)
3 x 250 mL beakers
Thermometer
Stopwatch

45 mL 0.1 mol/L potassium permanganate solution
45 mL 0.5 mol/L oxalic acid
90 mL 4 mol/L sulfuric acid
Distilled water

IS6: Reaction Dynamics and Ocean Acidification

INVESTIGATION 6.1
2 x test tubes
Red litmus paper
Blue litmus paper

0.1 M HCl
0.1 M NaOH

INVESTIGATION 6.2
2 x 1 L minimum beaker or basin
100 mL beaker
50 mL beaker

INVESTIGATION 6.3
Watch glasses (or spotting tile)

0.1 mol/L hydrochloric acid (HCl)
0.1 mol/L nitric acid (HNO_3)
0.1 mol/L ethanoic acid (CH_3COOH)
0.1 mol/L citric acid ($C_6H_8O_7$)
0.1 mol/L sodium hydroxide (NaOH)
0.1 mol/L ammonia solution (NH_3)
0.1 mol/L sodium carbonate (Na_2CO_3)
0.1 mol/L sodium hydrogen carbonate ($NaHCO_3$)

Distilled water
pH paper

INVESTIGATION 6.4
Water bath or basin
Measuring cylinder
Clamp stand
Funnel
Alka Seltzer tablets (or similar effervescent tablets)

Cold water / warm water (~45°C)

Image credits

We acknowledge the generosity of those who have provided photographs or diagrams for this edition: • Felix Hicks for the laboratory safety diagram and the cation and anion diagrams • Ammonium chloride experiment photo: ©Andrew Lambert Photography, Science Photo Library • Electrolysis of water photo from Science Photo Library

We also acknowledge the photographers that have made their images available through **Wikimedia Commons** under Creative Commons Licences 2.0, 2.5, 3.0, or 4.0:
• Farmercarlos • Energy2D Charles Xie • Rakot13 • Bigest t • H. Raab • Tobias1984 • Borealis • Wilco Oelen • Cjp24 • Benutzer:the-viewer • Jeff Kubina • Nikthestunned • The RedBurn • Energy2D Charles Xie • Library of Congress • Ben Mills • Richard Weymouth • BXXXDCC • Leiem • W. Oelen • Brocken Inaglory

Contributors identified by coded credits are: **KP**: Kent Pryor, **NASA**: National Aeronautics and Space Administration, **NASA/JPL**: NASA Jet Propulsion Laboratory, **NOAA**: National Oceanic and Atmospheric Administration, **USDE**: United States Department of Energy **USGS**: United States Geological Survey.

Royalty free images, purchased by BIOZONE International Ltd, are used throughout this workbook and have been obtained from the following sources:
• iStock images Corel Corporation from their Professional Photos CD-ROM collection; ©Digital Vision; Gazelle Technologies Inc.; PhotoDisc®, Inc. USA, www.photodisc.com • 3D images created using Bryce, Poser, and Pymol

Index